# Geometry of Quantum Theory

# Geometry

## of

# Quantum Theory

*By*

## V. S. VARADARAJAN

*Department of Mathematics*
*University of California*
*Los Angeles, California*

---

VOLUME I

---

# D. VAN NOSTRAND COMPANY, INC.

### Princeton, New Jersey

*Toronto*　　　　　　　*London*　　　　　　　*Melbourne*

VAN NOSTRAND REGIONAL OFFICES: *New York, Chicago, San Francisco*

D. VAN NOSTRAND COMPANY, LTD., *London*

D. VAN NOSTRAND COMPANY (Canada), LTD., *Toronto*

D. VAN NOSTRAND AUSTRALIA PTY. LTD., *Melbourne*

Library of Congress Catalog Card No. 68-20923

PRINTED IN THE UNITED STATES OF AMERICA

*TO MY PARENTS*

# PREFACE

The present work is the first volume of a substantially enlarged version of the mimeographed notes of a course of lectures first given by me in the Indian Statistical Institute, Calcutta, India, during 1964-65. When it was suggested that these lectures be developed into a book, I readily agreed and took the opportunity to extend the scope of the material covered.

No background in physics is in principle necessary for understanding the essential ideas in this work. However, a high degree of mathematical maturity is certainly indispensable. It is safe to say that I aim at an audience composed of professional mathematicians, advanced graduate students, and, hopefully, the rapidly increasing group of mathematical physicists who are attracted to fundamental mathematical questions.

Over the years, the mathematics of quantum theory has become more abstract and, consequently, simpler. Hilbert spaces have been used from the very beginning and, after Weyl and Wigner, group representations have come in conclusively. Recent discoveries seem to indicate that the role of group representations is destined for further expansion, not to speak of the impact of the theory of several complex variables and function-space analysis. But all of this pertains to the world of interacting subatomic particles; the more modest view of the microscopic world presented in this book requires somewhat less. The reader with a knowledge of abstract integration, Hilbert space theory, and topological groups will find the going easy.

Part of the work which went into the writing of this book was supported by the National Science Foundation Grant No. GP-5224. I have profited greatly from conversations with many friends and colleagues at various institutions. To all of them, especially to R. Arens, R. J. Blattner, R. Ranga Rao, K. R. Parthasarathy, and S. R. S. Varadhan, my sincere thanks. I want to record my deep thanks to my colleague Don Babbitt who read through the manuscript carefully, discovered many mistakes, and was responsible for significant improvement of the manuscript. My apologies are due to all those whose work has been ignored or, possibly, incorrectly (and/or insufficiently) discussed. Finally, I want to acknowledge that this book might never have made its way into print but for my wife. She typed the entire manuscript, encouraged me when my enthusiasm went down, and made me understand some of the meaning of our ancient words,

कर्मण्येवाधिकारस्ते मा फलेषु कदाचन । .*

To her my deep gratitude.

V. S. VARADARAJAN

*Spring, 1968*

* *Bhagavadgita, 2:47a.*

# TABLE OF CONTENTS

## PART ONE
## PROJECTIVE GEOMETRY

# INTRODUCTION

As laid down by Dirac in his great classic [1], the principle of superposition of states is the fundamental concept on which the quantum theory of atomic systems is to be erected. Dirac's development of quantum mechanics on an axiomatic basis is undoubtedly in keeping with the greatest traditions of the physical sciences. The scope and power of this principle can be recognized at once if one recalls that it survived virtually unmodified throughout the subsequent transition to a relativistic view of the atomic world. It must be pointed out, however, that the precise mathematical nature of the superposition principle was only implicit in the discussions of Dirac; we are indebted to John von Neumann for explicit formulation. In his characteristic way, he discovered that the set of experimental statements of a quantum mechanical system formed a projective geometry—the projective geometry of subspaces of a complex, separable, infinite dimensional Hilbert space. With this as a point of departure, he carried out a mathematical analysis of the axiomatic foundations of quantum mechanics which must certainly rank among his greatest achievements [1] [3] [4] [5] [6].

Once the geometric point of view is accepted, impressive consequences follow. The automorphisms of the geometry describe the dynamical and kinematical structure of quantum mechanical systems, thus leading to the *linear* character of quantum mechanics. The covariance of the physical laws under appropriate space-time groups consequently expresses itself in the form of projective unitary representations of these groups. The economy of thought as well as the unification of method that this point of view brings forth is truly immense; the Schrödinger equation, for example, is obtained from a representation of the time-translation group, the Dirac equation from a representation of the inhomogeneous Lorentz group. This development is the work of many mathematicians and physicists. However, insofar as the mathematical theory is concerned, no contribution is more outstanding than that of Eugene P. Wigner. Beginning with his famous article on time inversion and throughout his great papers on relativistic invariance [1] [3] [4] [5] [6], we find a beautiful and coherent approach to the mathematical description of the quantum mechanical world which achieves nothing less than the fusion of group theory and quantum mechanics, and moreover does this without compromising in any manner the axiomatic principles formulated by Dirac and von Neumann.

My own interest in the mathematical foundations of quantum mechanics received a great stimulus from the inspiring lectures given by Professor George W. Mackey at the University of Washington in Seattle during the summer of 1961. The present volumes are in great part the result of my interest in a detailed elaboration of the main features of the theory sketched by Mackey in those lectures. In sum, my indebtedness to Professor Mackey's lectures and to the books and papers of von Neumann and Wigner is immense and carries through this entire work.

There exist today many expositions of the basic principles of quantum mechanics. At the most sophisticated mathematical level, there are the books of von Neumann [1], Hermann Weyl [1] and Mackey [1]. But, insofar as I am aware, there is no account of the technical features of the geometry and group theory of quantum mechanical systems that is both reasonably self-contained and comprehensive enough to be able to include Lorentz invariance. Moreover, recent re-examinations of the fundamental ideas by numerous mathematicians have produced insights that have substantially added to our understanding of quantum foundations. From among these I want to single out for special mention Gleason's proof that quantum mechanical states are represented by the so-called density matrices, Mackey's extensive work on systems of imprimitivity and group representations, and Bargmann's work on the cohomology of Lie groups, particularly of the physically interesting groups and their extensions. All of this has made possible a conceptually unified and technically cogent development of the theory of quantum mechanical systems from a completely geometric point of view. The present work is an attempt to present such an approach.

Our approach may be described by means of a brief outline of the contents of the three parts that make up the two volumes of this work. Part One begins by introducing the viewpoint of von Neumann according to which every physical system has in its background a certain orthocomplemented lattice whose elements may be identified with the experimentally verifiable propositions about the system. For classical systems this lattice (called the logic of the system) is a Boolean $\sigma$-algebra while for quantum systems it is highly nondistributive This points to the relevance of the theory of complemented lattices to the axiomatic foundations of quantum mechanics. In the presence of modularity and finiteness of rank, these lattices decompose into a direct sum of irreducible ones, called geometries. A typical example of a geometry is the lattice of subspaces of a finite dimensional vector space over a division ring. The theory of these vector geometries is taken up in Chapters III and IV. The isomorphisms of such a geometry are induced in a natural fashion by semilinear transformations. Orthocomplementations are induced by definite semi-bilinear forms which are symmetric with respect to suitable involutive anti-automorphisms of the basic division ring. If the division ring is the reals, complexes or quaternions, this leads to the Hilbert space structures. In Chapter V, we examine the relation between axiomatic geometry and analytic geometry along classical lines with suitable modifications in order to handle the infinite dimensional case also. The main result of this chapter is the theorem which asserts that an abstractly given generalized geometry (i.e., one whose dimension need not be finite) of rank $\geqq 4$ is isomorphic to the lattice of all finite dimensional subspaces of a vector space over a division ring. The division ring is an invariant of the lattice.

Part Two, which concludes Volume I, analyzes the structure of the logics of quantum mechanical systems. In Chapter VI, we introduce the notion of an abstract logic ( = orthocomplemented weakly modular $\sigma$-lattice) and the observables and states associated with it. It is possible that certain observables need not be simultaneously observable. It is proved that for a given family of observables to be simultaneously measurable, it is necessary and sufficient that the observables of the family be classically related, i.e., that there exists a Boolean sub $\sigma$-algebra of the logic in question to which all the members of the given family are associated. Given an observable and a state, it is shown how to compute the probability distribution of the observable in that state. In Chapter VII, we take up the problem of singling out the logic of all subspaces of a Hilbert space by a set of neat axioms. Using the results of Chapter V, it is proved that the standard logics are precisely the projective ones. The analysis of the notions of an observable and a state carried out in Chapter VI now leads to the correspondence between observables and self-adjoint operators, and between the pure states and the rays of the underlying Hilbert space. The automorphisms of the standard logics are shown to be induced by the unitary and antiunitary operators. With this the von Neumann program of a deductive description of the principles of quantum mechanics is completed. The remarkable fact that there is a Hilbert space whose self-adjoint operators represent the observables and whose rays describe the (pure) states is thus finally established to be a consequence of the projective nature of the underlying logic.

Volume II, which constitutes the third and final part of the work, deals with specialized questions. The main problem is that of a covariant description of a quantum mechanical system, the covariance being with respect to suitable symmetry groups of the system. The theory of such systems leads to sophisticated problems of harmonic analysis on locally compact groups. Chapters VIII, IX, and X are devoted to these purely mathematical questions. The results obtained are then applied to yield the basic physical results in Chapters XI and XII. In Chapter XI, the Schrödinger equation is obtained and the relations between the Heisenberg and Schrödinger formulations of quantum mechanics are analyzed. The usual expressions for the position, momentum, and energy observables of a quantum mechanical particle are shown to be inevitable consequences of the basic axioms and the requirement of covariance. In addition, a classification of single particle systems is obtained in terms of the spin of the particle. The spin of a particle, which is so characteristic of quantum mechanics, is a manifestation of the *geometry* of the configuration space of the particle.

The final chapter of Volume II discusses the description of free particles from the relativistic viewpoint. The results of Chapters VIII, IX and X are used to obtain a classification of these particles in terms of their mass and spin. With each particle it is possible to associate a vector bundle whose square integrable sections constitute the Hilbert space of the particle. These abstract results lead to the standard transformation formulae for the (one particle) states under the elements of the relativity group. By taking Fourier transforms, it is possible to associate with each particle a definite wave equation. In particular, the Dirac equation of the free electron is obtained in this manner. The same methods lead to the localization in space, for a given time instant, of the particles of nonzero rest mass. The chapter ends with an analysis of Galilean relativity. It is shown that the free particles which are governed by Galilei's principle of relativity are none other than the Schrödinger particles of *positive* mass and arbitrary spin.

With this the program of obtaining a geometric view of the quantum mechanical world is completed. It is my belief that no other approach leads so clearly and smoothly to the fundamental results. It may be hoped that such methods may also lead to a successful description of the world of interacting particles and their fields. The realization of such hopes seems to be a matter for the future.

V. S. VARADARAJAN

# PART ONE

# PROJECTIVE GEOMETRY

# CHAPTER I

# BOOLEAN ALGEBRAS ON A CLASSICAL PHASE SPACE

## 1. THE CLASSICAL PHASE SPACE

We begin with a brief account of the usual description of a classical mechanical system with a finite number of *degrees of freedom*. Associated with such a system there is an integer $n$, and an open set $M$ of the $n$-dimensional space $R^n$ of $n$-tuples $(x_1, x_2, \cdots, x_n)$ of real numbers. $n$ is called the *number* of degrees of freedom of the system. The points of $M$ represent the possible *configurations* of the system. A *state* of the system at any instant of time is specified completely by giving a $2n$-tuple $(x_1, x_2, \cdots, x_n, p_1, \cdots, p_n)$ such that $(x_1, \cdots, x_n)$ represents the configuration and $(p_1, \cdots, p_n)$ the momentum vector, of the system at that instant of time. The possible states of the system are thus represented by the points of the open set $M \times R^n$ of $R^{2n}$. The law of evolution of the system is specified by a smooth function $H$ on $M \times R^n$, called the *Hamiltonian* of the system. If $(x_1(t), \cdots, x_n(t), p_1(t), \cdots, p_n(t))$ represents the state of the system at time $t$, then the functions $x_i(\cdot)$, $p_i(\cdot)$, $i = 1, 2, \cdots, n$, satisfy the well known differential equations:

$$\frac{dx_i}{dt} = \frac{\partial H}{\partial p_i}, \qquad i = 1, 2, \cdots, n,$$

**(1)**

$$\frac{dp_i}{dt} = -\frac{\partial H}{\partial x_i}, \qquad i = 1, 2, \cdots, n.$$

For most of the systems which arise in practice these equations have unique solutions for all $t$ in the sense that given any real number $t_0$, and a point $(x_1{}^0, x_2{}^0, \cdots, x_n{}^0, p_1{}^0, \cdots, p_n{}^0)$ of $M \times R^n$, there exists a unique differentiable map $t \to (x_1(t), \cdots, x_n(t), p_1(t), \cdots, p_n(t))$ of $R^1$ into $M \times R^n$ such that $x_i(\cdot)$ and $p_i(\cdot)$ satisfy the equations (1) with the *initial conditions*

**(2)** $\qquad x_i(t_0) = x_i{}^0, \quad p_i(t_0) = p_i{}^0, \qquad i = 1, 2, \cdots, n.$

If we denote by $s$ an arbitrary point of $M \times R^n$, it then follows in the standard fashion that for any $t$ there exists a mapping $D(t)(s \to D(t)s)$

of $M \times R^n$ into itself with the property that if $s$ is the state of the system at time $t_0$, $D(t)s$ is the state of the system at time $t+t_0$. The transformations $D(t)$ are one-one, map $M \times R^n$ onto itself and satisfy the equations:

$$D(0) = I \quad \text{(the identity mapping)},$$
$$(3) \qquad\qquad D(-t) = D(t)^{-1},$$
$$D(t_1+t_2) = D(t_1)D(t_2).$$

If, in addition, $H$ is an indefinitely differentiable function, then the $D(t)$ are also indefinitely differentiable and the correspondence $t \to D(t)$ defines a one-parameter differentiable transformation group of $M \times R^n$ so that the map $t, s \to D(t)s$ of $R^1 \times M \times R^n$ into $M \times R^n$ is indefinitely differentiable. The set $M \times R^n$ of all the possible states of the system is called the *phase space* of the system.

In the formulation described above, the physical quantities or the *observables* of the system are described by real valued functions on $M \times R^n$. For example, if the system is that of a single particle of mass $m$ which moves under some potential field, then $n = 3$, $M = R^3$, and the Hamiltonian $H$ is given by

$$(4) \qquad H(x_1,x_2,x_3,p_1,p_2,p_3) = \frac{1}{2m}\,(p_1{}^2+p_2{}^2+p_3{}^2) + V(x_1,x_2,x_3).$$

The function $s \to (p_1{}^2+p_2{}^2+p_3{}^2)/2m$ is the kinetic energy of the particle and the function $s \to V(x_1,x_2,x_3)$ is the potential energy of the particle. The function $s \to p_i$ $(i = 1, 2, 3)$ represents the $x_i$-component of the momentum of the particle. In the general case, if $f$ is a function on $M \times R^n$ which describes an observable, then $f(s)$ gives the value of that observable when the system is in the state $s$.

This formulation of the basic ideas relating to the mechanics of a classical system can be generalized significantly (Mackey [1], Sternberg [1]). Briefly, this generalization consists in replacing the assumption that $M$ is an open subset of $R^n$ by the more general one that $M$ is an abstract $C^\infty$ manifold of dimension $n$. The set of all possible configurations of the system is now $M$, and for any $x \in M$, the momenta of the system at this configuration are the elements of the vector space $M_x{}^*$, which is the dual of the *tangent vector space* $M_x$ of $M$ at $x$. The phase space of the system is then the set of all possible pairs $(x,p)$, where $x \in M$ and $p \in M_x{}^*$. This set, say $S$, comes equipped with a natural differentiable structure under which it is a $C^\infty$ manifold of dimension $2n$, the so-called *cotangent bundle* of $M$. The manifold $S$ admits further a canonical 2-form which is everywhere nonsingular and this gives rise to a natural isomorphism $J$ of the module of all $C^\infty$ vector fields on $S$ onto the module of all 1-forms (both being considered as modules over the ring of $C^\infty$ functions on $S$). The dynamical development of the system is then specified by a $C^\infty$ function $H$ on $S$, the *Hamiltonian* of the system. If $t \to s(t)$ is a curve representing a possible evolution of the system, then we have the differential equations:

$$(5) \qquad \frac{ds(t)}{dt} = [J^{-1}(dH)](s(t)).$$

Here $ds(t)/dt$ is the tangent vector to $S$ at the point $s(t)$ along the curve $t \to s(t)$ and $J^{-1}(dH)$ is the vector field on $S$ corresponding to the 1-form $dH$; the right side of the equation (5) being the value of this vector field at the point $s(t)$ of $S$. In the special case when $M$ is an open set in $R^n$ and $x_1, x_2, \cdots, x_n$ are the global affine coordinates on $M$, $S$ is canonically identified with $M \times R^n$ and, under this identification, $J$ goes over into the map which transforms the vector field

$$\sum_{i=1}^{n} A_i(\partial/\partial x_i) + \sum_{i=1}^{n} B_i(\partial/\partial p_i)$$

into the 1-form

$$- \sum_{i=1}^{n} B_i \, dx_i + \sum_{i=1}^{n} A_i \, dp_i.$$

The equation (5) then goes over to (1) (cf. Chevalley [1], Helgason [1] for a discussion of the general theory of differentiable manifolds).

In this general setup, the dynamical development of the system is given by the integral curves of the vector field $J^{-1}(dH)$. It is necessary to assume that the integral curves are defined for *all* values of the time parameter $t$. One can then use the standard theory of vector fields to deduce the existence of a diffeomorphism $D(t)$ of $S$ for each $t$ such that the correspondence $t \to D(t)$ satisfies the conditions (3), and the map $t, s \to D(t)s$ of $R^1 \times S$ into $S$ is $C^\infty$. If the system is at the state $s$ at time $t_0$, then its state at time $t + t_0$ is $D(t)s$. The physical observables of the system are then represented by real valued functions on $S$. A special class of Hamiltonian functions, analogous to (4), may be defined in this general framework. Let $x \to \langle . \, , . \rangle_x$ be a $C^\infty$ Riemannian metric on $M$, $\langle . \, , . \rangle_x$ being a positive definite inner product on $M_x \times M_x$. For each $x \in M$, we then have a natural isomorphism $p \to p^*$ of $M_x^*$ onto $M_x$ such that $p(u) = \langle u, p^* \rangle_x$ for all $p \in M_x^*$ and for all $u \in M_x$. The analogue of (4) is then the Hamiltonian $H$ given by

$$(6) \qquad H(x,p) = \langle p^*, p^* \rangle_x + V(x),$$

where $V$ is a $C^\infty$ function on $M$. The function $x, p \to \langle p^*, p^* \rangle_x$ then represents the kinetic energy of the system in question.

It may be pointed out that one can introduce the concept of the *momenta* of the system in this setup. Let

$$(7) \qquad \gamma : t \to \gamma_t$$

be a one-parameter group of *symmetries* of the configuration space $M$, i.e., $\gamma(t \to \gamma_t)$ is a one-parameter group of $C^\infty$ diffeomorphisms of $M$ onto itself such that the map $t, x \to \gamma_t(x)$ of $R^1 \times M$ into $M$ is $C^\infty$. The infinitesimal generator of $\gamma$ is a $C^\infty$ vector field, say $X_\gamma$, on $M$; for any $x \in M$ and any real valued $C^\infty$ function $f$ defined around $x$,

$$(X_\gamma f)(x) = \left\{ \frac{d}{dt} f(\gamma_{-t}(x)) \right\}_{t=0}.$$

$X_\gamma$ defines, in a natural fashion, a $C^\infty$ function $\mu_\gamma$ on $S$. In fact, if $x \in M$ and $p \in M_x{}^*$,

$$\mu_\gamma(x,p) = p(X_\gamma(x))$$

(here $X_\gamma(x)$ denotes the tangent vector to $M$ at $x$ which is the value of $X_\gamma$ at $x$). The observable corresponding to the function $\mu_\gamma$ is called the *momentum* of the system *corresponding to the one-parameter group of symmetries* $\gamma$. If $M = R^n$, if $x_1, \cdots, x_n$ are the global affine coordinates on $M$, and if

$$\gamma_t{}^c(x_1, \cdots, x_n) = x_1 - tc_1, \cdots, x_n - tc_n,$$

then the observable corresponding to $\mu_\gamma c$ is called the *component of the linear momentum along* $(c_1, \cdots, c_n)$. In the same case, if

$$\gamma_t^{i,j}(x_1, \cdots, x_n) = (y_1, \cdots, y_n),$$

where

$$y_r = x_r, \quad r \neq i, j,$$

$$y_i = x_i \cos t + x_j \sin t, \quad y_j = -x_i \sin t + x_j \cos t,$$

then the observable corresponding to $\mu_\gamma^{i,j}$ is called the *angular momentum with respect to a rotation in the i-j plane*. A straightforward calculation shows that in the case when $M = R^n$, $S = R^n \times R^n$, and $x_1, \cdots, x_n, p_1, \cdots, p_n$ are global coordinates on $S$ $((x_1, \cdots, x_n, p_1, \cdots, p_n)$ depicts $\sum_{i=1}^n p_i(dx_i)_x)$,

$$\mu_\gamma c(x,p) = c_1 p_1 + \cdots + c_n p_n,$$

and

$$\mu_\gamma^{i,j}(x,p) = x_i p_j - x_j p_i.$$

Suppose now that $M$ is a general $C^\infty$ manifold and $S$ its cotangent bundle. If $f$ and $g$ are two $C^\infty$ functions on $S$, then we can form $J^{-1}(df)$, which is a $C^\infty$ vector field on $S$, and apply it to $g$ to get another $C^\infty$ function on $S$, denoted by $[f,g]$:

(8) $$[f,g] = (J^{-1}(df))g.$$

$[f,g]$ is called the *Poisson Bracket* of $f$ with $g$. If we use local coordinates $x_1, \cdots, x_n$ on $M$ and the induced coordinates $x_1, \cdots, x_n, p_1, \cdots, p_n$ on $S$ (so that $(x_1, \cdots, x_n, p_1, \cdots, p_n)$ represents $\sum_i p_i(dx_i)$), then $J$ goes over into the map which (locally) sends $\sum_i A_i(\partial/\partial x_i) + \sum_i B_i(\partial/\partial p_i)$ into $-\sum_i B_i\,dx_i + \sum_i A_i\,dp_i$, and $[f,g]$ becomes

$$(9) \qquad [f,g] = \sum_i \left(\frac{\partial f}{\partial p_i}\frac{\partial g}{\partial x_i} - \frac{\partial f}{\partial x_i}\frac{\partial g}{\partial p_i}\right).$$

The map $f, g \to [f,g]$ is bilinear, skew symmetric, and satisfies the identity

$$[[f,g],h]+[[g,h],f]+[[h,f],g] = 0,$$

as is easily verified from (9). If $X$ is any $C^\infty$ vector field on $M$ and $\mu_X$ is the $C^\infty$ function on $S$ defined by

$$\mu_X(x,p) = p(X(x)),$$

then one can verify, using (9), that

$$\mu_{aX+bY} = a\mu_X+b\mu_Y \qquad (a,\ b\ \text{constants}),$$

$$\mu_{[X,Y]} = [\mu_X,\mu_Y],$$

where $[X,Y]$ is the *Lie bracket* of the vector fields $X$ and $Y$. If $f$ is any $C^\infty$ function on $M$ and $f^0$ is the lifted function on $S$, i.e.,

$$f^0(x,p) = f(x),$$

then we may use (9) once again to check that

$$[\mu_X,f^0] = (Xf)^0$$

for any $C^\infty$ vector field $X$ on $M$.

In many problems, there is a Lie group $G$ which acts on $M$ and provides the natural symmetries of the problem. For $g \in G$ we write $x \to g \cdot x$ for the symmetry associated with $g$ and assume that $g, x \to g \cdot x$ is $C^\infty$ from $G \times M$ into $M$. In such problems, one restricts oneself to the momenta specified by the one-parameter groups of $M$. If $\mathfrak{g}$ is the Lie algebra of $G$ (cf. Chevalley [1]) and if we associate for $X \in \mathfrak{g}$, the vector field on $M$ denoted by $X$ also and defined by

$$(Xf)(x) = \left(\frac{d}{dt}f(\exp tX \cdot x)\right)_{t=0},$$

then we obtain the relations

$$(10) \qquad \begin{aligned} \mu_{[X,Y]} &= [\mu_X,\mu_Y], \\ [\mu_X,f^0] &= (Xf)^0 \end{aligned}$$

between the configuration observables $f^0$ and the momentum observables $\mu_X$. These relations are usually referred to as *commutation rules*.

## 2. THE LOGIC OF A CLASSICAL SYSTEM

We shall now examine the algebraic aspects of a general classical system. In view of the discussion carried out just now, it is clear that for any classical system $\mathfrak{S}$ there is associated a space $S$ called the phase space of $\mathfrak{S}$. The states of the system are in one-one correspondence with the points of $S$. The notion of a state is so formulated that if one knows the state of the system at an instant of time $t_0$, and also the dynamical law of evolution of the system, then one can determine the state of the system at time $t + t_0$. The observables or physical quantities which are of interest to the observer are then represented by real valued functions on $S$. If $f$ is the function corresponding to a particular observable, its value $f(s)$ at the point $s$ of $S$ is interpreted as the value of the physical quantity when the system is in the state $s$. If $s$ is the state of the system at time $t_0$, we can write $D(t)s$ for the state of the system at time $t + t_0$. We thus have a trans-formation $D(t)$ of $S$ into itself. For each $t$, $D(t)$ is invertible and maps $S$ onto itself. The correspondence $t \to D(t)$ satisfies the equations (3). $t \to D(t)$ is then a one-parameter group of transformations of $S$. It is called the *dynamical group* of the system $\mathfrak{S}$.

These concepts make sense in every classical system. In the case of any such system the most general statement which can be made about it is one which asserts that the value of a certain observable lies in a real number set $E$. If the observable is represented by the function $f$ on $S$, then such a statement is equivalent to the statement that the state of the system lies in the set $f^{-1}(E)$ of the space $S$. In other words, the physically meaningful statements that can be made about the system are in correspondence with certain subsets of $S$. The inclusion relations for subsets naturally correspond to implications of statements. In mathematical terms, this means that at the background of the classical system there is a Boolean algebra of subsets of the space $S$, the elements of which represent the statements about the physical system. It is natural to call this Boolean algebra the *logic* of the system.

Suppose now that $\mathfrak{S}$ is a system which does not follow the laws of classical mechanics. Then one cannot associate with it a phase space in general. It is nevertheless meaningful to consider the totality of experimentally verifiable statements which may be made about the system. This collection, which may be called the *logic* of $\mathfrak{S}$, comes equipped with the relations of implication and negation which convert it into a complemented partially ordered set. For a classical system this partially ordered set is a Boolean algebra. Clearly, it is possible to conceive of mechanical systems whose logics are not Boolean algebras. *We take the point of view that quantum mechanical systems are those whose logics form some sort of projective geometries and which are consequently nondistributive lattices.* With such a point of view it is possible to understand the role played by simultaneously observable quantities, the uncertainty relations, and the complementarity principles. These phenomena, which are so peculiar to quantum systems, will then be seen to be consequences of the nondistributive nature of the logic in the background of the system $\mathfrak{S}$.

It might seem a bit surprising that the basic assumption on a quantum system is that its logic is not a distributive lattice. It would be natural to argue that statements about a physical system should obey the same rules as the rules of ordinary set theory. The well known critiques of von Neumann and Heisenberg answer this question (von Neumann [1], Birkhoff-von Neumann [1], Heisenberg [1]). The point is that only *experimentally verifiable statements* are to be regarded as members of the logic of the system. Consequently, as it happens in many questions in atomic physics, it may be impossible to verify experimentally statements which involve the values of two physical quantities of the system—for example, measurements of the position and momentum of an electron. One can verify statements about one of them but not, in general, those which involve both of them. What the basic assumptions imply is that the statements regarding position or momentum form two Boolean subalgebras of the logic but that there is in general no Boolean algebra which contains both of these Boolean subalgebras.

Before beginning an analysis of the logic of general quantum mechanical systems it would be helpful to recast at least some of the features of the formulation given in section 1 in terms of the logic of the classical system. In the first place it is natural to strengthen the hypothesis and assume that the logic of a given classical system $\mathfrak{S}$ is a Boolean $\sigma$-algebra, say $\mathscr{L}$, of subsets of $S$, the phase space of $\mathfrak{S}$. Suppose now, that an observable associated with the system is represented by the real valued function $f$ on $S$. The statements concerning the observable are then those which assert that its value lies in an arbitrary Borel set $E$ of the real line and these are represented by the subsets $f^{-1}(E)$ of $S$. The observable can thus be represented, without any loss of physical content, equally by the map $E \to f^{-1}(E)$ of the class of Borel subsets of the real line into $\mathscr{L}$. The range of this mapping is a sub-$\sigma$-algebra, say $\mathscr{L}_f$. Suppose $g$ is a real valued Borel function on the real line. Then, the observable represented by the function $g \circ f\ (s \to g(f(s)))$ can also be represented by the map $E \to f^{-1}(g^{-1}(E))$ from which we conclude that $\mathscr{L}_{g \circ f}$ is contained in $\mathscr{L}_f$.

In order to formulate the general features of a classical mechanical system in terms of its logic $\mathscr{L}$, it is therefore necessary to determine to what extent an abstract $\sigma$-algebra $\mathscr{L}$ can be regarded as a $\sigma$-algebra of subsets of some space $S$; further to determine the class of mappings from the $\sigma$-algebra of Borel sets of the real line into $\mathscr{L}$ which correspond to real valued functions on $S$; and to clarify the concept of functional dependence in this general context. We shall now proceed to a discussion of these questions.

## 3. BOOLEAN ALGEBRAS

Let $\mathscr{L}$ be a nonempty set. $\mathscr{L}$ is said to be *partially ordered* if there is a relation $<$ between some pairs of elements of $\mathscr{L}$ such that (i) $a < a$ for all $a$ in $\mathscr{L}$; (ii) $a < b$ and $b < a$ imply $a = b$; (iii) $a < b$ and $b < c$ imply $a < c$. If $\mathscr{L}$ is partially ordered, there is at most one element called the *null* or *zero* element and denoted by 0, such that $0 < a$ for all $a$ in $\mathscr{L}$. Similarly there is at most one element called the *unit* element and denoted by 1, such that $a < 1$ for all $a$ in $\mathscr{L}$. More generally, for any nonempty subset $F$ of $\mathscr{L}$ there exists at most one element $c$ of $\mathscr{L}$ such that (i) $a < c$ for all $a \in F$; (ii) if $d$ is any element of $\mathscr{L}$ such that $a < d$ for all $a \in F$, then $c < d$. We shall write $\bigvee_{a \in F} a$ for $c$ whenever it exists. If $F$ is a finite set, say $F = \{a_1, \cdots, a_n\}$, it is customary to write $\bigvee_{i=1}^{n} a_i$ or $a_1 \vee a_2 \vee \cdots \vee a_n$ instead of $\bigvee_{a \in F} a$. In an analogous fashion, for any subset $F$ of $\mathscr{L}$ there exists at most one element $c$ such that (i) $c < a$ for all $a \in F$; (ii) if $d$ is any element of $\mathscr{L}$ such that $d < a$ for all $a \in F$, then $d < c$; we denote it by $\bigwedge_{a \in F} a$ whenever it exists. If $F$ is a finite set, say $F = \{a_1, \cdots, a_n\}$, we often write $\bigwedge_{i=1}^{n} a_i$ or $a_1 \wedge a_2 \wedge \cdots \wedge a_n$ instead of $\bigwedge_{a \in F} a$. The partially ordered set $\mathscr{L}$ is called a *lattice* if

(11)    (i)  0 and 1 exist in $\mathscr{L}$ and $0 \neq 1$,
         (ii)  $\bigvee_{a \in F} a$ and $\bigwedge_{a \in F} a$ exist for all finite subsets $F$ of $\mathscr{L}$.

Suppose that $\mathscr{L}$ is a lattice. Given any element $a$ of $\mathscr{L}$, an element $a'$ of $\mathscr{L}$ is said to be a *complement* of $a$ if $a \wedge a' = 0$ and $a \vee a' = 1$. $a$ is then a complement of $a'$. $\mathscr{L}$ is said to be *complemented* if, given any element, there exists at least one complement of it. It is obvious that 0 and 1 have the unique complements 1 and 0, respectively. A lattice $\mathscr{L}$ is said to be *distributive* if for any three elements $a$, $b$, $c$ of $\mathscr{L}$, the identities

$$a \wedge (b \vee c) = (a \wedge b) \vee (a \wedge c),$$
$$a \vee (b \wedge c) = (a \vee b) \wedge (a \vee c)$$

are satisfied. A complemented distributive lattice is called a *Boolean algebra*. A *Boolean $\sigma$-algebra* $\mathscr{L}$ is a Boolean algebra in which $\bigwedge_{a \in F} a$ and $\bigvee_{a \in F} a$ exist for every countable subset $F$ of $\mathscr{L}$.

Every element in a Boolean algebra has a unique complement. Suppose in fact that $\mathscr{L}$ is a Boolean algebra and that $a$ is an element with two complements $a_1$ and $a_2$. Then, one has

$$a_1 = a_1 \wedge (a \vee a_2) = (a_1 \wedge a) \vee (a_1 \wedge a_2) = a_1 \wedge a_2 < a_2;$$

similarly, $a_2 < a_1$, so that $a_1 = a_2$. The unique complement of $a$ is denoted by $a'$. Using the standard manipulations of set theory it is easy to show that $(\bigwedge_{a \in F} a)' = \bigvee_{a \in F} a'$ and $(\bigvee_{a \in F} a)' = \bigwedge_{a \in F} a'$ for any finite subset $F$ of $\mathcal{L}$. If $\mathcal{L}$ is a Boolean $\sigma$-algebra, then the same identities remain valid even when $F$ is countably infinite. If $\mathcal{L}$ is any Boolean algebra and $a$, $b$ are elements in it with $a < b$, $c = a' \wedge b$ is the unique element of $\mathcal{L}$ such that $a \wedge c = 0$ and $a \vee c = b$; $c$ is called *the complement of $a$ in $b$*. Since $c = b \wedge a'$, $c < a'$ (cf. Birkhoff [1] and Sikorski [1] for the general theory of Boolean algebras and $\sigma$-algebras).

A *homomorphism* of a Boolean algebra $\mathcal{L}_1$ into a Boolean algebra $\mathcal{L}_2$ is a map $h$ of $\mathcal{L}_1$ into $\mathcal{L}_2$ such that (i) $h(0) = 0$, $h(1) = 1$; (ii) $h(a') = h(a)'$ for all $a$ in $\mathcal{L}_1$; (iii) $h(a \vee b) = h(a) \vee h(b)$, $h(a \wedge b) = h(a) \wedge h(b)$ for all $a$, $b$ in $\mathcal{L}_1$. If $h$ is a homomorphism and $a < b$, then $h(a) < h(b)$. An *isomorphism* of $\mathcal{L}_1$ onto $\mathcal{L}_2$ is a homomorphism $h$ of $\mathcal{L}_1$ onto $\mathcal{L}_2$ such that $h(a) = 0$ if and only if $a = 0$; in this case $h$ is also one-one.

The class of *all* subsets of any set is a Boolean algebra under set inclusion and set complementation. However, obviously this is not the most general Boolean algebra since infinite unions and intersections exist in it. Suppose now that $X$ is a topological space. The class of subsets of $X$ which are both open and closed (open-closed) is obviously a Boolean algebra. A well known theorem of Stone [1] asserts that every Boolean algebra is isomorphic to one such and that, if we require the topological space to be compact Hausdorff as well as totally disconnected, it is essentially uniquely determined by the Boolean algebra. We recall that a compact space is said to be *totally disconnected* if every open subset of it can be written as a union of open-closed subsets. We shall call a compact Hausdorff totally disconnected space a *Stone space*.

Let $\mathcal{L}$ be a Boolean algebra. A subset $\mathcal{M}$ of $\mathcal{L}$ is called a *dual ideal* if the following properties are satisfied:

(i)  $0 \notin \mathcal{M}$,

(ii)  if $a \in \mathcal{M}$ and $a < b$, then $b \in \mathcal{M}$,

(iii)  if $a, b \in \mathcal{M}$, then $a \wedge b \in \mathcal{M}$.

$\mathcal{M}$ is said to be *maximal* if it is properly contained in no other dual ideal.

The naturalness of the notion of maximal dual ideals can be seen in the following way. Let $X$ be a Stone space and $\mathcal{L} = \mathcal{L}(X)$ the Boolean algebra of all open-closed subsets of $X$. Then, for any $x \in X$, the collection $\mathcal{M}(x)$, where

$$\mathcal{M}(x) = \{A : A \in \mathcal{L}, x \in A\},$$

is easily seen to be a maximal dual ideal; it is also easy to check that the correspondence $x \to \mathcal{M}(x)$ is one-one if we notice that $X$ is Hausdorff. The concept of maximal dual ideals is central in the proof of Stone's theorem.

Suppose that $\mathscr{L}$ is an arbitrary Boolean algebra. Using Zorn's lemma one can show easily that maximal dual ideals of $\mathscr{L}$ exist. Let $X = X(\mathscr{L})$ be the set of all maximal dual ideals of $\mathscr{L}$. For any $a \in \mathscr{L}$ we define $X_a$ by

$$X_a = \{\mathscr{M} : \mathscr{M} \in X, a \in \mathscr{M}\},$$

$X_0 = \varnothing$, the null set, and $X_1 = X$. We shall say that a subset $A \subseteq X$ is *open* if $A$ is the union of sets of the form $X_a$. This definition defines the structure of a topology on $X$ called the *Stone topology*. We now have:

**Theorem 1.1** (*Stone* [1]). *Let $\mathscr{L}$ be a Boolean algebra and let $X = X(\mathscr{L})$ be the space of all maximal dual ideals of $\mathscr{L}$. Then, equipped with the Stone topology, $X$ becomes a Stone space. The map $a \to X_a$ is then an isomorphism of $\mathscr{L}$ with the Boolean algebra of all open-closed subsets of $X$. $X$ is determined by $\mathscr{L}$, among the class of Stone spaces, up to a homeomorphism. More generally, let $X$ and $Y$ be Stone spaces and let $\mathscr{L}(X)$ and $\mathscr{L}(Y)$ be their respective Boolean algebras of open-closed subsets. If $u$ is any isomorphism of $\mathscr{L}(Y)$ onto $\mathscr{L}(X)$, there exists a homeomorphism $h$ of $X$ onto $Y$ such that*

$$(12) \qquad\qquad u(A) = h^{-1}(A) \qquad (A \in \mathscr{L}(Y));$$

*moreover, $h$ is uniquely determined by* (12).

This theorem is very well known and we do not give its proof. The reader may consult the books of Birkhoff [1], Sikorski [1], and the paper of Stone [1] for the proof.

**Corollary 1.2.** *Let $X$ be a Stone space and let $\mathscr{L} = \mathscr{L}(X)$ be the Boolean algebra of open-closed subsets of $X$. If $t \to D_t(-\infty < t < \infty)$ is any one-parameter group of automorphisms of $\mathscr{L}$, there exists a unique one-parameter group $t \to h_t$ of homeomorphisms of $X$ onto itself such that for all $t$ and $A \in \mathscr{L}$, $D_t(A) = h_t^{-1}(A)$.*

**Proof.** Theorem 1.1 ensures the existence and uniqueness of each $h_t$. If $t_1$, $t_2$ are real, then $h_{t_1 + t_2}$ and $h_{t_1} \circ h_{t_2}$ induce the same automorphism $D_{t_1 + t_2}$ of $\mathscr{L}$, so that $h_{t_1 + t_2} = h_{t_1} \circ h_{t_2}$.

The theorem of Stone shows that there is essentially no distinction between an abstract Boolean algebra and a Boolean algebra of sets. If one deals with Boolean $\sigma$-algebras, the situation becomes somewhat less straightforward. We shall now describe the modifications necessary when one replaces Boolean algebras by Boolean $\sigma$-algebras.

If $\mathscr{L}_1$ and $\mathscr{L}_2$ are Boolean $\sigma$-algebras, and $h$ a map of $\mathscr{L}_1$ into $\mathscr{L}_2$, $h$ is called a $\sigma$-*homomorphism* if (i) $h(0) = 0$, $h(1) = 1$; (ii) $h(a') = h(a)'$ for all $a \in \mathscr{L}_1$; and (iii) if $F$ is any subset of $\mathscr{L}_1$ which is finite or countably infinite, $h(\bigvee_{a \in F} a) = \bigvee_{a \in F} h(a)$ and $h(\bigwedge_{a \in F} a) = \bigwedge_{a \in F} h(a)$. Suppose $\mathscr{L}_1$

and $\mathcal{L}_2$ are two Boolean $\sigma$-algebras and $h$ a $\sigma$-homomorphism of $\mathcal{L}_1$ onto $\mathcal{L}_2$. The set $\mathcal{N} = \{a : a \in \mathcal{L}_1, h(a) = 0\}$ is a subset of $\mathcal{L}_1$ with the properties: (i) $0 \in \mathcal{N}$, $1 \notin \mathcal{N}$; (ii) if $a \in \mathcal{N}$ and $b < a$, then $b \in \mathcal{N}$; (iii) if $F$ is a countable subset of $\mathcal{N}$, $\bigvee_{a \in F} a \in \mathcal{N}$. $\mathcal{N}$ is called the *kernel* of $h$. Suppose conversely $\mathcal{L}$ is a Boolean $\sigma$-algebra and $\mathcal{N}$ a subset of $\mathcal{L}$ with properties (i) to (iii) listed above. We shall say that elements $a$ and $b$ of $\mathcal{L}$ are equivalent, $a \sim b$, if $a \wedge b'$ and $b \wedge a'$ are in $\mathcal{N}$. It is easily verified that $\sim$ is an equivalence relation. Let $\overline{\mathcal{L}}$ be the set of all equivalence classes, and for any $a$ in $\mathcal{L}$, let $\overline{a}$ denote the unique equivalence class containing $a$. We define $\overline{a} < \overline{b}$ whenever there are elements $a$ in $\overline{a}$, and $b$ in $\overline{b}$ such that $a < b$. It is then easily shown that $\overline{\mathcal{L}}$ is a Boolean $\sigma$-algebra whose zero and unit elements are, respectively, $\overline{0}$ and $\overline{1}$, and that the map $a \rightarrow \overline{a}$ is a $\sigma$-homomorphism of $\mathcal{L}$ onto $\overline{\mathcal{L}}$ with kernel $\mathcal{N}$. We write $\overline{\mathcal{L}} = \mathcal{L}/\mathcal{N}$.

**Theorem 1.3** (*Loomis* [1]). *Let $\mathcal{L}$ be a Boolean $\sigma$-algebra. Then there exists a set $X$, a $\sigma$-algebra $\mathcal{S}$ of subsets of $X$, and a $\sigma$-homomorphism $h$ of $\mathcal{S}$ onto $\mathcal{L}$.*

**Proof.** Let $X$ be a Stone space such that the lattice $\mathcal{L}' = \mathcal{L}(X)$ of open-closed subsets of $X$ is isomorphic to the Boolean algebra $\mathcal{L}$. Let $\mathcal{S}$ denote the smallest $\sigma$-algebra of subsets of $X$ containing $\mathcal{L}'$. We denote by $\cup$ and $\cap$ the operations of set union and set intersection for subsets of $X$, and by $\vee$ and $\wedge$ the lattice-theoretic operations in $\mathcal{L}$ and $\mathcal{L}'$.

If $A_1, A_2, \cdots$ is any sequence of sets in $\mathcal{L}'$, then $\bigvee_n A_n = A$ exists in $\mathcal{L}'$ since $\mathcal{L}'$ is isomorphic to $\mathcal{L}$ and $\mathcal{L}$ is a $\sigma$-algebra. Since $A$ is the smallest element of $\mathcal{L}'$ containing all the $A_n$, it follows that the set $A - \bigcup_n A_n$ cannot contain any element of $\mathcal{L}'$ as a subset. The sets in $\mathcal{L}'$ form a base for the topology of $X$ and hence we conclude that $A - \bigcup_n A_n$ cannot contain any nonnull open set. Since $\bigcup_n A_n$ is open, this shows that $A - \bigcup_n A_n$ is a closed nondense set.

Consider now the class $\mathcal{S}_1$ of all sets $A \in \mathcal{S}$ with the property that for some $B$ in $\mathcal{L}'$, $(A - B) \cup (B - A)$ is of the first category. If $B_1$ and $B_2$ are elements of $\mathcal{L}'$ such that $(A - B_i) \cup (B_i - A)$ is of the first category $(i = 1, 2)$, then it will follow that $(B_1 - B_2) \cup (B_2 - B_1)$ is of the first category, which is not possible (by the category theorem of Baire) unless $B_1 = B_2$. Thus, for any $A$ in $\mathcal{S}_1$ there exists a *unique* $B = h_1(A)$ in $\mathcal{L}'$ such that $(A - B) \cup (B - A)$ is of the first category. Clearly $\mathcal{L}' \subseteq \mathcal{S}_1$, and for $A \in \mathcal{L}'$, $h_1(A) = A$.

We claim that $\mathcal{S}_1$ is a $\sigma$-algebra. Since

$$(A - B) \cup (B - A) = (A' - B') \cup (B' - A')$$

(primes denoting complementation in $X$), we see that for any $A$ in $\mathcal{S}_1$,

$A'$ is in $\mathscr{S}_1$ and $h_1(A')=h_1(A)'$. Suppose $A_1, A_2, \cdots$ is any sequence in $\mathscr{S}_1$. Write $B_n=h_1(A_n)$, $A=\bigcup_n A_n$, $B=\bigvee_n B_n$, $B_0=\bigcup_n B_n$. By what we said above, $B-B_0$ is a closed nondense set. Moreover, as $B_0 \subseteq B$, we have

$$(A-B) \cup (B-A) \subseteq \{(A-B_0) \cup (B_0-A)\} \cup (B-B_0)$$
$$\subseteq \bigcup_n \{(A_n-B_n) \cup (B_n-A_n)\} \cup (B-B_0).$$

As all members of the right side are of the first category, this proves that $A \in \mathscr{S}_1$ and $h_1(A)=\bigvee_n h_1(A_n)$. In a similar fashion we can show that $\bigcap_n A_n$ lies in $\mathscr{S}_1$ and $h_1(\bigcap_n A_n)=\bigwedge_n h_1(A_n)$.

The conclusions of the preceding paragraph show that $\mathscr{S}_1$, is a Boolean $\sigma$-algebra $\subseteq \mathscr{S}$. Since $\mathscr{S}_1$ contains $\mathscr{L}'$, $\mathscr{S}_1 = \mathscr{S}$. Moreover, we see at the same time that $h_1$ is a $\sigma$-homomorphism of $\mathscr{S}$ onto $\mathscr{L}'$. If we write $h=k \circ h_1$ where $k$ is an isomorphism of $\mathscr{L}'$ onto $\mathscr{L}$, then $h$ is a $\sigma$-homomorphism of $\mathscr{S}$ onto $\mathscr{L}$.

**Remark.** Let $\mathscr{S}$ be the $\sigma$-algebra of Borel sets on the unit interval $[0,1]$, $\mathscr{N}$ the class of Borel sets of Lebesgue measure 0, and $\mathscr{L} = \mathscr{S}/\mathscr{N}$. Then $\mathscr{L}$ is a Boolean $\sigma$-algebra. We can obviously define Lebesgue measure $\lambda$ as a countably additive function $\lambda$ on $\mathscr{L}$; $\lambda$ is strictly positive in the sense that for any $a \neq 0$ of $\mathscr{L}$, $\lambda(a)$ is positive. From this it follows that any family of mutually disjoint elements of $\mathscr{L}$ is countable. On the other hand, since $\mathscr{S}$ is countably generated, so is $\mathscr{L}$. However, any $\sigma$-algebra of subsets of some space $X$ which is countably generated can be proved to have atoms, that is, minimal elements. Since $\mathscr{L}$ does not have atoms, $\mathscr{L}$ cannot be isomorphic to any $\sigma$-algebra of sets.

## 4. FUNCTIONS

We now take up the second question raised in section 2, namely, the problem of describing the calculus of functions on a set $X$ entirely in terms of the Boolean $\sigma$-algebra of subsets of $X$ with respect to which all these functions are measurable. The results are summarized in theorems 1.4 and 1.6 of this section.

Let $X$ be any set of points $x$ and $\mathscr{S}$ a Boolean $\sigma$-algebra of subsets of $X$. A function $f$ from $X$ into a complete separable metric space $Y$ is said to be $\mathscr{S}$-measurable if $f^{-1}(E) \in \mathscr{S}$ for all Borel sets $E \subseteq Y$. If $f$ is $\mathscr{S}$-measurable, the mapping $E \rightarrow f^{-1}(E)$ is a $\sigma$-homomorphism of the $\sigma$-algebra $\mathscr{B}(Y)$ of Borel subsets of $Y$ into $\mathscr{S}$. Suppose now $\mathscr{L}$ is an abstract Boolean $\sigma$-algebra. We shall then define a *Y-valued observable associated with* $\mathscr{L}$ to be any $\sigma$-homomorphism of $\mathscr{B}(Y)$ into $\mathscr{L}$. If $Y=R^1$, the real line, we call these observables *real valued* and refer to them simply as *observables*. From our definition of $\sigma$-homomorphisms we see that a map $u(E \rightarrow u(E))$

of $\mathscr{B}(Y)$ into $\mathscr{L}$ is a $Y$-valued observable associated with $\mathscr{L}$ if and only if
(i) $u(\varnothing)=0$, $u(Y)=1$; (ii) $u(Y-E)=u(E)'$ for all $E$ in $\mathscr{B}(Y)$; (iii) if
$E_1, E_2, \cdots$ is any sequence of Borel sets in $Y$, $u(\bigcup_n E_n)=\bigvee_n u(E_n)$ and
$u(\bigcap_n E_n)=\bigwedge_n u(E_n)$.

**Theorem 1.4** *Let $X$ be a set, $\mathscr{S}$ a Boolean $\sigma$-algebra of subsets of $X$ and
$h$ a $\sigma$-homomorphism of $\mathscr{S}$ onto a Boolean $\sigma$-algebra $\mathscr{L}$. Suppose further
that $u(E \to u(E))$ is any (real valued) observable associated with $\mathscr{L}$. Then
there exists an $\mathscr{S}$-measurable real valued function $f$ defined on $X$ such that*

$$(13) \qquad u(E) = h(f^{-1}(E))$$

*for all Borel sets $E \subseteq R^1$. $f$ is essentially unique in the sense that if $g$ is any
$\mathscr{S}$-measurable real valued function defined on $X$ such that $u(E)=h(g^{-1}(E))$
for all Borel sets $E \subseteq R^1$, the set $\{x : x \in X, f(x) \neq g(x)\}$ belongs to the kernel
of $h$.*

**Proof.** We begin with a simple observation. Suppose $A$ and $B$ are two
subsets of $X$ in $\mathscr{S}$ such that $A \subseteq B$, and $c$ any element of $\mathscr{L}$ such that
$h(A) < c < h(B)$. Then we can select a set $C$ in $\mathscr{S}$ such that $A \subseteq C \subseteq B$ and
$h(C)=c$. In fact, since $h$ maps $\mathscr{S}$ onto $\mathscr{L}$, there exists $C_1$ in $\mathscr{S}$ such that
$h(C_1)=c$. If we define $C=(C_1 \cap B) \cup A$, then $A \subseteq C \subseteq B$ while

$$h(C) = (h(C_1) \wedge h(B)) \vee h(A) = (c \wedge b) \vee a = c.$$

We now come to the proof of theorem 1.4. Let $r_1, r_2, \cdots$ be any distinct
enumeration of the rational numbers in $R^1$ and let $D_i$ be the interval
$\{t : t \in R^1, t < r_i\}$. Evidently, $u(D_i) < u(D_j)$ whenever $r_i < r_j$. We shall now
construct sets $A_1, A_2, \cdots$ in $\mathscr{S}$ such that (a) $h(A_i)=u(D_i)$ for all $i=1, 2, 3$,
$\cdots$; (b) $A_i \subseteq A_j$ whenever $r_i < r_j$. Let $A_1$ be any set in $\mathscr{S}$ such that
$h(A_1)=u(D_1)$. Suppose $A_1, A_2, A_3, \cdots, A_n$ in $\mathscr{S}$ have been constructed
such that (i) $h(A_i)=u(D_i)$ for $i=1, 2, \cdots, n$; (ii) $A_i \subseteq A_j$ whenever $r_i < r_j$,
$1 \leq i, j \leq n$. We shall construct $A_{n+1}$ as follows. Let $(i_1, i_2, \cdots, i_n)$ be the
permutation of $(1, 2, \cdots, n)$ such that $r_{i_1} < r_{i_2} < \cdots < r_{i_n}$. Then, there
exists a unique $k$ such that $r_{i_k} < r_{n+1} < r_{i_{k+1}}$ (we define $r_{i_0} = -\infty$ and
$r_{i_{n+1}} = +\infty$), and by the observation made in the preceding paragraph,
we can select $A_{n+1}$ in $\mathscr{S}$ such that $A_{i_k} \subseteq A_{n+1} \subseteq A_{i_{k+1}}$ (we define $A_{i_0} = \varnothing$,
$A_{i_{n+1}}=X$). The collection $\{A_1, A_2, \cdots, A_{n+1}\}$ then has the same pro-
perties relative to $r_1, r_2, \cdots, r_{n+1}$ as $\{A_1, \cdots, A_n\}$ had relative to
$r_1, r_2, \cdots, r_n$. It thus follows by induction that there exists a sequence
$A_1, A_2 \cdots$ of sets in $\mathscr{S}$ with the properties (a) and (b). As

$$h\left(\bigcap_j A_j\right) = \bigwedge_j u(D_j) = u\left(\bigwedge_j D_j\right) = 0,$$

we may, by replacing $A_k$ by $A_k - \bigcap_j A_j$ if necessary, assume that

$\bigcap_j A_j = \varnothing$. Further $h(\bigcup_j A_j) = \bigvee_j u(D_j) = u(\bigvee_j D_j) = 1$ so that $h(N) = 0$, where $N = X - \bigcup_j A_j$. We now define a function $f$ as follows:

(14)
$$f(x) = \begin{cases} 0 & \text{if } x \in N, \\ \inf\{r_j : x \in A_j\} & \text{if } x \in \bigcup_j A_j. \end{cases}$$

Clearly, $f$ is finite everywhere. Moreover, for any $k$,

$$f^{-1}(D_k) \cap (X - N) = \bigcup_{j : r_j < r_k} A_j,$$

so that $f$ is $\mathscr{S}$-measurable. Further,

$$\begin{aligned} h(f^{-1}(D_k)) &= h\Big( \bigcup_{j : r_j < r_k} A_j \Big) \\ &= \bigvee_{j : r_j < r_k} u(D_j) \\ &= u(D_k), \end{aligned}$$

so that $h(f^{-1}(E)) = u(E)$ whenever $E = D_k$ for some $k$. Since the class of all $E$ for which this equation is valid is a Boolean $\sigma$-algebra, we conclude that $h(f^{-1}(E)) = u(E)$ for all Borel sets $E$.

It remains to examine the uniqueness. Let $g$ be any real valued $\mathscr{S}$-measurable function on $X$ such that $h(g^{-1}(E)) = u(E)$ for all Borel sets $E$. Then, if we write $D_k{}'$ for $R^1 - D_k$,

$$\begin{aligned} M &= \{x : x \in X, f(x) \neq g(x)\} \\ &= \bigcup_k \{(f^{-1}(D_k) \cap g^{-1}(D_k{}')) \cup (f^{-1}(D_k{}') \cap g^{-1}(D_k))\}, \end{aligned}$$

so that

$$\begin{aligned} h(M) &= \bigvee_k \{u(D_k) \wedge u(D_k{}')\} \\ &= 0. \end{aligned}$$

This shows that $M$ belongs to the kernel of $h$. This completes the proof of the theorem.

**Lemma 1.5.** *Let $X$ be a set, $\mathscr{S}$ a $\sigma$-algebra of subsets of $X$ and $f$ an $\mathscr{S}$-measurable mapping of $X$ into $R^n$. Suppose $\mathscr{S}^\sim = \{f^{-1}(F) : F \in \mathscr{B}(R^n)\}$. Then to any $\mathscr{S}^\sim$-measurable real function $c$ on $X$ there corresponds a real valued Borel function $c^\sim$ on $R^n$ such that $c(x) = c^\sim(f(x))$ for all $x \in X$.*

**Proof.** Since $c$ is $\mathscr{S}^\sim$-measurable, there exists a sequence $c_n$ $(n = 1, 2, \cdots)$ of $\mathscr{S}^\sim$-measurable functions such that (i) each $c_n$ takes only finitely many values; (ii) $c_n(x) \to c(x)$ for all $x \in X$. For any $n$, let $A_{n1}, A_{n2}, \cdots, A_{nk_n}$ be disjoint subsets of $X$ whose union is $X$ such that $c_n$ is a constant, say $a_{ni}$, on $A_{ni}$, the $a_{ni}$ being distinct for $i = 1, 2, \cdots, k_n$. Since $c_n$ is $\mathscr{S}^\sim$-measurable, $A_{ni} \in \mathscr{S}^\sim$; so there exists a Borel set $B_{ni}$ of $R^n$ such that $A_{ni} = f^{-1}(B_{ni})$

$(i = 1, 2, \cdots, k_n)$. Replacing $B_{ni}$ by $B_{ni} - \bigcup_{j<i} B_{nj}$ if necessary, we may assume that the $B_{ni}$ are disjoint. Let us define the function $c_n{}^\sim$ on $R^n$ as follows:

$$c_n{}^\sim(t) = \begin{cases} a_{ni} & \text{if } t \in B_{ni}, \\ 0 & \text{if } t \notin \bigcup_i B_{ni}. \end{cases}$$

Clearly $c_n{}^\sim$ is Borel and $c_n(x) = c_n{}^\sim(f(x))$ for all $x$ in $X$. Let us define $c^\sim$ on $R^n$ as follows:

$$c^\sim(t) = \begin{cases} \lim_{n \to \infty} c_n{}^\sim(t) & \text{if the limit exists}, \\ 0 & \text{otherwise}. \end{cases}$$

Clearly $c^\sim$ is Borel. Since $c_n(x) = c_n{}^\sim(f(x))$ and $\lim c_n(x)$ exists and is equal to $c(x)$ for all $x$ in $X$, $c^\sim(f(x)) = c(x)$ for all $x$ in $X$.

Let $\mathscr{L}$ be a Boolean $\sigma$-algebra. $\mathscr{L}_1 \subseteq \mathscr{L}$ is said to be a *sub-$\sigma$-algebra* if (i) $0, 1 \in \mathscr{L}_1$; (ii) if $a \in \mathscr{L}_1$, then $a' \in \mathscr{L}_1$; (iii) if $a_1, a_2, \cdots$ are in $\mathscr{L}_1$, then $\bigvee_n a_n$ and $\bigwedge_n a_n$ are in $\mathscr{L}_1$. A sub-$\sigma$-algebra $\mathscr{L}_1$ is said to be *separable* if there exists a countable subset $D$ of $\mathscr{L}$ such that $\mathscr{L}_1$ is the smallest sub-$\sigma$-algebra of $\mathscr{L}$ containing $D$.

**Theorem 1.6.** (i) *Let $\mathscr{L}$ be a Boolean $\sigma$-algebra and $u(E \to u(E))$ an observable associated with $\mathscr{L}$. Then the range $\mathscr{L}_u = \{u(E) : E \in \mathscr{B}(R^1)\}$ of $u$ is a separable Boolean sub-$\sigma$-algebra of $\mathscr{L}$. Conversely, if $\mathscr{L}_1$ is a separable Boolean sub-$\sigma$-algebra of $\mathscr{L}$, there exists an observable $u$ associated with $\mathscr{L}$ such that $\mathscr{L}_1$ is the range of $u$.*

(ii) *Let $u_i$ $(i = 1, 2, \cdots, n)$ be observables associated with $\mathscr{L}$, and $\mathscr{L}_i$ $(i = 1, 2, \cdots, n)$ their respective ranges. Suppose $\mathscr{L}_0$ is the smallest sub-$\sigma$-algebra of $\mathscr{L}$ containing all the $\mathscr{L}_i$. Then there exists a unique $\sigma$-homomorphism $u$ of $\mathscr{B}(R^n)$ (the $\sigma$-algebra of Borel subsets of the $n$-dimensional space $R^n$) onto $\mathscr{L}_0$ such that for any Borel set $E$ of $R^1$, $u_i(E) = u(p_i{}^{-1}(E))$, where $p_i$ is the projection $(t_1, t_2, \cdots, t_n) \to t_i$ of $R^n$ onto $R^1$. If $\varphi$ is any real valued Borel function on $R^n$, the map $E \to u(\varphi^{-1}(E))(E \in \mathscr{B}(R^1))$ is an observable associated with $\mathscr{L}$ whose range is contained in $\mathscr{L}_0$. Conversely, if $v(E \to v(E))$ is any observable associated with $\mathscr{L}$ such that the range of $v$ is contained in $\mathscr{L}_0$, there exists a real valued Borel function $\varphi$ on $R^n$ such that $v(E) = u(\varphi^{-1}(E))$ for all $E$.*

**Proof.** If $u$ is an observable with range $\mathscr{L}_u$, $\mathscr{L}_u$ is obviously the smallest sub-$\sigma$-algebra of $\mathscr{L}$ containing all the $u(E)$, where $E$ is any open interval of $R^1$ with rational end points. This shows that $\mathscr{L}_u$ is separable.

Suppose conversely that $\mathscr{L}_1 \subseteq \mathscr{L}$ is a separable sub-$\sigma$-algebra of $\mathscr{L}$. By theorem 1.3 there exists a set $X$, a $\sigma$-algebra $\mathscr{S}$ of subsets of $X$, and a $\sigma$-homomorphism $h$ of $\mathscr{S}$ onto $\mathscr{L}$. Let $\{A_n : n = 1, 2, \cdots\}$ be a countable family of sets of $\mathscr{S}$ such that $\mathscr{L}_1$ is the smallest sub $\sigma$-algebra of $\mathscr{L}$

containing all the $h(A_n)$. We denote by $\mathscr{S}_0$ the smallest $\sigma$-algebra of subsets of $X$ containing all the $A_n$. The function

$$c : x \to (\chi_{A_1}(x), \chi_{A_2}(x), \cdots, \chi_{A_n}(x), \cdots)$$

(where $\chi_A$ denotes the function which is 1 on $A$, and 0 on $X - A$) is $\mathscr{S}_0$-measurable from $X$ into the compact metric space $Y$ which is the product of countably many copies of the 2-point space consisting of 0 and 1. Moreover, it is obvious that each $A_n$ is of the form $c^{-1}(F)$ for some Borel set $F \subseteq Y$, and hence $\mathscr{S}_0 = \{c^{-1}(F) : F \text{ Borel in } Y\}$. Now, by a classical theorem (Kuratowski [1]), there exists a Borel isomorphism $d$ of $Y$ onto $R^1$, so that the function $c_1 : x \to d(c(x))$ is an $\mathscr{S}_0$-measurable real valued function and $\mathscr{S}_0 = \{c_1^{-1}(E) : E \text{ Borel in } R^1\}$. If we now define, for any Borel set $E$ of $R^1$, $u(E)$ by the equation

$$u(E) = h(c_1^{-1}(E)),$$

then $u$ is an observable associated with $\mathscr{L}$ whose range is $\mathscr{L}_1$. This proves (i).

We now come to the proof of (ii). Suppose $u_1, u_2, \cdots, u_n$ are observables associated with $\mathscr{L}$, having ranges $\mathscr{L}_1, \cdots, \mathscr{L}_n$, respectively. Each $\mathscr{L}_i$ is separable and hence $\mathscr{L}_0$, the smallest sub-$\sigma$-algebra of $\mathscr{L}$ containing all the $\mathscr{L}_i$, is also separable. Let $X$, $\mathscr{S}$, and $h$ have the same significance as in the proof of (i). By theorem 1.4, there exists a real valued $\mathscr{S}$-measurable function $f_i$ on $X$ such that $u_i(E) = h(f_i^{-1}(E))$ for all Borel subsets $E$ of $R^1$. Let $\tilde{f}$ be the map $x \to (f_1(x), \cdots, f_n(x))$ of $X$ into $R^n$. Then $\tilde{f}$ is $\mathscr{S}$-measurable. The map $u : F \to h(\tilde{f}^{-1}(F))$ is then a $\sigma$-homomorphism of $\mathscr{B}(R^n)$ into $\mathscr{L}$ such that $u_i(E) = u(p_i^{-1}(E))$ for all $E \in \mathscr{B}(R^1)$. Since $\mathscr{B}(R^n)$ is the smallest $\sigma$-algebra of subsets of $R^n$ containing all the sets $p_i^{-1}(E)$, it is clear that the range of $u$ is $\mathscr{L}_0$. The uniqueness of $u$ is obvious.

For any real Borel function $\varphi$ on $R^n$, $E \to u(\varphi^{-1}(E))$ is an observable associated with $\mathscr{L}$ whose range is obviously contained in $\mathscr{L}_0$. Suppose now that $v$ is an observable associated with $\mathscr{L}$ whose range $\mathscr{L}_v \subseteq \mathscr{L}_0$. If we use the notations of the previous paragraph, and define $\mathscr{S}^\sim$ by

$$\mathscr{S}^\sim = \{\tilde{f}^{-1}(F) : F \in \mathscr{B}(R^n)\},$$

then $h$ maps $\mathscr{S}^\sim$ onto $\mathscr{L}_0$. Applying theorem 1.4 to $\mathscr{S}^\sim$ and $v$, we infer the existence of a real valued $\mathscr{S}^\sim$-measurable Borel function $c$ on $X$ such that $h(c^{-1}(E)) = v(E)$ for all Borel sets $E$ of $R^1$. By lemma 1.5, since $c$ is $\mathscr{S}^\sim$-measurable, there exists a real valued Borel function $\varphi$ on $R^n$ such that $c(x) = \varphi(\tilde{f}(x))$ for all $x \in X$. If now $E$ is any Borel set on the line, we have:

$$u(\varphi^{-1}(E)) = h(\tilde{f}^{-1}(\varphi^{-1}(E)))$$
$$= h(c^{-1}(E))$$
$$= v(E).$$

This proves (ii) and completes the proof of the theorem.

**Remark.** The uniqueness of $u$, guaranteed by (ii) of theorem 1.6 shows that $u$ is independent of the constructs $X$, $\mathscr{S}$, and $h$, used in its construction. Consequently, for any real Borel function $\varphi$ on $R^n$, the map $E \to u(\varphi^{-1}(E))$ is uniquely determined by $u_1, u_2, \cdots, u_n$ and $\varphi$. It is natural to denote this observable associated with $\mathscr{L}$ by $\varphi(u_1, u_2, \cdots, u_n)$.

# CHAPTER II
# PROJECTIVE GEOMETRIES

## 1. COMPLEMENTED MODULAR LATTICES

As we mentioned previously, the point of departure of our discussion of quantum phenomenology is the observation that the partially ordered set of experimentally verifiable statements associated with an atomic system is a lattice which does not possess the distributivity properties of the Boolean algebras associated with classical systems. We therefore begin a discussion of some elementary properties of such lattices.

We recall that a lattice $\mathscr{L}$ is complemented if for any element $a$ in $\mathscr{L}$ there exists an element $b$ in $\mathscr{L}$ such that

$$a \wedge b = 0,$$
(1)
$$a \vee b = 1.$$

We shall call $b$ a *complement* of $a$. In general, $b$ is not uniquely determined by $a$. We shall call the lattice *modular* if for any three elements $a$, $b$, $c$ of $\mathscr{L}$ for which $c < a$, one has:

(2)
$$a \wedge (b \vee c) = (a \wedge b) \vee c.$$

Obviously, a Boolean algebra is a complemented modular lattice. A typical example of a complemented modular lattice which is not a Boolean algebra is the lattice of linear manifolds of a finite dimensional vector space. More precisely, let $\mathbf{D}$ be a division ring, $n$ an integer $> 0$, and $\mathscr{L}$ the lattice of linear manifolds of an $n$-dimensional vector space $V$ over $\mathbf{D}$. Evidently $\mathscr{L}$ is complemented. However, when $n$ is $\geq 2$, complementation is not unique. Consequently, the lattice in question is not a Boolean algebra. We shall usually write $\mathscr{L} = \mathscr{L}(V, \mathbf{D})$. We notice that in the above example it is not necessary to take $\mathbf{D}$ to be commutative. In case the division ring is not commutative we shall understand by a vector space a *left vector space* over $\mathbf{D}$ (cf. Jacobson [1]).

We have remarked that given an element $a$ of $\mathscr{L}$, a complemented modular lattice, $a$ may have many complements. Suppose, however, that $b$ and $c$ are complements of $a$ and $b < c$. Then $b = c$. In fact, we have $c = c \wedge 1 = c \wedge (a \vee b) = (c \wedge a) \vee b = b$ by using modularity.

By a *chain* in a lattice $\mathscr{L}$ we mean a strictly increasing finite sequence of nonzero elements, i.e., $\{a_1, \cdots, a_n\}$, $a_1 < a_2 < \cdots < a_n$, $a_1 \neq 0$, $a_i \neq a_j$ if $i \neq j$. The number of elements, $n$, in the chain is called the *length* of the chain. We shall say that $\mathscr{L}$ has finite *rank* if there is an integer $k$ such that every chain in the lattice has at most $k$ elements. In such a case the exact upper bound of the lengths of the chains of the lattice is called the *dimension* of the lattice. An element $x$ in $\mathscr{L}$ is called a *point* if it is nonzero and if it has the further property that, for any element $y < x$, either $y = x$ or $y = 0$. In other words, points are minimal elements of a lattice. If $\mathscr{L} = \mathscr{L}(V, \mathbf{D})$, points of $\mathscr{L}$ are precisely the linear manifolds of $V$ of dimension 1. Of course, if $\mathscr{L}$ is arbitrary, points need not exist. However, we shall prove that if the lattice is of finite rank, points exist and in fact every element will then be a lattice sum of at most finitely many points. Under suitable restrictions the number of independent points whose lattice sum is a given element will be an invariant attached to that element. In this way one obtains the dimension function on the lattice, whose existence is equivalent to the modularity of the lattice.

## 2. THE DIMENSION FUNCTION

**Lemma 2.1.** *Let $\mathscr{L}$ be a lattice of finite rank. Then $\mathscr{L}$ is a complete lattice. That is, for an arbitrary collection of elements $\{a_\alpha\}$ in $\mathscr{L}$, $\bigvee_\alpha a_\alpha$ and $\bigwedge_\alpha a_\alpha$ exist.*

**Proof.** Suppose $\{a_\alpha\}$ is an arbitrary family of elements of the lattice. We shall prove that $\bigvee_\alpha a_\alpha$ exists. It is enough to prove the existence of indices $\alpha_1, \cdots, \alpha_r$ such that every $a_\alpha$ satisfies the inclusion:

$$a_\alpha < a_{\alpha_1} \vee a_{\alpha_2} \vee \cdots \vee a_{\alpha_r}.$$

This will then prove that the family $\{a_\alpha\}$ has a sum and that the sum is $\bigvee_{i=1}^r a_{\alpha_i}$. Suppose that such a finite set of indices does not exist. Then one can construct by induction an infinite sequence of indices $\alpha_1, \alpha_2, \cdots$ such that the elements $b_1, b_2, \cdots$, where

$$b_j = a_{\alpha_1} \vee a_{\alpha_2} \vee \cdots \vee a_{\alpha_j},$$

are strictly increasing, i.e., $b_i < b_j$, $b_i \neq b_j$ for $i < j$. This contradicts the finiteness of the rank of the lattice. The proof that $\bigwedge_\alpha a_\alpha$ exists proceeds in the same way with unions replaced by intersections and increasing chains replaced by decreasing ones. This proves the lemma.

Let $\mathscr{L}$ be a complemented lattice. By a *dimension function* on $\mathscr{L}$ we mean a real valued function $d(a \to d(a))$ defined on $\mathscr{L}$ with the following properties:

(3)
$\quad$ (i) $d(0) = 0,\quad d(a) \geq 0\quad$ for all $a \in \mathscr{L}$,
$\quad$ (ii) if $a < b$ and $\quad a \neq b$, then $\quad d(a) < d(b)$,
$\quad$ (iii) $d(a \vee b) + d(a \wedge b) = d(a) + d(b)\quad$ for all $a, b \in \mathscr{L}$.

The pair $(\mathscr{L},d)$ (or $\mathscr{L}$, by abuse of notation) is called a *dimension lattice*. If $\mathscr{L} = \mathscr{L}(V,\mathbf{D})$, the lattice of linear manifolds in an $n$-dimensional vector space $V$ over some division ring $\mathbf{D}$, and if for each linear manifold $a$ we put $d(a) =$ dimension of $a$, then $(\mathscr{L},d)$ is a dimension lattice.

**Lemma 2.2.** *Let* $(\mathscr{L},d)$ *be a dimension lattice. Then* $\mathscr{L}$ *is modular.*

**Proof.** Let $a$, $b$, $c$ be three elements of $\mathscr{L}$ such that $c < a$. We have to prove $a \wedge (b \vee c) = (a \wedge b) \vee c$. Since $b, c < b \vee c$, we have:

$$(a \wedge b) \vee c < a \wedge (b \vee c).$$

Since $\mathscr{L}$ is a dimension lattice, it is enough to prove that $d(a \wedge (b \vee c))$ and $d((a \wedge b) \vee c))$ are equal; i.e., (cf. (iii) of (3)),

$$d(a) + d(b \vee c) - d(a \vee b \vee c) = d(a \wedge b) + d(c) - d(a \wedge b \wedge c).$$

However,

$$
\begin{aligned}
d(a) + d(b \vee c) - d(a \vee b \vee c) &= d(a) + d(b \vee c) - d(a \vee b) \\
&= d(a) + (d(b) + d(c) - d(b \wedge c)) \\
&\quad - (d(a) + d(b) - d(a \wedge b)) \\
&= d(c) - d(b \wedge c) + d(a \wedge b) \\
&= d(a \wedge b) + d(c) - d(a \wedge b \wedge c).
\end{aligned}
$$

The lemma is proved.

We shall say that a set of distinct points $\{x_1, \cdots, x_n\}$ of $\mathscr{L}$ is *independent* if for each $i$, $x_i \not< \bigvee_{j \neq i} x_j$. The construction of the dimension function of a modular lattice depends on the properties of this notion of independence.

**Lemma 2.3.** *Let* $\mathscr{L}$ *be a complemented modular lattice, $a$, $b$ elements of $\mathscr{L}$, and $a'$ a complement of $a$. Let $a < b$. Then $c = a' \wedge b$ is a complement of $a$ in $b$, i.e.,*

(4)
$$a \wedge c = 0, \quad and \quad a \vee c = b.$$

*Moreover, if $u$, $v$ are arbitrary elements and $w$ is a complement of $u \wedge v$ in $v$, then $w$ is also a complement of $u$ in $u \vee v$.*

**Proof.** By modularity,

$$
\begin{aligned}
b &= b \wedge 1 \\
&= b \wedge (a \vee a') \\
&= a \vee (b \wedge a')
\end{aligned}
$$

while

$$a \wedge c = a \wedge b \wedge a'$$
$$< a \wedge a'$$
$$= 0.$$

For the second assertion, note first that $w \wedge u < w \wedge u \wedge v = 0$. Further, $v = (u \wedge v) \vee w < u \vee w$ while $u < u \vee w$ trivially, showing $u \vee v < w \vee u$. As $u \vee w < u \vee v$ obviously, $w$ is a complement of $u$ in $u \vee v$.

**Lemma 2.4.** *Let $\mathscr{L}$ be a complemented modular lattice. If $a$, $b$, $c$ are elements of $\mathscr{L}$ such that $a \wedge b = 0$ and $c \wedge (a \vee b) = 0$, then $a \wedge (b \vee c) = 0$ and $b \wedge (c \vee a) = 0$.*

**Proof.** We have, by modularity, since $b < a \vee b$,

$$(a \vee b) \wedge (b \vee c) = b \vee (c \wedge (a \vee b))$$
$$= b.$$

On the other hand, since $b < b \vee c$, we have also

$$(a \vee b) \wedge (b \vee c) = b \vee (a \wedge (b \vee c)).$$

Thus, $b = b \vee (a \wedge (b \vee c))$. Therefore, $a \wedge (b \vee c) < b$, hence $< a \wedge b = 0$. Thus $a \wedge (b \vee c) = 0$. The second conclusion, $b \wedge (c \vee a) = 0$, is obtained by interchanging $a$ and $b$ in the first assertion. This proves the lemma.

**Lemma 2.5.** *Let $\mathscr{L}$ be a complemented modular lattice, $a$, $b \in \mathscr{L}$. If $a \wedge b = 0$, there exists a complement $x$ of $a$ such that $b < x$. If $a \vee b = 1$, there exists a complement $y$ of $a$ such that $y < b$.*

**Proof.** Let $a \wedge b = 0$. Suppose $c$ to be a complement of $a \vee b$. Then, by lemma 2.4, $a \wedge (b \vee c) = 0$. Further, $a \vee (b \vee c) = (a \vee b) \vee c = 1$. If $x = b \vee c$, $x$ is a complement of $a$ and $b < x$. Next, let $a \vee b = 1$. Let $y$ be a complement of $a \wedge b$ in $b$, i.e., $(a \wedge b) \wedge y = 0$, $(a \wedge b) \vee y = b$ (lemma 2.3). Then, as $y < b$, $y \wedge a < y \wedge a \wedge b = 0$, while $a < y \vee a$, $b = y \vee (a \wedge b) < y \vee a$, so that $a \vee b < a \vee y$; i.e., $a \vee y = 1$. Thus, we see that $y$ is a complement of $a$ and obviously $y < b$.

**Lemma 2.6.** *Let $s > 1$, and let $\{x_1, x_2, \cdots, x_s\}$ be a set of distinct points of a complemented modular lattice $\mathscr{L}$. Then the set $\{x_1, x_2, \cdots, x_s\}$ is independent if and only if for each $i = 2, 3, \cdots, s$,*

$$(5) \qquad\qquad x_i \not< \bigvee_{j=1}^{i-1} x_j.$$

**Proof.** The "only if" part is a trivial deduction from the definition of independence. For the "if" part, let us suppose $s > 1$ and that the set $\{x_1, \cdots, x_s\}$ has the property (5), i.e., that for each $i \geq 2$, $x_i$ is not contained in the lattice sum of $x_1, \cdots, x_{i-1}$. We shall prove that the set $\{x_1, \cdots, x_s\}$

is independent. Suppose that $\{x_1, \cdots, x_s\}$ is not independent, so that for some $j$, $x_j < \bigvee_{r \neq j} x_r$. Since (5) is satisfied for each $i \geq 2$, $j < s$. For any $t \leq s$, let

$$(6) \qquad\qquad\qquad y_t = \bigvee_{\substack{r \leq t \\ j \neq r}} x_r.$$

Let $s'$ be the smallest integer $\leq s$ such that $x_j < y_{s'}$. In view of (5) $s' > j$. Then $x_j \not< y_{s'-1}$ and hence, as $x_j$ is a point, $x_j \wedge y_{s'-1} = 0$. But as $s'-1 \geq j$, $x_j \vee y_{s'-1} = \bigvee_{i=1}^{s'-1} x_i$ and hence, by (5), $x_{s'} \wedge (x_j \vee y_{s'-1}) = 0$. By lemma 2.4, this implies that $x_j \wedge (x_{s'} \vee y_{s'-1}) = 0$. However, as $j \neq s'$,

$$x_{s'} \vee y_{s'-1} = y_{s'},$$

and so we have

$$x_j \wedge y_{s'} = 0,$$

which is impossible. The lemma is proved.

For any element $a$ in a complemented modular lattice we define its *dimension* to be the number of points in any independent set of points whose lattice sum is $a$. The next lemma asserts that this number is an invariant of the element $a$.

**Lemma 2.7.** *Let $a$ be an element of a complemented modular lattice $\mathcal{L}$. Let $x_1, \cdots, x_s$ and $y_1, \cdots, y_t$ be points such that the sets $\{x_1, \cdots, x_s\}$ and $\{y_1, \cdots, y_t\}$ are independent and*

$$(7) \qquad\qquad\qquad a = \bigvee_{j=1}^{s} x_j = \bigvee_{i=1}^{t} y_i.$$

*Then $s = t$.*

**Proof.** It is enough to show that $s \leq t$, since the other inequality will follow by interchanging the $x$'s and $y$'s. Consider the set $\{x_1, y_1, y_2, \cdots, y_t\}$. $x_1$ is a point and $x_1 < a = \bigvee_i y_i$. Consequently this set is not independent and hence, by lemma 2.6, there is a $j$ with $1 \leq j \leq t$ such that $y_j$ is contained in the lattice sum of $x_1, y_1, y_2, \cdots, y_{j-1}$, i.e., the points of the set $\{x_1, y_1, \cdots, y_t\} - \{y_j\}$ have as lattice sum once again $a$. Consider now the ordered set $\{x_2, x_1, y_1, \cdots, y_t\}$ (with $y_j$ omitted). Once again this set is not independent, since $x_2$ is contained in the lattice sum of the others and consequently some member of this sequence is contained in the lattice sum of the preceding members. Such a member cannot be an $x$ since the $x$'s are independent. It has therefore to be a $y$, say $y_k$. This $y_k$ is contained in the lattice sum of $x_2, x_1, y_1, \cdots, y_{k-1}$ and consequently the ordered set $x_2, x_1, y_1, \cdots, y_t$ ($y_j, y_k$ both omitted) has as lattice sum once again $a$. We can proceed now adjoining $x_3$ to this and to argue as before. At each stage of this argument we drop out a $y$, and the elements which remain have always $a$ for their lattice sum. The process will have to terminate before all the $y$'s get dropped out, as otherwise the $y$'s will have to be exhausted without the $x$'s being so, and then $a$ will be the lattice sum of a proper subset of the $x$'s, which is impossible, since the $x$'s are independent. The fact that the $x$'s are exhausted before the $y$'s implies that $s \leq t$.

**Theorem 2.8.** *Let $\mathscr{L}$ be a complemented modular lattice of finite rank. Then every element of $\mathscr{L}$ is a lattice sum of points. Moreover, there exists a unique function d on $\mathscr{L}$ such that*

(8)
$\qquad$ (i) *$(\mathscr{L},d)$ is a dimension lattice,*
$\qquad$ (ii) *$d(x) = 1$ for all points $x \in \mathscr{L}$.*

*A complemented lattice of finite rank is modular if and only if it possesses a dimension function.*

**Proof.** We first show that if $a \in \mathscr{L}$ and $a \neq 0$, there is a point $x < a$. In fact, points are minimal elements of $\mathscr{L}$ and, consequently, the nonexistence of any point $x < a$ implies that there is an infinite sequence $a = a_0, a_1, a_2, \cdots$ such that $a_j < a_i$ and $a_j \neq a_i$ if $i < j$. This contradicts the finiteness of the rank of $\mathscr{L}$. Suppose next that $a \in \mathscr{L}$, $a \neq 0$. Let $b$ be the lattice sum of all points $x < a$ (lemma 2.1). If $b \neq a$, there exists, by lemma 2.3, an element $c$ such that $b \wedge c = 0$, $b \vee c = a$; clearly $c \neq 0$. From our first observation it follows that there exists a point $y < c$. Then, however, $y \wedge b = 0$ which contradicts the definition of $b$. Hence $b = a$.

Suppose now $a \in \mathscr{L}$, $a \neq 0$. If $\{x_1, x_2, \cdots, x_s\}$ is an independent set of points with $x_i < a$ for all $i$, the elements $y_i$, where $y_i = \bigvee_{j \leq i} x_j$, have the property that $y_i < y_j$, $y_i \neq y_j$ for $i < j$. Consequently $s \leq k$, the rank of $\mathscr{L}$. This shows that there are maximal finite sets $\{x_1, \cdots, x_s\}$ of independent points with $x_i < a$ for all $i$. The reasoning in the preceding paragraph makes it clear that $a = \bigvee_{i=1}^s x_i$ for any such maximal set. By lemma 2.7, the number $s$ depends only on $a$ and not on the maximal set in question. We write $d(a)$ for this number. We write $d(0) = 0$. $a \to d(a)$ is then a well-defined function on $\mathscr{L}$. Note that if $a \neq 0$, there is at least one point $x < a$ so that $d(a) \geq 1$.

We shall now prove that $d$ is a dimension function on $\mathscr{L}$. (i) of (3) is trivial. (ii) is a consequence of the fact that $d(a) > 0$ for all $a \neq 0$ and of (iii). In fact, if $a < b$, $a \neq b$, there is a $c \neq 0$ (lemma 2.3) such that $a \wedge c = 0$, $a \vee c = b$ and then, by (iii), $d(b) = d(a) + d(c) > d(a)$ as $d(c) > 0$.

It now remains to prove (iii) of (3). We prove this in two stages. First, let $a, b \in \mathscr{L}$ with $a \wedge b = 0$. We intend to show that $d(a \vee b) = d(a) + d(b)$. Let $\{x_1, x_2, \cdots, x_s\}$ be a set of independent points whose lattice sum is $a$ and let $\{y_1, y_2, \cdots, y_t\}$ be a set of independent points whose lattice sum is $b$. The set $\{x_1, x_2, \cdots, x_s, y_1, y_2, \cdots, y_t\}$ has lattice sum $a \vee b$. We claim that this set is an independent set. Otherwise, some member of it is contained in the lattice sum of the preceding members (lemma 2.6).

Such a member can not be an $x$ since the $x_j$ are independent. Therefore, there will be a $j$ such that $y_j$ is contained in the lattice sum of $a, y_1, \cdots, y_{j-1}$. But by modularity we have, as $a \wedge b = 0$,

$$y_j < \left( \bigvee_{r=1}^{j} y_r \right) \wedge \left( a \vee \bigvee_{r=1}^{j-1} y_r \right) = \bigvee_{r=1}^{j-1} y_r.$$

This contradicts the independence of the $y$'s. Thus the set

$$\{x_1, x_2, \cdots, x_s, y_1, y_2, \cdots, y_t\}$$

is independent and hence the dimension of $a \vee b$ is $s+t$. Since $s$ and $t$ are obviously the dimensions of $a$ and $b$, respectively, we have the equation

(9)                    $d(a \vee b) = d(a) + d(b).$

We now come to the general case of the additivity formula for the dimension function. Let $a$ and $b$ be two arbitrary elements. Let $c$ be a complement of $a \wedge b$ in $b$. Then, by lemma 2.3, $c$ is also a complement of $a$ in $a \vee b$. From the additivity proved in the preceding paragraph we may conclude that $d(a \vee b) = d(a) + d(c)$ and $d(b) = d(a \wedge b) + d(c)$. From this it follows at once that

$$d(a \vee b) + d(a \wedge b) = d(a) + d(b).$$

$(\mathscr{L}, d)$ is thus shown to be a dimension lattice. Evidently, $d(x) = 1$ for all points $x$. This shows that (i) and (ii) of (8) are true.

Let $d'$ be any function on $\mathscr{L}$ such that (i) and (ii) of (8) are satisfied. If $a \in \mathscr{L} \neq 0$ and $a = \bigvee_{j=1}^{s} x_j$ where $\{x_1, x_2, \cdots, x_s\}$ is independent, then $d(a) = s$; on the other hand, if $y_r = \bigvee_{j \leq r} x_j$, then $y_{r-1} \wedge x_r = 0$, $y_{r-1} \vee x_r = y_r$ so that $d'(y_r) = d'(y_{r-1}) + 1$, showing by induction that $d'(a) = s$ also. This proves that $d = d'$.

Since, by lemma 2.2, any dimension lattice is modular, all assertions of theorem 2.8 are proved.

We call a dimension function $d$ on $\mathscr{L}$ *canonical* if $d(x) = 1$ for all points $x \in \mathscr{L}$.

## 3. GEOMETRIES

Let $X$ be a set having $n$ elements, $\mathscr{L}$ the Boolean algebra of all subsets of $X$, and for $A \subseteq X$ let $d(A)$ be the number of points of $A$. Then $d$ is the canonical dimension function of $\mathscr{L}$. At the other extreme, and what is more relevent to our purposes, are the lattices $\mathscr{L}(V, \mathbf{D})$, $\mathbf{D}$ being a division ring and $V$ a vector space of dimension $n (< \infty)$ over $\mathbf{D}$. We devote this section to the description of a method of singling out the lattices of the form $\mathscr{L}(V, \mathbf{D})$ from the class of all dimension lattices.

Let $\mathscr{L}$ be a complemented modular lattice. An element $a$ is said to be in the *center* of $\mathscr{L}$ if it has a unique complement in $\mathscr{L}$. $\mathscr{L}$ is said to be *irreducible* if the only elements belonging to its center are 0 and 1. An irreducible complemented modular lattice of finite rank is called a *geometry*.

We now proceed to analyze the properties of the center of a complemented modular lattice. We begin with a lemma.

**Lemma 2.9.** *Let $\mathscr{L}$ be a complemented modular lattice, $a$ an element in its center, and $a'$ its complement. If $a \wedge y = 0$, then $y < a'$.*

**Proof.** By lemma 2.5 there is a complement $b$ of $a$ such that $y < b$. Since $a$ is in the center, $b = a'$. Hence $y < a'$.

**Lemma 2.10.** *Let $\mathscr{L}$ be a complemented modular lattice, $a$ an element of $\mathscr{L}$, and $a'$ a complement of $a$. Then in order that $a$ be in the center of $\mathscr{L}$ it is necessary and sufficient that*

$$(10) \qquad x = (x \wedge a) \vee (x \wedge a')$$

*for all $x \in \mathscr{L}$. In particular, if $a$ is in the center of $\mathscr{L}$, so is $a'$.*

**Proof.** Suppose $a \in \mathscr{L}$ and (10) is satisfied for all $x$. We shall prove that $a'$ is the unique complement of $a$. Suppose in fact that $b$ is a complement of $a$. Then we have by (10), as $b \wedge a = 0$,

$$b = (b \wedge a) \vee (b \wedge a') = (b \wedge a').$$

Consequently, $b < a'$, so that $a' = a' \wedge (a \vee b) = b$ by modularity. Conversely, suppose $a$ is in the center of $\mathscr{L}$. We shall prove (10), i.e., that

$$x = (x \wedge a) \vee (x \wedge a')$$

for an arbitrary element $x$ of $\mathscr{L}$. Clearly, $(x \wedge a) \vee (x \wedge a') < x$. It is thus enough to prove the reverse inclusion. Since $\mathscr{L}$ is complemented we can find an element $y$ such that $(x \wedge a) \wedge y = 0$, $(x \wedge a) \vee y = x$; by lemma 2.3, $y \wedge a = 0$. From lemma 2.9 it follows that $y < a'$ and hence we conclude that $y < x \wedge a'$. Consequently

$$x = (x \wedge a) \vee y < (x \wedge a) \vee (x \wedge a').$$

The last assertion follows if we note that (10) is symmetric in $a$ and $a'$. Lemma 2.9 is completely proved.

For any $a$ in the center of $\mathscr{L}$ we write $a'$ for its unique complement; $(a')' = a$.

**Theorem 2.11.** *Let $\mathscr{L}$ be a complemented modular lattice and let $\mathscr{C}$ be its center. Then $\mathscr{C}$ is a Boolean algebra.*

**Proof.** From lemma 2.10 it follows that if $a$ is in the center, then so is $a'$.

Moreover, $a$ and $a'$ are the unique complements of each other. Suppose now $a$ and $b \in \mathscr{C}$. Consider the element $a' \wedge b'$ and let $x$ be any complement of $a' \wedge b'$. Since $a' \wedge b' < a'$, $x \vee a' = 1$. Therefore there exists, by lemma 2.5, a complement of $a'$ contained in $x$. However, by lemma 2.10, $a$ is the unique complement of $a'$. Hence $a < x$. Similarly, $b < x$. Hence $a \vee b < x$ which shows that $(a \vee b) \wedge (a' \wedge b') = 0$. Suppose now $z$ is any complement of $a \vee b$. Then, as $a < a \vee b$, $a \wedge z = 0$ so that $z < a'$ by lemma 2.9. Similarly $z < b'$ showing $z < a' \wedge b'$. We have already seen that $(a' \wedge b') \wedge (a \vee b) = 0$. We may therefore conclude that $a' \wedge b'$ is the unique complement of $a \vee b$. This proves that $a \vee b$ lies in $\mathscr{C}$ and that $(a \vee b)' = a' \wedge b'$. Replacing $a$, $b$ by $a'$, $b'$, respectively, we may conclude that $a \wedge b$ lies in $\mathscr{C}$. Thus the center of $\mathscr{L}$ is a sublattice of $\mathscr{L}$ closed under complementation. Moreover, for $a, b \in \mathscr{C}$, $(a \vee b)' = a' \wedge b'$, and $(a \wedge b)' = a' \vee b'$.

To prove now that $\mathscr{C}$ is a Boolean algebra we must prove distributivity. Since for $a, b \in \mathscr{C}$ we have $(a \vee b)' = a' \wedge b'$ and $(a \wedge b)' = a' \vee b'$, it is enough to verify one of the distributive laws. We shall prove that if $a, b, c \in \mathscr{C}$, then

$$a \wedge (b \vee c) = (a \wedge b) \vee (a \wedge c).$$

Since $(a \wedge b) \vee (a \wedge c) < a \wedge (b \vee c)$, it is enough to prove that

$$a \wedge (b \vee c) < (a \wedge b) \vee (a \wedge c).$$

We have, since $b \in \mathscr{C}$, by (10),

$$a \wedge (b \vee c) = \{a \wedge (b \vee c) \wedge b\} \vee \{a \wedge (b \vee c) \wedge b'\}$$
$$= (a \wedge b) \vee \{a \wedge b' \wedge (b \vee c)\}.$$

Let $y$ be a complement of $b \wedge c$ in $c$. Then it follows from lemma 2.3 that $y$ is a complement of $b$ in $b \vee c$. In view of lemma 2.9, $y < b'$ and hence $y < b' \wedge (b \vee c)$. Since $(b \vee c) \wedge b'$ is also a complement of $b$ in $b \vee c$ (cf. lemma 2.3), we must have $y = (b \vee c) \wedge b'$. Hence, as $y < c$, $b' \wedge (b \vee c) < c$. Consequently,

$$a \wedge (b \vee c) = (a \wedge b) \vee \{a \wedge b' \wedge (b \vee c)\}$$
$$< (a \wedge b) \vee (a \wedge c).$$

This proves that $\mathscr{C}$ is a Boolean algebra in view of our earlier remarks.

**Corollary 2.12.** *A complemented modular lattice is a Boolean algebra if and only if every element has a unique complement.*

If **D** is a division ring and $n$ an integer $\geq 2$, then the lattice of linear manifolds of a vector space $V$ of dimension $n$ over **D** is obviously a geometry. We shall call this the *geometry of the vector space $V$*.

Let $\mathscr{L}$ be any complemented modular lattice, and let $\mathscr{C}$ be the center of $\mathscr{L}$. If $\mathscr{L}$ is a Boolean algebra, $\mathscr{C} = \mathscr{L}$ while $\mathscr{C} = \{0,1\}$ if $\mathscr{L}$ is a geometry.

We shall now prove that in the general case $\mathscr{L}$ can be decomposed, over $\mathscr{C}$, as a direct sum of geometries. To do this we need to make precise the notion of a direct sum. Let $\mathscr{L}_1, \cdots, \mathscr{L}_k$ be lattices with zero elements $0_1, 0_2, \cdots, 0_k$ and unit elements $1_1, 1_2, \cdots, 1_k$, respectively. Let

$$(11) \qquad \mathscr{L} = \mathscr{L}_1 \times \mathscr{L}_2 \times \cdots \times \mathscr{L}_k$$

and let $a_i, b_i \in \mathscr{L}_i$, $i = 1, 2, \cdots, k$. We define

$$(12) \qquad (a_1, \cdots, a_k) < (b_1, \cdots, b_k)$$

to mean

$$(13) \qquad a_i < b_i \quad \text{for} \quad i = 1, 2, \cdots, k.$$

It follows that under this partial ordering $\mathscr{L}$ becomes a lattice with null element $(0_1, \cdots, 0_k)$ and unit element $(1_1, \cdots, 1_k)$, called the *direct sum* of the $\mathscr{L}_i$.

**Lemma 2.13.** *Let $\mathscr{L}$ be a complemented modular lattice of finite rank and let $\mathscr{C}$ be its center. If $x \in \mathscr{L}$ and $c_1, \cdots, c_k \in \mathscr{C}$, then*

$$(14) \qquad x \wedge \left( \bigvee_{j=1}^{k} c_j \right) = \bigvee_{j=1}^{k} (x \wedge c_j).$$

**Proof.** It is obviously sufficient to prove (14) when $k = 2$, since the general case follows then easily by induction on $k$. Let $k = 2$ and $c_1, c_2 \in \mathscr{C}$. By lemma 2.10,

$$x \wedge (c_1 \vee c_2) = \{(x \wedge (c_1 \vee c_2)) \wedge c_1\} \vee \{(x \wedge (c_1 \vee c_2)) \wedge c_1'\}$$
$$= (x \wedge c_1) \vee \{x \wedge ((c_1 \vee c_2) \wedge c_1')\}.$$

Since $\mathscr{C}$ is a Boolean algebra, $(c_1 \vee c_2) \wedge c_1' = c_1' \wedge c_2$. Moreover

$$x \wedge c_1 = (x \wedge c_1) \vee (x \wedge c_2 \wedge c_1)$$

so that

$$x \wedge (c_1 \vee c_2) = (x \wedge c_1) \vee \{x \wedge (c_1' \wedge c_2)\} \vee \{(x \wedge c_2) \wedge c_1\}$$
$$= (x \wedge c_1) \vee \{((x \wedge c_2) \wedge c_1') \vee (x \wedge c_2 \wedge c_1)\}$$
$$= (x \wedge c_1) \vee (x \wedge c_2)$$

as $c_1 \in \mathscr{C}$. This proves the lemma.

**Theorem 2.14.** *Every complemented modular lattice of finite rank is isomorphic to a direct sum of geometries.*

**Proof.** Let $\mathscr{L}$ be a complemented modular lattice of finite rank and let $\mathscr{C}$ be its center. Since $\mathscr{C}$ is also of finite rank, its associated Stone space is finite and hence there are nonzero elements $c_1, c_2, \cdots, c_k \in \mathscr{C}$ such that (i) $c_i \wedge c_j = 0$ for $i \neq j$, $c_1 \vee c_2 \vee \cdots \vee c_k = 1$, (ii) $\mathscr{C}$ is precisely the set of all elements of the form $c_{i_1} \vee c_{i_2} \vee \cdots \vee c_{i_r}$ $(1 \leq i_1, \cdots, i_r \leq k)$. Let $\mathscr{L}_j = \{a : a < c_j\}$. $\mathscr{L}_j$ is a lattice with $0$ and $c_j$ as its null and unit elements, respectively. Let $\overline{\mathscr{L}}$ be the direct sum of the lattices $\mathscr{L}_j$. For any element $x$ of $\mathscr{L}$ let us consider the element

(15) $$\overline{x} = (x \wedge c_1, x \wedge c_2, \cdots, x \wedge c_k)$$

of $\overline{\mathscr{L}}$. Lemma 2.13 implies that for any $x$ of $\mathscr{L}$ the equation

(16) $$x = (x \wedge c_1) \vee (x \wedge c_2) \vee \cdots \vee (x \wedge c_k)$$

holds. From (16) it follows immediately that the mapping

(17) $$x \to \overline{x}$$

is an isomorphism of $\mathscr{L}$ with $\overline{\mathscr{L}}$. We now claim that each $\mathscr{L}_j$ is a geometry. Suppose that $a < c_j$, and that $a$ lies in the center of $\mathscr{L}_j$. Then there exists a unique complement $b$ of $a$ in $\mathscr{L}_j$. Clearly $a \wedge b = 0$ and $a \vee b = c_j$. If $x$ is a complement of $a$ in $\mathscr{L}$, $x \wedge c_j$ is a complement of $a$ in $c_j$ (lemma 2.3) so that $x \wedge c_j = b$. Since $x \vee c_j = 1$ and $c_j \in \mathscr{C}$, we see by lemma 2.5 that $c_j' < x$. Thus $b \vee c_j' < x$. By lemma 2.4, $b \vee c_j'$ is also a complement of $a$. Consequently $x = b \vee c_j'$. This shows that $a$ has a unique complement in $\mathscr{L}$. By definition of the $c_i$'s, $a = 0$ or $a = c_j$. This proves that each $\mathscr{L}_j$ is a geometry. Theorem 2.14 is thus completely proved.

Let $\mathscr{L}$ be a complemented modular lattice of finite rank and $d$ its canonical dimension function. $d(1) = n$ is the dimension of $\mathscr{L}$. An element $a \in \mathscr{L}$ is called a *line* if $d(a) = 2$, and it is called a *plane* if $d(a) = 3$. It is called a *hyperplane* if $d(a) = n - 1$. If $a$ and $b$ are distinct points of $\mathscr{L}$, $d(a \vee b) = 2$ and hence $a \vee b$ is a line. It is called the line *joining* $a$ and $b$. If $a$ and $b$ are distinct lines in $\mathscr{L}$ and $a \wedge b \neq 0$, then $d(a \wedge b) = 1$ so that $a \wedge b$ is a point called the *meet of the lines a and b*. In this case, the identity $d(a \vee b) = d(a) + d(b) - d(a \wedge b)$ shows that $a \vee b$ is a plane, called the *plane of a and b*. If $a, b \in \mathscr{L}$, we say that $a$ *lies in* $b$ if and only if $a < b$. If $a, b, c$ are three distinct points and $c$ lies on the line joining $a$ and $b$, then it is easily shown that $a$ lies on the line joining $b$ and $c$, and $b$ lies on the line joining $a$ and $c$. In this case, we say that $a, b, c$ are *collinear*. In this manner we make contact with traditional geometric terminology.

**Theorem 2.15.** *A complemented modular lattice $\mathscr{L}$ of finite rank is a geometry if and only if every line in $\mathscr{L}$ has at least three points lying in it.*

**Proof.** Suppose $\mathscr{L}$ is not a geometry. Then there exists an element $a$ other than $0$ and $1$ which belongs to the center of $\mathscr{L}$. Let $x$ be a point $< a$ and $y$ a point $< a'$, where $a'$ is the complement of $a$. Let $m$ be the line $x \vee y$. We shall prove that if a point is on $m$, then it is either $x$ or $y$. Since $m$ has rank 2, and $x < m \wedge a < m$, $m \wedge a$ has either rank 1 or 2. If it has rank 2, then it must coincide with $m$; but then $y < m \wedge a$, which is impossible, since $y < a'$. Thus $m \wedge a$ has rank 1 which means that $m \wedge a = x$. Similarly, $m \wedge a' = y$. Suppose now $z$ is a point of $m$. Since $a$ is in the center of $\mathscr{L}$, we have:

$$z = (z \wedge a) \vee (z \wedge a'),$$

and since $z$ is a point, each of $z \wedge a$ and $z \wedge a'$ is either 0 or a point. Both cannot be points because then they would be distinct and $z$ would have rank 2. Therefore, one is a point and the other is zero. Suppose, for example, that $z \wedge a$ is a point. Then

$$z \wedge a < m \wedge a = x,$$

and hence $z = x$. If $z \wedge a'$ is a point, $z = y$. This proves that if every line has at least three points, then $\mathscr{L}$ is a geometry.

We shall now prove the converse. Let $\mathscr{L}$ be a geometry and let $x$ and $y$ be two distinct points of $\mathscr{L}$ such that the line $x \vee y$ has no point lying on it other than $x$ and $y$. We shall construct an element of the center of $\mathscr{L}$ such that it contains $x$ while its complement contains $y$. This will then contradict the assumption that $\mathscr{L}$ is a geometry.

To construct the required central element we proceed as follows. We introduce the *set* $A$ defined as follows:

(18)  $A = \{t : t \text{ a point} \neq x \text{ such that the line } x \vee t \text{ has only 2 points on it}\}.$

$A$ is nonempty since $y \in A$. We shall first prove by induction the assertion $(S_n)$ that if $z$ is a point such that $z < x_1 \vee \cdots \vee x_n$, where $x_1, x_2, \cdots, x_n \in A$, then $z \neq x$ and $z$ is also in $A$. We first prove $(S_2)$. Let $n = 2$, and $x_1 \neq x_2$, $x_1, x_2 \in A$. Since $x$ is distinct from $x_1$ and $x_2$, it is clear that $x$ cannot be on the line joining $x_1$ and $x_2$ since this would mean that $x_2$ is on the line joining $x$ and $x_1$ which will then have the three distinct points $x, x_1, x_2$. Suppose now that $z$ is a point distinct from $x_1$ and $x_2$ lying on the line joining $x_1$ and $x_2$. $z \neq x$ as we saw just now. We claim that the line joining $x$ and $z$ has only the points $x$ and $z$ on it. Suppose, in fact, that $u$ is a point other than $x$ and $z$ on this line. The triple $\{x, x_1, x_2\}$ is independent and hence if $c = x \vee x_1 \vee x_2$, $d(c) = 3$. If $m, m'$ are any two distinct lines in $c$, $m \wedge m'$ is a point. Now $u$ is a point $< c$. The lines $x_1 \vee x_2$ and $x \vee z$ are distinct lines containing $z$ and hence the intersection

$$(x_1 \vee x_2) \wedge (x \vee z)$$

must consist of the point $z$. Consequently, $u \nleq x_2 \vee z$ and hence $x_2 \vee u$ and $x \vee x_1$ are distinct lines both $< c$. They meet once again in a point, say, $v$. Since the line joining $x$ and $x_1$ has only two points, $v$ is either $x$ or $x_1$. If $v = x$, then $u = x$; if $v = x_1$, then $u = z$; both of which being impossible, it follows that the line joining $x$ and $z$ cannot have any other point lying on it. This proves $(S_2)$. Suppose now that the statement $(S_n)$ has been proved for some $n$. Let $x_1, x_2, \cdots, x_{n+1}$ be distinct points which are independent, distinct from $x$, and with the property that the line joining $x$ and $x_j$ has only two points on it for any $j$. Let $u$ be a point such that $u \neq x_j$ for all $j$ and $u < \bigvee_{j=1}^{n+1} x_j$. The elements $x_1 \vee \cdots \vee x_n$ and $u \vee x_{n+1}$ have dimensions $n$ and $2$, respectively; hence by the property of the dimension function we conclude that $(u \vee x_{n+1}) \wedge (x_1 \vee \cdots \vee x_n)$ has dimension $1$ and hence is a point, say $t$. Now $t < x_1 \vee \cdots \vee x_n$ and, by the inductive hypothesis, $t \neq x$ and the line joining $x$ and $t$ has only two points on it. Since $u$ lies now on the line joining $t$ and $x_{n+1}$, we conclude from the previous argument that $u \neq x$ and that the line joining $x$ and $u$ has only two points on it. This induction establishes immediately the validity of $(S_n)$ for all $n$ and shows that any point which is contained in the lattice sum of a finite number of elements of $A$ is also in $A$. Let us denote the lattice sum of the elements of $A$ as $b$. $b \neq 0$ as $y < b$ and $b \neq 1$ as $x \wedge b = 0$, whereas for any point $t < b$, the line $x \vee t$ has only two points on it.

Suppose now there are no points of $\mathscr{L}$ other than $x$ and those $< b$. Then $x$ is the unique complement of $b$ and we would have $b$ central. We therefore assume that there are points $z$ of $\mathscr{L}$ such that $z \neq x$, $z \not< b$. Let $u$ be a point $< b$. Since $z \not< b$ and $z \neq x$, the line joining $x$ and $z$ has one more point on it, say $v$, $v \neq x$, $v \neq z$. We claim that the line joining $z$ and $u$ has only two points on it. Suppose this is not true. Let $w$ be a point on the line joining $z$ and $u$ distinct from $z$ and $u$. Then the lattice sum of $x$, $z$ and $u$ is a plane. The lines $x \vee u$ and $w \vee v$ are distinct and are $< x \vee z \vee u$ so that they must meet in a point. This point cannot be either $x$ or $u$ and hence we have a third point on the line joining $x$ and $u$ which is impossible. Thus $z$ has the property that the line joining $z$ and $u$ has only two points on it. By the above argument we conclude that if $B$ is the set of points $z$ defined as

$$B = \{z : z \not< b, z \vee u \text{ has only 2 points on it for all } u < b\},$$

then every point contained in the lattice sum of the points of $B$ is also in $B$. Let $c = \bigvee \{z : z \in B\}$. The argument that we have just given shows that if a point is not $< b$, then it is in $c$. This proves at once that $c$ is the unique complement of $b$ and hence that $b$ is in the center of $\mathscr{L}$. Obviously $x < c$ while $y < b$. This proves that the lattice $\mathscr{L}$ is not a geometry and completes the proof of theorem 2.15.

## 4. COORDINATIZATION

We have seen that if $\mathbf{D}$ is any division ring and $V$ is a (left) vector space of dimension $n$ over $\mathbf{D}$, the lattice $\mathscr{L}(V, \mathbf{D})$ is a geometry of dimension $n$.

The converse is also true, roughly speaking. In fact, the fundamental theorem of Projective Geometry takes the following form:

**Theorem 2.16.** *Let $\mathscr{L}$ be a geometry of dimension $n \geq 4$. Then there exists a division ring $\mathbf{D}$ such that $\mathscr{L}$ is isomorphic to $\mathscr{L}(V, \mathbf{D})$, where $V$ is a vector space of dimension $n$ over $\mathbf{D}$. If $n = \dim \mathscr{L} = 3$, then in order that $\mathscr{L}$ be isomorphic to the lattice $\mathscr{L}(V, \mathbf{D})$ for some division ring $\mathbf{D}$ and some vector space $V$ over $\mathbf{D}$, it is necessary and sufficient that $\mathscr{L}$ be Desarguesian. $\mathbf{D}$ is uniquely determined by $\mathscr{L}$ up to isomorphism. In particular, if $\mathbf{D}_1$, $\mathbf{D}_2$ are two division rings and $V_1$, $V_2$ two vector spaces of dimension $n$ over $\mathbf{D}_1$, $\mathbf{D}_2$, respectively, then the geometries $\mathscr{L}(V_1, \mathbf{D}_1)$ and $\mathscr{L}(V_2, \mathbf{D}_2)$ are isomorphic if and only if $\mathbf{D}_1$ and $\mathbf{D}_2$ are isomorphic division rings.*

The proof of this theorem is long and complicated (cf. Seidenberg [1] and Heyting [1]). We remark also that the division ring $\mathbf{D}$ is a field (commutative) if and only if the theorem of Pappus is valid in the geometry $\mathscr{L}(V, \mathbf{D})$. We shall discuss the second part of this theorem in the next chapter. The first part is examined, in a more general context, in Chapter V.

# CHAPTER III

# LATTICE ISOMORPHISMS AND SEMILINEAR TRANSFORMATIONS

## 1. DETERMINATION OF THE LATTICE ISOMORPHISMS

If we let $\mathcal{L}$ and $\mathcal{L}'$ represent the geometries of two vector spaces $V$ and $V'$ (over the same division ring), the maps of $\mathcal{L}$ onto $\mathcal{L}'$ which preserve the order are natural objects of study from the geometric point of view. To every linear isomorphism of $V$ onto $V'$ we can obviously associate an isomorphism of $\mathcal{L}$ onto $\mathcal{L}'$. The question naturally arises whether every lattice isomorphism of $\mathcal{L}$ onto $\mathcal{L}'$ can be constructed in this manner. It turns out that this is not quite so and that we have to include the so-called semilinear transformations in order to be able to describe all the lattice isomorphisms. At the same time, if we use the appropriate definitions, the class of semilinear transformations is adequate to describe all isomorphisms of $\mathcal{L}$ onto $\mathcal{L}'$, even when $V$ and $V'$ are defined over different but isomorphic division rings. Theorem 3.1, the fundamental result of this chapter, makes precise the remarks just made.

Let $\mathbf{D}$, $\mathbf{D}'$, be isomorphic division rings and let $V$, $V'$ be finite dimensional vector spaces over $\mathbf{D}$ and $\mathbf{D}'$, respectively. Let

$$(1) \qquad \sigma : c \to c^\sigma \qquad (c \in \mathbf{D})$$

be an isomorphism of $\mathbf{D}$ onto $\mathbf{D}'$. A map

$$(2) \qquad L : v \to Lv$$

of $V$ into $V'$ is called *semilinear relative to* $\sigma$, or, briefly, *$\sigma$-linear*, if

$$(3) \qquad \begin{aligned} L(v_1 + v_2) &= Lv_1 + Lv_2 \qquad (v_1, v_2 \in V), \\ L(cv) &= c^\sigma Lv \qquad (v \in V, c \in \mathbf{D}). \end{aligned}$$

$L$ is said to be a $\sigma$-linear isomorphism if, in addition to (3), $Lv = 0$ implies $v = 0$ $(v \in V)$. $L$ is an isomorphism if and only if $L$ maps $V$ onto $V'$.

If $L$ is a $\sigma$-linear transformation of $V$ into $V'$ and $M$ a linear manifold of $V$, then

$$L[M] = \{Lv : v \in M\}$$

is evidently a linear manifold of $V'$. If $L$ is an isomorphism of $V$ onto $V'$, then it is obvious that the map

(4) $$\xi_L : M \to L[M]$$

is an isomorphism of the lattice $\mathscr{L}(V,\mathbf{D})$ of subspaces of $V$ onto the lattice $\mathscr{L}(V',\mathbf{D}')$ of subspaces of $V'$. We shall say that $\xi_L$ is induced by the $\sigma$-linear isomorphism $L$. Now let $d'$ be any nonzero element of $\mathbf{D}'$. If we define

(5) $$c^\tau = d'c^\sigma d'^{-1} \qquad (c \in \mathbf{D}),$$

(6) $$L'v = d'Lv \qquad (v \in V),$$

then it is easy to verify that $\tau$ $(c \to c^\tau)$ is an isomorphism of $\mathbf{D}$ onto $\mathbf{D}'$ and that $L'$ is a $\tau$-linear isomorphism of $V$ onto $V'$. We shall say that $\sigma$ and $\tau$ are *conjugate* if (5) is satisfied for a suitable nonzero $d'$. (6) implies that for any linear manifold $M \subseteq V$, $L[M] = L'[M]$, and hence it follows that the induced isomorphisms $\xi_L$ and $\xi_{L'}$ are identical. Notice that if $\mathbf{D}$ and $\mathbf{D}'$ are fields, $\sigma$ and $\tau$ are conjugate if and only if $\sigma = \tau$.

**Theorem 3.1.** *Let* $\mathbf{D}$ *and* $\mathbf{D}'$ *be division rings and let* $V$ *and* $V'$ *be vector spaces of dimension* $n$ *over* $\mathbf{D}$ *and* $\mathbf{D}'$, *respectively. Let* $n \geq 3$. *Then, in order that the geometries* $\mathscr{L}(V,\mathbf{D})$ *and* $\mathscr{L}(V',\mathbf{D}')$ *be isomorphic, it is necessary and sufficient that* $\mathbf{D}$ *and* $\mathbf{D}'$ *be isomorphic. Let us suppose that* $\mathbf{D}$ *and* $\mathbf{D}'$ *are isomorphic. Let* $\sigma$ *be an isomorphism of* $\mathbf{D}$ *onto* $\mathbf{D}'$ *and* $L$ *a* $\sigma$-*linear isomorphism of* $V$ *onto* $V'$. *Then the map* $\xi_L(M \to L[M])$ *is an isomorphism of* $\mathscr{L}(V,\mathbf{D})$ *onto* $\mathscr{L}(V',\mathbf{D}')$. *Conversely, if* $\xi$ *is any isomorphism of* $\mathscr{L}(V,\mathbf{D})$ *onto* $\mathscr{L}(V',\mathbf{D}')$, *there exists an isomorphism* $\sigma$ *of* $\mathbf{D}$ *onto* $\mathbf{D}'$ *and a* $\sigma$-*linear isomorphism* $L$ *of* $V$ *onto* $V'$ *such that* $\xi = \xi_L$. *If* $\tau$ *is another isomorphism of* $\mathbf{D}$ *onto* $\mathbf{D}'$ *and* $L'$ *a* $\tau$-*linear isomorphism of* $V$ *onto* $V'$, *then* $\xi_L = \xi_{L'}$, *if and only if for some nonzero* $d' \in \mathbf{D}'$ *one has:*

(6)
$$c^\tau = d'c^\sigma d'^{-1} \qquad (c \in \mathbf{D}),$$
$$L'v = d'Lv \qquad (v \in V).$$

**Proof.** Suppose to start with that $\mathbf{D}$ and $\mathbf{D}'$ are isomorphic. Let $\sigma$ be an isomorphism of $\mathbf{D}$ onto $\mathbf{D}'$. Let $\{v_1, \cdots, v_n\}$ and $\{v_1', \cdots, v_n'\}$ be bases for $V$ and $V'$, respectively. Then $L$, defined by

$$L : \sum_{i=1}^{n} c_i v_i \to \sum_{i=1}^{n} c_i^\sigma v_i',$$

is a $\sigma$-linear isomorphism of $V$ onto $V'$. Consequently, $\xi_L$ is an isomorphism of $\mathscr{L}(V,\mathbf{D})$ onto $\mathscr{L}(V',\mathbf{D}')$ which shows that $\mathscr{L}(V,\mathbf{D})$ and $\mathscr{L}(V',\mathbf{D}')$ are isomorphic. We have moreover seen in the remarks preceding theorem 3.1 that for any $\sigma$-linear isomorphism $L$ of $V$ onto $V'$, $\xi_L$ is an isomorphism of $\mathscr{L}(V,\mathbf{D})$ onto $\mathscr{L}(V',\mathbf{D}')$ and that $\xi_L = \xi_{L'}$ if $L$ and $L'$ are related as in (5) and (6).

We shall now prove the converses. The proof is essentially that given by Baer [1]. We have arranged it in the form of a series of lemmas. Let $\xi$ be an isomorphism of $\mathscr{L}(V,\mathbf{D})$ onto $\mathscr{L}(V',\mathbf{D}')$.

Let $x \in V$. We write

(7)                     $\mathbf{D} \cdot x = \{dx : d \in \mathbf{D}\}.$

$\mathbf{D}' \cdot x'$ is defined similarly for $x' \in V'$. If $c \in \mathbf{D}$ and $c \neq 0$, then $\mathbf{D} \cdot x = \mathbf{D} \cdot (cx)$. Suppose $x \in V$, $x' \in V'$. We write $x \sim x'$ when and only when

(8)                 $x \neq 0, \quad x' \neq 0, \quad \xi(\mathbf{D} \cdot x) = \mathbf{D}' \cdot x',$

where $\xi$ is the given isomorphism of $\mathscr{L}(V,\mathbf{D})$ onto $\mathscr{L}(V',\mathbf{D}')$.

**Lemma 3.2.** *Let $x \in V$, $x' \in V'$ and let $x \sim x'$. Then, for any $y \in V$ with $y \neq 0$ and $\mathbf{D} \cdot y \neq \mathbf{D} \cdot x$, there exists a unique $y' \in V'$ such that*

(9)                 $y \sim y' \quad and \quad x - y \sim x' - y'.$

**Proof.** Let $y''$ be some nonzero vector in $\xi(\mathbf{D} \cdot y)$. Since $\xi$ is a lattice isomorphism it follows that for some $a, b \in \mathbf{D}'$,

$$\xi(\mathbf{D} \cdot (x-y)) = \mathbf{D}' \cdot (ax' + by'').$$

Since $\mathbf{D} \cdot y \neq \mathbf{D} \cdot x$, $\mathbf{D} \cdot (x-y)$ is distinct from both $\mathbf{D} \cdot x$ and $\mathbf{D} \cdot y$ and hence $a \neq 0$, $b \neq 0$. Define $y'$ by

$$y' = -(a^{-1}b)y''.$$

Then $y' \neq 0$, $y \sim y'$, and $x - y \sim x' - y'$.

To prove the uniqueness of $y'$, suppose that $z' \neq 0$ is in $V'$ such that $y \sim z'$, $x - y \sim x' - z'$. Then for $a, b \in \mathbf{D}'$, which are both nonzero,

$$z' = ay',$$
$$x' - z' = b(x' - y'),$$

from which it follows that $x' = bx' + (a-b)y'$. Since $\mathbf{D}' \cdot x'$ and $\mathbf{D}' \cdot y'$ are distinct, this implies that $b = 1$ and $a - b = 0$ so that $a = 1$ and $y' = z'$.

Now let $x \in V$, $x' \in V'$, and let $x \sim x'$. We define the mapping $T_{x,x'}$ by

(10)   $\begin{aligned} &T_{x,x'}(0) = 0, \\ &T_{x,x'}(y) = y' \quad \text{if} \quad y \in V, \quad y \neq 0, \quad \text{and} \quad \mathbf{D} \cdot y \neq \mathbf{D} \cdot x, \end{aligned}$

where $y' \in V'$ satisfies (9). Note that $T_{x,x'}(y)$ is not defined for a nonzero $y$ unless $\mathbf{D} \cdot y \neq \mathbf{D} \cdot x$.

**Lemma 3.3.** *Let $x, y, z \in V$ be independent. Then*

(11)   (a)　$\mathbf{D} \cdot (y-z) = (\mathbf{D} \cdot y \vee \mathbf{D} \cdot z) \wedge (\mathbf{D} \cdot (x-y) \vee \mathbf{D} \cdot (x-z)),$
       (b)　$\mathbf{D} \cdot (x-y-z) = (\mathbf{D} \cdot (x-y) \vee \mathbf{D} \cdot z) \wedge (\mathbf{D} \cdot (x-z) \vee \mathbf{D} \cdot y),$
       (c)　$\mathbf{D} \cdot (y+z) = (\mathbf{D} \cdot y \vee \mathbf{D} \cdot z) \wedge (\mathbf{D} \cdot x \vee \mathbf{D} \cdot (x-y-z)).$

**Proof.** In view of the independence of $x$, $y$ and $z$, each element occurring in the lattice intersection on the right-hand side of the above equations is of dimension 2, and hence the lattice intersections themselves are, because of independence of $x$, $y$ and $z$, of dimension 1. Thus, to prove the equations written above, it is obviously sufficient to check that the vectors which appear in the left-hand sides of the above equations belong to the linear manifolds appearing in the right-hand side. However, this is obvious in every case. This proves the lemma.

**Lemma 3.4.** *Let* $x \in V$, $x' \in V'$ *and let* $x \sim x'$. *Further let* $y \neq 0$, $\mathbf{D} \cdot y \neq \mathbf{D} \cdot x$, *and* $T_{x,x'}(y) = y'$. *Then* $y \sim y'$ *and* $T_{y,y'}(x) = x'$.

**Proof.** Since $y, y' \neq 0$, $y \sim y'$. Moreover, since $x - y \sim x' - y'$, one has $y - x \sim y' - x'$. Therefore we conclude from (10) that

$$T_{y,y'}(x) = x'.$$

This proves the lemma.

**Lemma 3.5.** *Let* $x$, $y$, $z$ *be independent vectors of* $V$. *Let* $x \sim x'$ *and let* $y' = T_{x,x'}(y)$ *and* $z' = T_{x,x'}(z)$. *Then*

(12) $$T_{y,y'}(z) = z'.$$

**Proof.** We first note that the independence of $x$, $y$, and $z$ guarantees that $T_{x,x'}(y)$, $T_{x,x'}(z)$, and $T_{y,y'}(z)$ are defined. We must show that

$$y \sim y', \quad y - z \sim y' - z'.$$

Since $x$, $y$, $z$ are independent, $y - z \neq 0$. Since, by lemma 3.4, $x \sim x'$, $y \sim y'$, $z \sim z'$, and since $\xi$ is a lattice isomorphism, $x'$, $y'$, $z'$ are independent. In particular, $y' - z' \neq 0$. Moreover, we obtain from (a) of (11), using the independence of $x'$, $y'$, $z'$,

$$\xi(\mathbf{D} \cdot (y - z)) = (\xi(\mathbf{D} \cdot y) \vee \xi(\mathbf{D} \cdot z)) \wedge (\xi(\mathbf{D} \cdot (x - y)) \vee \xi(\mathbf{D} \cdot (x - z)))$$
$$= (\mathbf{D}' \cdot y' \vee \mathbf{D}' \cdot z') \wedge (\mathbf{D}' \cdot (x' - y') \vee \mathbf{D}' \cdot (x' - z'))$$
$$= \mathbf{D}' \cdot (y' - z').$$

This proves that $y - z \sim y' - z'$.

**Lemma 3.6.** *Let* $x, y, z$ *be independent, let* $x \sim x'$, *and let us write* $y' = T_{x,x'}(y)$ *and* $z' = T_{x,x'}(z)$. *Then*

(13)
    (a) $\quad x - y - z \sim x' - y' - z'$,
    (b) $\quad y + z \sim y' + z'$.

**Proof.** Since $x'$, $y'$, $z'$ are independent, $x' - y' - z' \neq 0$, $y' + z' \neq 0$. Therefore, (13) will be proved if we show that

$$\xi(\mathbf{D} \cdot (x - y - z)) = \mathbf{D}' \cdot (x' - y' - z'),$$
$$\xi(\mathbf{D} \cdot (y + z)) = \mathbf{D}' \cdot (y' + z').$$

Now, $\{x,y,z\}$ and $\{x',y',z'\}$ are both independent sets and $\xi$ is a lattice isomorphism. Further, as $T_{x,x'}(y)=y'$ and $T_{x,x'}(z) = z'$, $\xi(\mathbf{D}\cdot(x-y)) = \mathbf{D}'\cdot(x'-y')$ and $\xi(\mathbf{D}\cdot(x-z))=\mathbf{D}'\cdot(x'-z')$. We therefore obtain from (b) of (11),

$$\xi(\mathbf{D}\cdot(x-y-z)) = (\mathbf{D}'\cdot(x'-y') \vee \mathbf{D}'\cdot z') \wedge (\mathbf{D}'\cdot(x'-z') \vee \mathbf{D}'\cdot y')$$
$$= \mathbf{D}'\cdot(x'-y'-z').$$

This proves (a) of (13). We know now that $x-y-z \sim x'-y'-z'$. But then we obtain from (c) of (11),

$$\xi(\mathbf{D}\cdot(y+z)) = (\mathbf{D}'\cdot y' \vee \mathbf{D}'\cdot z') \wedge (\mathbf{D}'\cdot x' \vee \mathbf{D}'\cdot(x'-y'-z'))$$
$$= \mathbf{D}'\cdot(y'+z').$$

This shows that (b) of (13) is true. The lemma is proved.

**Lemma 3.7.** *Let* $x \sim x'$. *Let* $y$ *and* $z$ *be vectors of* $V$ *such that*

$$(\mathbf{D}\cdot y \vee \mathbf{D}\cdot z) \wedge \mathbf{D}\cdot x = 0.$$

*Then*

(14) $$T_{x,x'}(y+z) = T_{x,x'}(y)+T_{x,x'}(z).$$

**Proof.** The case when one or both of $y$ and $z$ are equal to 0 is a trivial consequence of the definition of $T_{x,x'}$ in (10). We may (and do) therefore assume that $y \neq 0$, $z \neq 0$. Notice that if $y+z \neq 0$, the assumption that $(\mathbf{D}\cdot y \vee \mathbf{D}\cdot z) \wedge \mathbf{D}\cdot x=0$ implies that $\mathbf{D}\cdot(y+z) \neq \mathbf{D}\cdot x$, $\mathbf{D}\cdot y \neq \mathbf{D}\cdot x$ and $\mathbf{D}\cdot z \neq \mathbf{D}\cdot x$. This means that $T_{x,x'}(y)$, $T_{x,x'}(z)$ and $T_{x,x'}(y+z)$ are all defined. Three cases arise.

*Case 1: $x$, $y$, $z$ are independent.* Then, from (13) we obtain the relations $x-y-z \sim x'-y'-z'$, $y+z \sim y'+z'$, which imply that

$$T_{x,x'}(y+z) = y'+z'.$$

From this we obtain (14) immediately.

*Case 2: $\mathbf{D}\cdot y = \mathbf{D}\cdot z$, but $y+z \neq 0$.* In this case, as dim $V \geq 3$, there is a nonzero vector $w$ such that $w$, $x$, and $y$ are independent. Since $y+z \neq 0$, the sets $\{x,w,y+z\}$ and $\{x,w+y,z\}$ are independent. We have, from case 1,

$$T_{x,x'}(w+y+z) = T_{x,x'}(w)+T_{x,x'}(y+z)$$

while

$$T_{x,x'}(w+y+z) = T_{x,x'}(w+y)+T_{x,x'}(z)$$
$$= T_{x,x'}(w) + T_{x,x'}(y)+T_{x,x'}(z),$$

so that

$$T_{x,x'}(y+z) = T_{x,x'}(y)+T_{x,x'}(z).$$

*Case 3:* $\mathbf{D} \cdot y = \mathbf{D} \cdot z$, $y + z = 0$. In this case, let $w$ be as in case 2. Then the vectors $w$, $x$, $y$ are independent and the vectors $x$, $w + y$, $z$ are independent and we have, since $w + y + z = w$,

$$T_{x,x'}(w) = T_{x,x'}(w + y + z) = T_{x,x'}(w + y) + T_{x,x'}(z)$$
$$= T_{x,x'}(w) + T_{x,x'}(y) + T_{x,x'}(z),$$

from which it follows, as $T_{x,x'}(0) = 0$, that

$$T_{x,x'}(y + z) = T_{x,x'}(y) + T_{x,x'}(z).$$

This completes the proof of the lemma if we notice that the assumptions $y \neq 0$, $z \neq 0$, $(\mathbf{D} \cdot y \vee D \cdot z) \wedge \mathbf{D} \cdot x = 0$ imply that the three cases discussed above are the only possible ones.

Since the dimension of $V$ is at least 3, we can choose 3 vectors $u_1$, $u_2$, $u_3$ of $V$ which are independent. Let $u_1' \in V'$ be such that $u_1 \sim u_1'$ and let $u_2'$, $u_3' \in V'$ be defined by

(15)
$$u_2' = T_{u_1,u_1'}(u_2),$$
$$u_3' = T_{u_1,u_1'}(u_3).$$

From lemma 3.4 it follows that $u_i \sim u_i'$ for $i = 1, 2, 3$ and

$$T_{u_2,u_2'}(u_1) = T_{u_3,u_3'}(u_1) = u_1'.$$

**Lemma 3.8.** *If $i$, $j$ are two distinct elements of $\{1,2,3\}$, then*

(16)
$$u_j' = T_{u_i,u_i'}(u_j).$$

**Proof.** In view of lemma 3.4 we have, when $x \sim x'$ and $y \sim y'$,

$$T_{x,x'}(y) = y' \quad \text{if and only if} \quad T_{y,y'}(x) = x'.$$

In order to prove (16) it remains only to show that

$$u_3' = T_{u_2,u_2'}(u_3),$$

but this follows from (12).

We shall now define a mapping $L$ of $V$ into $V'$. We set

(17)
$$L0 = 0.$$

If $x \neq 0$ there will exist an integer $i$ such that $1 \leq i \leq 3$ and $\mathbf{D} \cdot x \neq \mathbf{D} \cdot u_i$; we then set

(17a)
$$Lx = T_{u_i,u_i'}(x).$$

**Lemma 3.9.** *$L$ is well defined and $Lu_i = u_i'$ for $i = 1, 2, 3$.*

**Proof.** We have to show that if $x \neq 0$ is in $V$ and if $i$ and $j$ are two distinct elements of $\{1,2,3\}$ such that $\mathbf{D} \cdot x \neq \mathbf{D} \cdot u_i$, $\mathbf{D} \cdot x \neq \mathbf{D} \cdot u_j$, then

$$T_{u_i,u_i'}(x) = T_{u_j,u_j'}(x).$$

Two cases arise.

*Case 1: $x$, $u_i$, $u_j$ are independent.* In this case the result follows from (12); for, we have from (17) and (16),

$$Lx = T_{u_i,u_i'}(x),$$

$$u_j' = T_{u_i,u_i'}(u_j),$$

so that

$$T_{u_j,u_j'}(x) = T_{u_i,u_i'}(x).$$

*Case 2: $\mathbf{D} \cdot x \subseteq (\mathbf{D} \cdot u_i) \vee (\mathbf{D} \cdot u_j)$.* Let $k$ be the remaining integer between 1 and 3 such that $i$, $j$, $k$ is a permutation of 1, 2, 3. Since $u_1$, $u_2$, $u_3$ are independent, $x$, $u_i$, $u_k$ are independent and $x$, $u_j$, $u_k$ are independent. Hence, from case 1, we have:

$$T_{u_i,u_i'}(x) = T_{u_k,u_k'}(x)$$
$$= T_{u_j,u_j'}(x).$$

This proves the lemma if we notice that the equations $Lu_i = u_i'$ $(1 \leq i \leq 3)$ are consequences of (16).

**Lemma 3.10.** *$L$ is additive; i.e., if $y$ and $z$ are vectors of $V$, then*

$$(18) \qquad\qquad L(y+z) = Ly + Lz.$$

**Proof.** If $y$ or $z$ is 0, then (18) is trivial as $L0 = 0$. We may assume therefore that both of them are nonzero. Then there exists an integer $i$ between 1 and 3 such that

$$\mathbf{D} \cdot u_i \wedge (\mathbf{D} \cdot y \vee \mathbf{D} \cdot z) = 0.$$

Then from (14) we have:

$$L(y+z) = T_{u_i,u_i'}(y+z)$$
$$= T_{u_i,u_i'}(y) + T_{u_i,u_i'}(z)$$
$$= Ly + Lz.$$

This proves (18).

**Lemma 3.11.** *$L$ is an isomorphism between the additive abelian groups $V$ and $V'$.*

**Proof.** We see from (17) that $Ly = 0$ if and only if $y = 0$. It is thus enough to prove that $L$ maps $V$ onto $V'$. Let $x' \neq 0$ be in $V'$. Then as $\xi$ maps $\mathscr{L}(V,\mathbf{D})$ onto $\mathscr{L}(V',\mathbf{D}')$, there exists an $a \in \mathscr{L}(V,\mathbf{D})$ of dimension 1 such that $\xi(a) = \mathbf{D}' \cdot x'$. Let $i(1 \leq i \leq 3)$ be such that $a \neq \mathbf{D} \cdot u_i$. Then $\mathbf{D}' \cdot u_i' \neq \mathbf{D}' \cdot x'$. The vector $x' + u_i'$ is nonzero and distinct from both $x'$ and $u_i'$. Therefore there exists a $b$ in $\mathscr{L}(V,\mathbf{D})$ of dimension 1, distinct from $a$ and $\mathbf{D} \cdot u_i$ such that

$$\xi(b) = \mathbf{D}' \cdot (x' + u_i').$$

Let $z$ be a vector such that $z \neq 0$ and $\mathbf{D} \cdot z = a$. Then $b$ will be of the form

$$b = \mathbf{D} \cdot (c_1 u_i + c_2 z),$$

with $c_1, c_2 \in \mathbf{D}$. Clearly, $c_1, c_2$ are both $\neq 0$. Write $c = c_1^{-1} c_2$. Then

$$b = \mathbf{D} \cdot (u_i + cz).$$

Then, however, as $L$ is additive,

$$\xi(b) = \mathbf{D}' \cdot L(u_i + cz)$$
$$= \mathbf{D}' \cdot (u_i' + L(cz)).$$

But we have also

$$\xi(b) = \mathbf{D}' \cdot (u_i' + x').$$

This shows that $u_i' + x' \in \mathbf{D}' \cdot (u_i' + L(cz))$ and hence we infer that

$$x' = L(cz).$$

This completes the proof of lemma 3.11.

$L$ is thus an isomorphism between the additive abelian groups $V$ and $V'$ such that for any $x \neq 0$ in $V$, $Lx$ satisfies the relation $x \sim Lx$. We now examine the properties of $L$ relative to scalar multiplication. For any $x \neq 0$, $\mathbf{D} \cdot (cx) = \mathbf{D} \cdot x$ if $c \neq 0$, and hence $\mathbf{D}' \cdot (Lx) = \mathbf{D}' \cdot (L(cx))$. Consequently, there is a constant $g(c,x) \in \mathbf{D}'$ such that

$$(19) \qquad L(cx) = g(c,x)Lx,$$

with $g(c,x) \neq 0$. We define $g(0,x) = 0$ for all $x \neq 0$ so that the equation

$$L(cx) = g(c,x)Lx$$

is valid for all $x \neq 0$ of $V$ and for all $c$ of $\mathbf{D}$.

**Lemma 3.12.** *If $x$ and $y$ are vectors of $V$ which are $\neq 0$, then for any $c$ of $\mathbf{D}$, we have*

$$g(c,x) = g(c,y).$$

**Proof.** We assume, as we may, that $c \neq 0$. Two cases arise.
*Case 1: $x$ and $y$ are independent.* In this case, we have $x + y \neq 0$ and

$$L(c(x+y)) = g(c,x+y)L(x+y) = g(c,x+y)(Lx + Ly).$$

Also, however,

$$L(c(x+y)) = L(cx) + L(cy) = g(c,x)Lx + g(c,y)Ly.$$

Since $x \sim Lx$ and $y \sim Ly$, $Lx$ and $Ly$ are independent. Consequently,

$$g(c,x) = g(c,x+y) = g(c,y).$$

*Case 2: x and y are dependent, i.e.,* $\mathbf{D} \cdot x = \mathbf{D} \cdot y$. Let $w$ be a vector $\neq 0$ such that $\{x,w\}$ and $\{y,w\}$ are independent. Then we have, by case 1,

$$g(c,x) = g(c,w),$$
$$g(c,y) = g(c,w),$$

so that

$$g(c,x) = g(c,y).$$

This proves the lemma.

In view of this lemma we can define $\sigma(c \to c^\sigma)$ by the formula

(20) $$c^\sigma = g(c,x),$$

where $x \in V$ is nonzero. $\sigma$ is then a well-defined mapping of $\mathbf{D}$ into $\mathbf{D}'$.

**Lemma 3.13.** $\sigma(c \to c^\sigma)$ *is an isomorphism of* $\mathbf{D}$ *onto* $\mathbf{D}'$. *In particular,* $\mathbf{D}$ *and* $\mathbf{D}'$ *are isomorphic.*

**Proof.** Let $x \neq 0$ be in $V$. Let $c_1, c_2 \in \mathbf{D}$. Then $Lx \neq 0$ and

$$\begin{aligned}
(c_1 + c_2)^\sigma Lx &= L((c_1 + c_2)x) \\
&= L(c_1 x + c_2 x) \\
&= L(c_1 x) + L(c_2 x) \\
&= (c_1{}^\sigma + c_2{}^\sigma)Lx,
\end{aligned}$$

so that

$$(c_1 + c_2)^\sigma = c_1{}^\sigma + c_2{}^\sigma.$$

Further,

$$\begin{aligned}
(c_1 c_2)^\sigma Lx &= L(c_1(c_2 x)) \\
&= c_1{}^\sigma L(c_2 x) \\
&= c_1{}^\sigma c_2{}^\sigma Lx,
\end{aligned}$$

so that

$$(c_1 c_2)^\sigma = c_1{}^\sigma c_2{}^\sigma.$$

Since $L$ is one-one and onto, it is evident that $\sigma$ is one-one and onto. Lemma 3.13 is proved.

**Lemma 3.14.** $L$ *is a* $\sigma$-*linear isomorphism of* $V$ *onto* $V'$.

**Proof.** We have:

$$L(cx) = c^\sigma Lx$$

for $x \in V$ and $c \in \mathbf{D}$. Moreover, $L$ is an additive isomorphism of $V$ onto $V'$ by lemma 3.11. This proves that $L$ is a $\sigma$-linear isomorphism.

At this stage we know that the lattice isomorphism $\xi$ is induced by the $\sigma$-linear isomorphism $L$. We shall now complete the proof of the theorem by showing that the $L$ is essentially uniquely determined by $\xi$. Suppose $\tau(c \to c^\tau)$ is an isomorphism of $\mathbf{D}$ onto $\mathbf{D}'$ and $M$ a $\tau$-linear isomorphism of $V$ onto $V'$ such that $M$ also induces the lattice isomorphism $\xi$; i.e., $\xi_M = \xi_L = \xi$.

**Lemma 3.15.** *There exists an element $d' \neq 0$ of $\mathbf{D}'$ such that*

$$Mx = d'Lx$$

*for all $x \in V$ and*

$$c^\tau = d'c^\sigma d'^{-1}$$

*for all $c \in \mathbf{D}$.*

**Proof.** The mapping $M^{-1}L = N$ is evidently an additive isomorphism of $V$ onto itself. Moreover, if we define $\theta(c \to c^\theta)$ by

$$c^\theta = (c^\sigma)^{(\tau^{-1})},$$

then $\theta(c \to c^\theta)$ is an automorphism of the division ring $\mathbf{D}$ onto itself. Obviously

$$N(cx) = c^\theta Nx,$$

so that we may conclude that $N$ is a $\theta$-linear isomorphism of $V$ onto itself. Since $L$ and $M$ induce the same lattice isomorphism $\xi$, $N$ induces the identity automorphism of $\mathscr{L}(V, \mathbf{D})$ onto itself. This means that for any $x \neq 0$ in $V$ there is a $g(x) \neq 0$ in $\mathbf{D}$ such that

$$Nx = g(x)x.$$

We claim that $g(x)$ does not depend on $x$, $x \neq 0$. Suppose that $x$ and $y$ are two vectors $\neq 0$. If they are independent we will have, since $N$ is additive,

$$\begin{aligned}
g(x+y)(x+y) &= N(x+y) \\
&= Nx + Ny \\
&= g(x)x + g(y)y,
\end{aligned}$$

so that

$$g(x) = g(x+y) = g(y).$$

On the other hand, if $x$ and $y$ were dependent, let $w$ be a vector $\neq 0$ such that $\{x,y\}$ and $\{y,w\}$ are independent. Then from the preceding case, we may conclude

$$\begin{aligned}
g(x) &= g(w), \\
g(y) &= g(w),
\end{aligned}$$

i.e.,

$$g(x) = g(y).$$

In other words, there is a single element $g \neq 0$ of $\mathbf{D}$ such that for all $x \in V$,

$$Nx = gx.$$

This shows that, if we define $d' = (g^\tau)^{-1}$,

$$Lx = M(gx)$$

$$= g^\tau Mx$$

$$= d'^{-1} Mx,$$

so that for all $x \in V$,

$$Mx = d' Lx.$$

Further, $c^\tau Mx = M(cx) = d'(L(cx)) = d' c^\sigma d'^{-1}(Mx)$, so that

$$c^\tau = d' c^\sigma d'^{-1}$$

for all $c \in \mathbf{D}$.

Lemmas 3.2 through 3.15 imply theorem 3.1, which is now completely proved.

Let $\mathbf{D} = \mathbf{D}'$. Then theorem 3.1 asserts that any lattice isomorphism $\xi$ of $\mathscr{L}(V,\mathbf{D})$ onto $\mathscr{L}(V',\mathbf{D})$ is induced by a semilinear isomorphism of $V$ onto $V'$. We shall say that $\xi$ is *linear* if there exists a linear isomorphism $L$ of $V$ onto $V'$, such that $\xi = \xi_L$. An automorphism $\sigma(c \to c^\sigma)$ of $\mathbf{D}$ is called *inner* if there is a $d \neq 0$ in $\mathbf{D}$ such that $c^\sigma = dcd^{-1}$ for all $c$ in $\mathbf{D}$.

**Theorem 3.16.** *Let $\mathbf{D}$ be a division ring and let $V$ and $V'$ be vector spaces of dimension $n$ ($\geq 3$) over $\mathbf{D}$. In order that every isomorphism of $\mathscr{L}(V,\mathbf{D})$ onto $\mathscr{L}(V',\mathbf{D})$ be linear, it is necessary and sufficient that every automorphism of $\mathbf{D}$ be inner.*

**Proof.** Let $\mathbf{D}$ be such that its automorphisms are all inner and let $\xi$ be an isomorphism of $\mathscr{L}(V,\mathbf{D})$ onto $\mathscr{L}(V',\mathbf{D})$. Then there exists an automorphism $\sigma(c \to c^\sigma)$ of $\mathbf{D}$ and a $\sigma$-linear isomorphism $L$ of the vector space $V$ onto the vector space $V'$ which induces $\xi$. Since $\sigma$ is inner, there exists an element $d_0 \neq 0$ of $\mathbf{D}$ such that, for all $c$ in $\mathbf{D}$,

$$c^\sigma = d_0 c d_0^{-1}.$$

If we define $M$ by

$$Mx = d_0^{-1}(Lx) \qquad (x \in V),$$

then it is trivial to check that $M$ is a linear transformation which maps $V$ onto $V'$ isomorphically and which induces the lattice isomorphism $\xi$.

Conversely, let every isomorphism of $\mathscr{L}(V,\mathbf{D})$ onto $\mathscr{L}(V',\mathbf{D})$ be linear. Let $\{x_1, \cdots, x_n\}$ and $\{x_1', \cdots, x_n'\}$ be bases in $V$ and $V'$, respectively.

Suppose that $\sigma(c \to c^\sigma)$ is an arbitrary automorphism of $\mathbf{D}$. Let $L$ be the map

$$L : \sum_{i=1}^{n} c_i x_i \to \sum_{i=1}^{n} c_i{}^\sigma x_i{}'.$$

$L$ is evidently a $\sigma$-linear isomorphism of $V$ onto $V'$. $\xi_L$, the induced isomorphism of $\mathscr{L}(V,\mathbf{D})$ on $\mathscr{L}(V',\mathbf{D})$ is linear by assumption, and hence $\xi_L = \xi_M$, where $M$ is a linear isomorphism of $V$ onto $V'$. By (5) of theorem 3.1 we have for some $d \neq 0$ in $\mathbf{D}$, $c^\sigma = dcd^{-1}$ for all $c \in \mathbf{D}$. $\sigma$ is therefore an inner automorphism of $\mathbf{D}$. Theorem 3.16 is thus proved completely.

**Remark.** Let $\xi$ be a linear isomorphism of $\mathscr{L}(V,\mathbf{D})$ onto $\mathscr{L}(V',\mathbf{D})$ and let $L_1$, $L_2$ be two *linear* isomorphisms of $V$ onto $V'$ such that $\xi = \xi_{L_1} = \xi_{L_2}$. From (5) and (6) we conclude that

$$L_1 x = d' L_2 x,$$
$$c = d' c d'^{-1},$$

for some $d'(\neq 0)$ in $\mathbf{D}$, all $x \in V$ and $c \in \mathbf{D}$. Therefore, $d'$ is in the center of $\mathbf{D}$.

## 2. EXAMPLES

We shall now discuss a few examples. We have great interest in three division rings: $\mathbf{R}$, the field of real numbers, $\mathbf{C}$, the field of complex numbers, and $\mathbf{Q}$, the division ring of quaternions.

(a) $\mathbf{R}$, *the field of real numbers.* We remark that every automorphism of $\mathbf{R}$ is trivial, i.e., is the identity automorphism. In fact, if $x \to x'$ is an automorphism of $\mathbf{R}$, $(x+y)' = x' + y'$ and $x^2 = x'^2$ so that $x \geq 0$ implies $x' \geq 0$. From this it is very easy to show that $x' = cx$ for all $x$. Due to the multiplicative nature of the mapping $x \to x'$, $c$ must be 1. Theorem 3.1 shows that every lattice isomorphism between the geometries of two real vector spaces of the same dimension ($\geq 3$) is induced by a real *linear* isomorphism between the vector spaces concerned and that, moreover, this isomorphism is unique to within multiplication by a nonzero real number.

(b) $\mathbf{C}$, *the field of complex numbers.* In this case, by using general field theory one can construct a great profusion of automorphisms of $\mathbf{C}$ (cf. Bourbaki [1], pp. 114–115). However, if the automorphism is analytically well behaved (measurable or maps bounded sets into bounded sets), then it is either the *identity* $c \to c$, or $(*) : c \to c^*$ ($a + ib \to a - ib$, $a$, $b$ real, $i^2 = -1$), the *conjugation*. Theorem 3.1 of course implies that if the automorphism $\xi$ of $\mathscr{L}(V,\mathbf{C})$ is induced by a $*$-linear (also called conjugate-linear) automorphism of $V$, it cannot be induced by a linear automorphism of $V$.

(c) **Q**, *the quaternions*. We begin by giving a brief description of this division ring. There are several ways to introduce the division ring of quaternions. It is convenient to use their matrix representations. We define:

$$(21) \quad 1 = \begin{pmatrix} 1 & 0 \\ 0 & 1 \end{pmatrix}, \quad \mathbf{j}_1 = \begin{pmatrix} i & 0 \\ 0 & -i \end{pmatrix}, \quad \mathbf{j}_2 = \begin{pmatrix} 0 & 1 \\ -1 & 0 \end{pmatrix}, \quad \mathbf{j}_3 = \begin{pmatrix} 0 & i \\ i & 0 \end{pmatrix},$$

where $i$ is a fixed square root of $-1$ in the complex number field. Let

$$(22) \quad \mathbf{Q} = \{\mathbf{q} : \mathbf{q} = q_0 1 + q_1 \mathbf{j}_1 + q_2 \mathbf{j}_2 + q_3 \mathbf{j}_3, \; q_0, \, q_1, \, q_2, \, q_3 \text{ real}\}.$$

**Q** is evidently a real vector space of dimension 4 over the field **R** of real numbers. Moreover, we obtain, through an easy computation:

$$(23) \quad \begin{aligned} \mathbf{j}_1{}^2 &= \mathbf{j}_2{}^2 = \mathbf{j}_3{}^2 = -1, \\ \mathbf{j}_1 \mathbf{j}_2 &= -\mathbf{j}_2 \mathbf{j}_1 = \mathbf{j}_3, \\ \mathbf{j}_2 \mathbf{j}_3 &= -\mathbf{j}_3 \mathbf{j}_2 = \mathbf{j}_1, \\ \mathbf{j}_3 \mathbf{j}_1 &= -\mathbf{j}_1 \mathbf{j}_3 = \mathbf{j}_2. \end{aligned}$$

If we write, for $\mathbf{q} = q_0 1 + q_1 \mathbf{j}_1 + q_2 \mathbf{j}_2 + q_3 \mathbf{j}_3$,

$$(24) \quad |\mathbf{q}| = +(q_0{}^2 + q_1{}^2 + q_2{}^2 + q_3{}^2)^{1/2},$$

then $\mathbf{q} \to |\mathbf{q}|$ is a nonnegative real valued function of $\mathbf{q} \in \mathbf{Q}$ which is zero if and only if the element $\mathbf{q}$ is zero. Obviously, $|\cdot|$ is a norm for **Q** and we have the property

$$(25) \quad |\mathbf{q} + \mathbf{q}'| \le |\mathbf{q}| + |\mathbf{q}'|.$$

**Q**, under $|\cdot|$, is complete.

For any $\mathbf{q} \in \mathbf{Q}$, let $\mathbf{q}^*$ denote the matrix adjoint to $\mathbf{q}$. If

$$\mathbf{q} = q_0 1 + \sum_{k=1}^{3} q_k \mathbf{j}_k,$$

then $\mathbf{q}^* \in \mathbf{Q}$ and $\mathbf{q}^* = q_0 1 - \sum_{k=1}^{3} q_k \mathbf{j}_k$. $\mathbf{q} \to \mathbf{q}^*$ is an involutive anti-automorphism of **Q**. We shall call it the *canonical conjugation* of **Q**. If $\mathbf{q} \in \mathbf{Q}$ and $\mathbf{q} \ne 0$, the element $\mathbf{q}' = |\mathbf{q}|^{-1} \cdot \mathbf{q}$ lies in **Q** and in fact

$$\mathbf{q}' = \begin{pmatrix} (q_0 + iq_1)/|\mathbf{q}|, & (q_2 + iq_3)/|\mathbf{q}| \\ (-q_2 + iq_3)/|\mathbf{q}|, & (q_0 - iq_1)/|\mathbf{q}| \end{pmatrix}.$$

Evidently $\mathbf{q}'$ is in $SU(2,\mathbf{C})$, the group of unitary matrices of order 2 and determinant one. Obviously, all such matrices can be obtained in this fashion and in fact $SU(2,\mathbf{C})$ coincides with the set of all

$$\mathbf{q} = q_0 \cdot 1 + \sum_{k=1}^{3} q_k \mathbf{j}_k$$

with $q_0^2 + q_1^2 + q_2^2 + q_3^2 = 1$, i.e., the set of all quaternions of norm one. Moreover,

(26) $\qquad \mathbf{Q} = \{c\mathbf{q} : c \text{ a real number} \geq 0, \text{ and } \mathbf{q} \in SU(2,\mathbf{C})\}.$

This proves that $\mathbf{Q}$ is closed under multiplication so that $\mathbf{Q}$ becomes an associative algebra over $\mathbf{R}$ with 1 as its unit. Since any element of $\mathbf{Q}$ is of this form, it is invertible as soon as it is $\neq 0$ so that any nonzero element of $\mathbf{Q}$ has an inverse. This shows that $\mathbf{Q}$ is a division ring. For $\mathbf{q} \in SU(2,\mathbf{C})$, $\mathbf{q}^{-1} = \mathbf{q}^*$. We have, for $\mathbf{q} = q_0 1 + \sum_{r=1}^{3} q_r \mathbf{j}_r$, $\mathrm{tr}(\cdot)$ denoting the trace,

(27) $\qquad\qquad\qquad \mathrm{tr}(\mathbf{q}) = 2q_0.$

By the invariance of trace, if $\mathbf{x} \in \mathbf{Q}$ is $\neq 0$,

(28) $\qquad\qquad\qquad \mathrm{tr}(\mathbf{x}\mathbf{q}\mathbf{x}^{-1}) = \mathrm{tr}(\mathbf{q}).$

Evidently,

(29) $\qquad\qquad\qquad |\mathbf{q}|^2 = \det \mathbf{q},$

and thus $q \to |\mathbf{q}|$ has in addition the multiplicative property:

(30) $\qquad\qquad\qquad |\mathbf{q}\mathbf{q}'| = |\mathbf{q}| \cdot |\mathbf{q}'|.$

A quaternion of norm 1 is called a *unit quaternion*. Under the topology we have given for $\mathbf{Q}$, the set $\mathbf{U}$ of unit quaternions is the compact non-commutative topological group $SU(2,\mathbf{C})$.

It is easy to see that a $2 \times 2$ matrix commutes with all unitary matrices of determinant 1 if and only if it is a scalar multiple of the identity matrix. This shows that only an element of the form $r\mathbf{1}$, $r$ a real number, can lie in the center of the division ring $\mathbf{Q}$. Thus the center of the division ring $\mathbf{Q}$ is identified with the real number field by the map:

$$r \to r\mathbf{1} \qquad (r \in \mathbf{R}).$$

We shall now prove that every automorphism of the division ring $\mathbf{Q}$ is an inner automorphism. More precisely, let $(\mathbf{x} \to \mathbf{x}^\sigma)$ be an automorphism of $\mathbf{Q}$. Then there exists an element $\mathbf{q}$ of $\mathbf{Q}$ with the property $|\mathbf{q}| = 1$, such that for all $\mathbf{x}$ in $\mathbf{Q}$

$$\mathbf{x}^\sigma = \mathbf{q}\mathbf{x}\mathbf{q}^{-1}.$$

Let us define $\mathbf{j}_k'\,(k=1,\,2,\,3)$ by the equation

$$\mathbf{j}_k' = \mathbf{j}_k^\sigma.$$

Since $\mathbf{j}_k'^2 = -1$, $\mathbf{j}_k'$ as an endomorphism of $\mathbf{C}^2$ has two eigenvalues $+i$ and $-i$, and hence there are linearly independent vectors $v^+$ and $v^-$ spanning $\mathbf{C}^2$ such that

$$\mathbf{j}_1'v^\pm = \pm iv^\pm.$$

Since $\mathbf{j}_1'\mathbf{j}_2'+\mathbf{j}_2'\mathbf{j}_1'=\mathbf{j}_1'\mathbf{j}_3'+\mathbf{j}_3'\mathbf{j}_1'=0$, $\mathbf{j}_2'^2=\mathbf{j}_3'^2=-1$ and $\mathbf{j}_2'\mathbf{j}_3'+\mathbf{j}_3'\mathbf{j}_2'=0$, it follows by a direct computation that for some nonzero $c \in \mathbf{C}$, the matrices $\mathbf{j}_2'$ and $\mathbf{j}_3'$ are given by

$$\mathbf{j}_2' : \begin{array}{l} v^+ \to -c^{-1}v^-, \\ v^- \to cv^+ \end{array} \qquad \mathbf{j}_3' : \begin{array}{l} v^+ \to ic^{-1}v^-. \\ v^- \to icv^+ \end{array}$$

If we write $w^+ = cv^+$, $w^- = v^-$, then the matrices of $\mathbf{j}_1'$, $\mathbf{j}_2'$, $\mathbf{j}_3'$ with respect to the basis $\{w^+, w^-\}$ coincide with $\mathbf{j}_1$, $\mathbf{j}_2$, $\mathbf{j}_3$, respectively. Consequently, there exists a nonsingular matrix $m$ of order 2 such that

$$\mathbf{x}^\sigma = m\mathbf{x}m^{-1}$$

for all $\mathbf{x} \in \mathbf{Q}$. Now for any $\mathbf{x} \in \mathbf{Q}$, $|\mathbf{x}| = \det(\mathbf{x})$ and hence $|\mathbf{x}^\sigma| = |\mathbf{x}|$. This means that $\mathbf{x}^\sigma \in SU(2,\mathbf{C})$ if and only if $\mathbf{x} \in SU(2,\mathbf{C})$. Writing the condition for $\mathbf{x}^\sigma$ to be unitary, we get $(m^*m)\mathbf{x}(m^*m)^{-1} = \mathbf{x}$. Since this is valid for all unitary $\mathbf{x}$, we conclude that for some $c \in \mathbf{C}$, $m^*m = cl$. Since $m^*m$ is positive definite, $c$ is real and $>0$. If we write $\mathbf{q} = c^{-1/2}m$, then $\mathbf{q}$ is unitary, $\det \mathbf{q} = 1$, and

$$\mathbf{x}^\sigma = \mathbf{q}\mathbf{x}\mathbf{q}^{-1}$$

for all $\mathbf{x} \in \mathbf{Q}$.

We remark that any isomorphism between the geometries of two vector spaces of the same dimension over $\mathbf{Q}$ can be induced by a linear isomorphism. This follows at once from theorem 3.16, as we have shown just now that all automorphisms of $\mathbf{Q}$ are inner.

Two quaternions are called *conjugate* if each can be transformed into the other by an (inner) automorphism. It is obviously of interest to examine the conjugacy classes of the quaternions. If two quaternions are conjugate they must have equal norm. For a positive real number $r$, the mapping $\mathbf{x} \to r\mathbf{x}$ permutes the conjugacy classes and hence it is enough to determine the conjugacy classes of the set of unit quaternions. Since two $2 \times 2$ unitary matrices of determinant 1 are conjugate if and only if they have the same eigenvalues up to a permutation, it follows that the quaternions

$$\mathbf{x}_\theta = \begin{pmatrix} e^{i\theta} & 0 \\ 0 & e^{-i\theta} \end{pmatrix} \qquad (0 \le \theta \le \pi)$$

are in one-one correspondence with the conjugacy classes. Moreover, since the correspondence

$$\theta \to e^{i\theta} + e^{-i\theta} = 2 \cos \theta$$

is one-one, we conclude that two unit quaternions $\mathbf{x}$ and $\mathbf{x}'$ are conjugate if and only if

$$\mathrm{tr}(\mathbf{x}) = \mathrm{tr}(\mathbf{x}').$$

In other words, two quaternions $\mathbf{x}$ and $\mathbf{x}'$ are conjugate if and only if

$$|\mathbf{x}| = |\mathbf{x}'|$$

and

$$\mathrm{tr}(\mathbf{x}) = \mathrm{tr}(\mathbf{x}').$$

# CHAPTER IV

# DUALITIES

## 1. DUALITIES AND SEMI-BILINEAR FORMS

Our aim in this chapter is to obtain a description of the anti-auto-morphisms of a geometry. Such a description will lead to the determination of the orthocomplementations associated with the real, complex, and quaternionic geometries. The result of this analysis is that orthocomplementations arise essentially from Hilbert space structures.

We begin with the concept of the dual of a division ring $\mathbf{D}$. Let $\mathbf{D}^0$ be the ring whose underlying set of elements is identical with that of $\mathbf{D}$, and in which addition and multiplication are defined in the following way:

$$
\begin{aligned}
x \oplus y &= x + y, \\
x \odot y &= yx.
\end{aligned}
\tag{1}
$$

It is evident that $\oplus$ and $\odot$ convert $\mathbf{D}^0$ into a division ring and that the identity mapping $x \to x$ is an anti-isomorphism of $\mathbf{D}$ onto $\mathbf{D}^0$. Moreover, any anti-automorphism of $\mathbf{D}$ can be regarded as an isomorphism between $\mathbf{D}$ and $\mathbf{D}^0$. $\mathbf{D}^0$ is said to be the division ring *dual* to $\mathbf{D}$.

Let $V$ be a vector space of dimension $n(<\infty)$ over $\mathbf{D}$. We define $V^*$, the dual of $V$, as the set of all mappings $\lambda$,

$$
\lambda : V \to \mathbf{D}
$$

of $V$ into $\mathbf{D}$ with the properties:

$$
\begin{aligned}
&\lambda(0) = 0, \\
&\lambda(au + bv) = a\lambda(u) + b\lambda(v) \qquad (a, b \in \mathbf{D}, u, v \in V).
\end{aligned}
\tag{2}
$$

We can convert $V^*$ into a vector space over the division ring $\mathbf{D}^0$. This is done by defining, for $\lambda_1, \lambda_2 \in V^*$ and $c \in \mathbf{D}^0$,

$$
\begin{aligned}
(\lambda_1 \oplus \lambda_2)(u) &= \lambda_1(u) + \lambda_2(u) \qquad (u \in V), \\
(c \odot \lambda_1)(u) &= \lambda_1(u)c \qquad\qquad (u \in V).
\end{aligned}
\tag{3}
$$

In view of the fact that for $a, b \in \mathbf{D}^0$ and $u \in V$,

$$
\begin{aligned}
((a \odot b) \odot \lambda)(u) &= \lambda(u)(a \odot b) \\
&= \lambda(u)ba \\
&= (a \odot (b \odot \lambda))(u),
\end{aligned}
$$

*50*

it easily follows that $V^*$ is a vector space over $\mathbf{D}^0$. $V^*$ and $V$ have the same dimension. If $\mathbf{D}$ is a field, then both $V$ and $V^*$ are vector spaces over $\mathbf{D}$ as $\mathbf{D} = \mathbf{D}^0$.

We shall now summarize a few known facts about the relations between $V$ and $V^*$. Let $\{v_1, \cdots, v_n\}$ be a basis for $V$. If we define $v_j^* \in V^*$ by

$$v_j^*\left(\sum_{k=1}^{n} x_k v_k\right) = x_j,$$

then $\{v_1^*, \cdots, v_n^*\}$ is a basis for $V^*$ which is called *the basis of $V^*$ dual to the basis* $\{v_1, \cdots, v_n\}$ of $V$. In fact, if $\lambda \in V^*$ and

$$\lambda(v_j) = a_j \qquad (j = 1, 2, \cdots, n),$$

then

$$\lambda\left(\sum_{j=1}^{n} x_j v_j\right) = \sum_{j=1}^{n} x_j a_j,$$

so that we have the equation

$$\lambda = \sum_{j=1}^{n} \lambda(v_j) \odot v_j^*.$$

Evidently

$$v_j^*(v_k) = \delta_{jk}.$$

For any linear manifold $M \subseteq V$, we define

(4) $$M^0 = \{\lambda : \lambda \in V^*, \quad \lambda(v) = 0 \quad \text{for all} \quad v \in M\}.$$

It is obvious that $M^0$ is a linear manifold of $V^*$. If $\{v_1, \cdots, v_n\}$ is a basis for $V$ such that $\{v_1, \cdots, v_r\}$ is a basis for $M$, and if $\{v_1^*, \cdots, v_n^*\}$ is the dual basis in $V^*$, then it follows that $\{v_{r+1}^*, \cdots, v_n^*\}$ is a basis for $M^0$. This shows that

(5) $$\dim M + \dim M^0 = n.$$

$M^0$ is called the *annihilator* of $M$. The division ring dual to $\mathbf{D}^0$ is evidently $\mathbf{D}$ itself. If we identify any $x$ of $V$ with the element $\lambda \to \lambda(x)$ of $(V^*)^*$, we see that $V$ becomes identified canonically with the second dual $(V^*)^*$ of $V$. We shall always so identify $V$ with $(V^*)^*$. If now $M$ is a linear manifold of $V$, we have the inclusion

$$M \subseteq (M^0)^0$$

and the dimension relation (5) shows that we have in fact

(6) $$M = (M^0)^0.$$

The correspondence

(7) $$M \to M^0$$

is thus a one-one mapping of the lattice $\mathcal{L}(V,\mathbf{D})$ onto the lattice $\mathcal{L}(V^*,\mathbf{D}^0)$ with the following properties:

(8)
$$\begin{aligned} &\text{(i)} \ 0^0 = V^*, \qquad V^0 = 0, \\ &\text{(ii)} \ M \subseteq N \ \text{ if and only if } \ N^0 \subseteq M^0. \end{aligned}$$

Let $\mathcal{L}$ and $\mathcal{L}'$ be two geometries of the same rank. A *duality* of $\mathcal{L}$ onto $\mathcal{L}'$ is a mapping

$$\xi : a \rightarrow \xi(a)$$

of $\mathcal{L}$ into $\mathcal{L}'$ such that

(9)
$$\begin{aligned} &\text{(i)} \ \xi \text{ is one-one and maps } \mathcal{L} \text{ onto } \mathcal{L}', \\ &\text{(ii)} \ a < b \ \text{ if and only if } \ \xi(b) < \xi(a). \end{aligned}$$

If $\xi$ is a duality, and $0'$ and $1'$ are, respectively, the null and unit elements of $\mathcal{L}'$, the relations (9) imply that

(10)
$$\begin{aligned} \xi(0) &= 1', \\ \xi(1) &= 0'. \end{aligned}$$

If $V$ is a vector space, and $V^*$ its dual, the correspondence

$$M \rightarrow M^0$$

is, by (8), a duality between the geometries $\mathcal{L}(V,\mathbf{D})$ and $\mathcal{L}(V^*,\mathbf{D}^0)$. If $\mathcal{L}$ is a geometry, we define a duality of $\mathcal{L}$ to be a duality of $\mathcal{L}$ onto itself.

Our purpose now is to determine the dualities of $\mathcal{L}(V,\mathbf{D})$. We begin by introducing the concept of a nonsingular semi-bilinear form. Let $\theta$ be an anti-automorphism of $\mathbf{D}$. We then define a *$\theta$-bilinear form* to be a map of $V \times V$ into $\mathbf{D}$,

$$\langle\, .\, ,\, .\, \rangle : x, y \rightarrow \langle x,y \rangle,$$

with the following properties:

(i) $\langle\, .\, ,\, .\, \rangle$ is a map of $V \times V$ into $\mathbf{D}$,

(ii) $\langle x_1 + x_2, y \rangle = \langle x_1,y \rangle + \langle x_2,y \rangle,$

(11) $\qquad \langle x, y_1 + y_2 \rangle = \langle x,y_1 \rangle + \langle x,y_2 \rangle$ for all $x_1, x_2, y \in V$ and

$$x, y_1, y_2 \in V,$$

(iii) $\langle cx,dy \rangle = c\langle x,y \rangle d^\theta$ for all $x, y \in V$ and $c, d \in \mathbf{D}$.

We shall call $\langle\, .\, ,\, .\, \rangle$ *right nonsingular* if

(12r) $\qquad \langle x,y \rangle = 0 \ $ for all $x \in V$ implies that $y = 0$,

and *left nonsingular* if

(12l) $\qquad \langle x,y \rangle = 0 \ $ for all $y \in V$ implies that $x = 0$.

We shall say that $\langle\, .\, ,\, .\, \rangle$ is *nonsingular* if it is both right and left nonsingular.

Given any anti-automorphism $\theta$ of $\mathbf{D}$ there exist nonsingular $\theta$-bilinear forms on $V \times V$. To see this, let $\{v_1, \cdots, v_n\}$ be a basis for $V$, and for any $x \in V$ let $c_1(x), \cdots, c_n(x) \in \mathbf{D}$ be defined by

$$x = \sum_{j=1}^{n} c_j(x)v_j.$$

For $x, y \in V$, let

$$\langle x,y \rangle = \sum_{j=1}^{n} c_j(x)c_j(y)^{\theta}.$$

It is then easily verified that $\langle \,.\,,\,.\, \rangle$ is a nonsingular $\theta$-bilinear form on $V \times V$.

**Theorem 4.1.** *Let $V$ be a vector space of dimension $n$ $(< \infty)$ over the division ring $\mathbf{D}$, $\theta$ an anti-automorphism of $\mathbf{D}$, and $\langle \,.\,,\,.\, \rangle$, a $\theta$-bilinear form on $V \times V$. Then $\langle \,.\,,\,.\, \rangle$ is nonsingular if and only if it is either right or left nonsingular. If $\langle \,.\,,\,.\, \rangle$ is nonsingular, the correspondence*

$$(13) \qquad\qquad M \to M',$$

*where, for any linear manifold $M$ of $V$,*

$$(14) \qquad M' = \{u : \langle x,u \rangle = 0 \quad \text{for all} \quad x \in M\}$$

*is a duality of $\mathscr{L}(V,\mathbf{D})$. Conversely, let $n \geq 3$, and let $\xi(M \to \xi(M))$ be a duality of $\mathscr{L}(V,\mathbf{D})$. Then, for all $M \subseteq V$,*

$$(15) \qquad \dim M + \dim \xi(M) = n.$$

*Moreover, there exists an anti-automorphism $\theta$ of $\mathbf{D}$, and a nonsingular $\theta$-bilinear form $\langle \,.\,,\,.\, \rangle$ on $V \times V$, such that for all $M$ in $\mathscr{L}(V,\mathbf{D})$,*

$$(16) \qquad \xi(M) = \{u : \langle x,u \rangle = 0 \quad \text{for all} \quad x \in M\}.$$

*If $\theta'$ is another anti-automorphism of $\mathbf{D}$ and $\langle \,.\,,\,.\, \rangle'$ a nonsingular $\theta'$-bilinear form on $V \times V$, then, in order that, for all linear manifolds $M \subseteq V$,*

$$\xi(M) = \{u : \langle x,u \rangle' = 0 \quad \text{for all} \quad x \in M\},$$

*it is necessary and sufficient that there exist a nonzero element $d$ of $\mathbf{D}$ such that for all $x, y \in V$,*

$$(17) \qquad\qquad \langle x,y \rangle' = \langle x,y \rangle d,$$

*and for any $c \in \mathbf{D}$,*

$$(18) \qquad\qquad c^{\theta'} = d^{-1}c^{\theta}d.$$

**Proof.** Let $\langle \,.\,,\,.\, \rangle$ be any $\theta$-bilinear form on $V \times V$. Let the mapping $\lambda(y \to \lambda_y)$ of $V$ into $V^*$ be defined by setting for any $y \in V$, $\lambda_y$ to be the element of $V^*$ given by

$$(19) \qquad\qquad \lambda_y(u) = \langle u,y \rangle \qquad (u \in V).$$

It follows from (11) that $y \to \lambda_y$ is a $\theta$-linear map of $V$ into $V^*$. It is obvious that right nonsingularity of $\langle . , . \rangle$ is equivalent to asserting that $\lambda(y \to \lambda_y)$ is one-one. On the other hand, it is clear from (12l) that $\langle . , . \rangle$ is left nonsingular if and only if $\lambda[V]^0 = 0$ which, in turn, is equivalent to $\lambda[V] = V^*$; i.e., $\lambda$ is onto. As dim $V < \infty$, $\lambda$ is one-one if and only if $\lambda[V] = V^*$ and hence $\langle . , . \rangle$ is nonsingular if and only if it is either right or left nonsingular.

Let us now assume that the form $\langle . , . \rangle$ is nonsingular. Then $\lambda$ is a $\theta$-linear *isomorphism* of $V$ onto $V^*$. Therefore

$$M \to \lambda[M]$$

is an isomorphism of $\mathscr{L}(V, \mathbf{D})$ onto $\mathscr{L}(V^*, \mathbf{D}^0)$. However, $M \to M^0$ is a duality of $\mathscr{L}(V, \mathbf{D})$ onto $\mathscr{L}(V^*, \mathbf{D}^0)$. Consequently, if

$$\xi(M) = \{u : \langle x, u \rangle = 0 \quad \text{for all } x \in M\}$$

for any linear manifold $M \subseteq V$, it is clear from (19) that $\lambda[\xi(M)] = M^0$ and hence that $M \to \xi(M)$ is a duality of $\mathscr{L}(V, \mathbf{D})$.

Conversely, let $\xi(M \to \xi(M))$ be any duality of $\mathscr{L}(V, \mathbf{D})$. Then it is easily seen that

$$\eta : M \to (\xi^{-1}(M))^0$$

is an isomorphism of $\mathscr{L}(V, \mathbf{D})$ onto $\mathscr{L}(V^*, \mathbf{D}^0)$. Since any isomorphism between two geometries preserves their canonical dimension functions we see that $\dim M = \dim(\xi^{-1}(M))^0$ for all $M$, and hence we obtain (15), from (5). Moreover, we deduce from theorem 3.1 the existence of an isomorphism $\theta$ of $\mathbf{D}$ onto $\mathbf{D}^0$ and a $\theta$-linear isomorphism $T$ of $V$ onto $V^*$ such that $T$ induces the isomorphism $\eta$ of $\mathscr{L}(V, \mathbf{D})$ onto $\mathscr{L}(V^*, \mathbf{D}^0)$. Thus, for all $M$ in $\mathscr{L}(V, \mathbf{D})$,

(20)                         $$M^0 = T[\xi(M)].$$

Evidently, $\theta$ is an anti-automorphism of $\mathbf{D}$. If we define $\langle . , . \rangle$ on $V \times V$ by

(21)                    $$\langle x, y \rangle = (Ty)(x) \qquad (x, y \in V)$$

then it follows from (20) that $y \in \xi(M)$ if and only if $Ty \in M^0$, i.e., if and only if $\langle x, y \rangle = 0$ for all $x \in M$. The fact that $T$ is a $\theta$-linear isomorphism of $V$ onto $V^*$ implies at once that $\langle . , . \rangle$ is a nonsingular $\theta$-bilinear form on $V \times V$ which moreover has the property that

$$\xi(M) = \{u : \langle x, u \rangle = 0 \quad \text{for all } x \in M\}.$$

Suppose, finally, that $\theta'$ is another anti-automorphism of $\mathbf{D}$ and $\langle . , . \rangle'$ a nonsingular $\theta'$-bilinear form on $V \times V$. Let

$$\xi'(M) = \{u : \langle x, u \rangle' = 0 \quad \text{for all } x \in M\}$$

for all linear manifolds $M \subseteq V$. The mapping $\lambda'(y \to \lambda_y')$ of $V$ into $V^*$ defined by

$$\lambda_y'(x) = \langle x,y \rangle'$$

is then a $\theta'$-linear isomorphism of $V$ onto $V^*$. $\xi = \xi'$ if and only if

$$(\xi'^{-1}(M))^0 = \eta(M)$$

for all linear manifolds $M \subseteq V$, i.e., if and only if $\lambda$ and $\lambda'$ induce the same isomorphism of $\mathscr{L}(V,\mathbf{D})$ onto $\mathscr{L}(V^*,\mathbf{D}^0)$. We know from (5) and (6) of Chapter III that this is true if and only if, for some nonzero $d \in \mathbf{D}^0$,

$$(22) \qquad \lambda_y' = d \odot \lambda_y \qquad (y \in V)$$

and $c^{\theta'} = d \odot c^\theta \odot d^{-1}$ for all $c \in \mathbf{D}$, i.e.,

$$c^{\theta'} = d^{-1}c^\theta d \qquad (c \in \mathbf{D}).$$

Equation (22) implies that

$$\langle x,y \rangle' = \langle x,y \rangle d \qquad (x,y \in V).$$

This completes the proof of theorem 4.1.

**Remark.** If $\mathbf{D}$ is a field, $\theta = \theta'$. In the general case discussed in theorem 4.1, we shall say that $\langle .\,,. \rangle$ induces $\xi$.

## 2. POLARITIES

A duality $\xi(M \to \xi(M))$ of $\mathscr{L}(V,\mathbf{D})$ is said to be a *polarity* if $M \subseteq \xi(\xi(M))$ for all linear manifolds $M \subseteq V$. Since, by (15), dim $M$ + dim $\xi(M) = n$, $\xi$ is a polarity if and only if

$$(23) \qquad \xi(\xi(M)) = M$$

for all linear manifolds $M \subseteq V$. $\xi$ is said to be *isotropic* if $M \subseteq \xi(M)$ for any *one-dimensional* linear manifold $M$. Our purpose in this section is to determine the conditions to be imposed on a $\theta$-bilinear form in order that the duality induced by it is a polarity. We begin with an analysis of isotropic polarities.

**Theorem 4.2.** *Let $V$ be a vector space of dimension $n$ over the division ring $\mathbf{D}$ ($3 \le n < \infty$). Then $\mathscr{L}(V,\mathbf{D})$ admits an isotropic polarity, if and only if $\mathbf{D}$ is a field and dim $V$ is even. Let $\mathbf{D}$ be a field, dim $V = 2N$, and let $\xi(M \to \xi(M))$ be an isotropic polarity of $\mathscr{L}(V,\mathbf{D})$. Then there exists a nonsingular skew-symmetric bilinear form $\langle .\,,. \rangle$ such that for any $M$ in $\mathscr{L}(V,\mathbf{D})$,*

$$\xi(M) = \{u : \langle x,u \rangle = 0 \quad \text{for all } x \in M\}.$$

*Moreover, there exists a basis* $\{x_1, y_1, x_2, y_2, \cdots, x_N, y_N\}$ *of* $V$ *such that*

$$
(24) \qquad \begin{aligned} \langle x_i, x_j \rangle &= \langle y_i, y_j \rangle = 0 \\ \langle x_i, y_j \rangle &= -\langle y_j, x_i \rangle = \delta_{ij} \end{aligned} \qquad (i, j = 1, 2, \cdots, N).
$$

*Finally, if* $\xi$ *and* $\xi'$ *are any two isotropic polarities of* $\mathscr{L}(V, \mathbf{D})$*, then there exists a linear automorphism* $T$ *of* $V$ *such that*

$$
(25) \qquad \xi' = \alpha \cdot \xi \cdot \alpha^{-1},
$$

*where* $\alpha$ *is the automorphism of the geometry* $\mathscr{L}(V, \mathbf{D})$*, induced by* $T$*.*

**Proof.** Let $\xi$ be an isotropic polarity of $\mathscr{L}(V, \mathbf{D})$. By theorem 4.1, there exists an anti-automorphism $\theta$ of $\mathbf{D}$ and a nonsingular $\theta$-bilinear form $\langle \, . \, , . \, \rangle$ on $V \times V$ inducing $\xi$. Since $\xi$ is isotropic,

$$
\mathbf{D} \cdot x \subseteq \xi(\mathbf{D} \cdot x),
$$

for any $x \in V$. Hence, $\langle x, x \rangle = 0$ for all $x \in V$. Consequently,

$$
\begin{aligned} 0 &= \langle x+y, \, x+y \rangle \\ &= \langle x, x \rangle + \langle y, y \rangle + \langle x, y \rangle + \langle y, x \rangle \\ &= \langle x, y \rangle + \langle y, x \rangle. \end{aligned}
$$

Thus

$$
(26) \qquad \langle x, y \rangle = -\langle y, x \rangle
$$

for all $x, y \in V$. For any $c$ in $\mathbf{D}$, however,

$$
(26a) \qquad \begin{aligned} \langle x, y \rangle c^\theta &= \langle x, cy \rangle \\ &= -\langle cy, x \rangle \\ &= -c \langle y, x \rangle \\ &= c \langle x, y \rangle. \end{aligned}
$$

Since $\langle \, . \, , . \, \rangle$ is nonsingular, we can find $x, y$ in $V$ such that $\langle x, y \rangle = 1$. We now conclude from (26a) that

$$
c = c^\theta.
$$

This means that $\theta$ is the identity. Since an anti-automorphism is an automorphism only if the division ring is commutative, we see that $\mathbf{D}$ must be commutative. Moreover, as $\theta$ is the identity, $\langle \, . \, , . \, \rangle$ is actually *bilinear*, and (26) shows that it is skew symmetric.

Let $x_1$ be a nonzero vector. Since $\langle \, . \, , . \, \rangle$ is nonsingular, there exists a $y_1$ such that

$$
\langle x_1, y_1 \rangle \neq 0.
$$

By multiplying $y_1$ by a constant, we may even assume that

$$
\langle x_1, y_1 \rangle = 1,
$$

and we have $\langle x_1,x_1 \rangle = \langle y_1,y_1 \rangle = 0$ and $\langle x_1,y_1 \rangle = 1$. Suppose now that $\{x_1, y_1; x_2, y_2; \cdots; x_r, y_r\}$ is a set of vectors for which

$$\langle x_i,x_j \rangle = \langle y_i,y_j \rangle = 0$$
$$\langle x_i,y_j \rangle = -\langle y_j,x_i \rangle = \delta_{ij} \qquad (i,j = 1, 2, \cdots, r)$$

and which is maximal with respect to this property. We claim that $\{x_1, y_1; \cdots; x_r, y_r\}$ is a basis for $V$. If $z = \sum_{i=1}^{r} a_i x_i + \sum_{i=1}^{r} b_i y_i$, then $\langle z,x_i \rangle = -b_i$ and $\langle z,y_i \rangle = a_i$ for $i = 1, 2, \cdots, r$. This means that $z = 0$ if and only if all the $a_i$'s and $b_i$'s are 0. Thus $\{x_1, y_1; \cdots; x_r, y_r\}$ is a linearly independent set. Let

$$R = \sum_{i=1}^{r} \mathbf{D} \cdot x_i + \sum_{i=1}^{r} \mathbf{D} \cdot y_i.$$

If $z = \sum_{i=1}^{r} a_i x_i + \sum_{i=1}^{r} b_i y_i \in R \cap \xi(R)$, then $0 = \langle z,x_i \rangle = -b_i$, $0 = \langle z,y_i \rangle = a_i$ so that $R \cap \xi(R) = 0$. As $\dim R + \dim \xi(R) = \dim V$, $V$ is the direct sum of $R$ and $\xi(R)$. In order to prove our claim that $\{x_1, y_1; \cdots; x_r, y_r\}$ is a basis for $V$, we must show now that $\xi(R) = 0$. Suppose $\xi(R) \neq 0$. Let $x_{r+1}$ be some nonzero vector in $\xi(R)$. As $\langle x_{r+1},y \rangle$ cannot vanish for all $y$, and as it vanishes for all $y \in R$, there exists a $y \in \xi(R)$ such that $\langle x_{r+1},y \rangle \neq 0$. By defining $y_{r+1}$ to be $cy$ for a suitable $c \in \mathbf{D}$, we may assume that $\langle x_{r+1},y_{r+1} \rangle = 1$. However, then $\{x_1, y_1; \cdots; x_{r+1}, y_{r+1}\}$ is a set having the same properties as $\{x_1, y_1; \cdots; x_r, y_r\}$. This contradicts the maximality of $\{x_1, y_1; \cdots; x_r, y_r\}$ and shows that $\{x_1, y_1; \cdots; x_r, y_r\}$ is a basis for $V$. If we put $N = r$, then $\dim V = 2N$, and the equations (24) are satisfied.

Let now $\dim V = 2N$ and $\mathbf{D}$ a field. Let $\{x_1, y_1; \cdots; x_N, y_N\}$ be a basis for $V$. For any $x \in V$, let $a_i(x)$ and $b_i(x) \in \mathbf{D}$ be defined by

$$x = \sum_{i=1}^{N} a_i(x)x_i + \sum_{i=1}^{N} b_i(x)y_i.$$

If $x, y \in V$, let us write

$$\langle x,y \rangle = \sum_{i=1}^{N} a_i(x)b_i(y) - \sum_{i=1}^{N} b_i(x)a_i(y).$$

It is then easily seen that $\langle .\,,. \rangle$ is a nonsingular skew-symmetric bilinear form on $V \times V$ and that the induced polarity of $\mathscr{L}(V,\mathbf{D})$ is isotropic.

If $\xi$ and $\xi'$ are any two isotropic polarities of $\mathscr{L}(V,\mathbf{D})$, then we have bases $\{x_1, y_1; \cdots; x_N, y_N\}$ and $\{x_1', y_1'; \cdots; x_N', y_N'\}$ for $V$ such that $\langle x_i,x_j \rangle = \langle y_i,y_j \rangle = 0$, $\langle x_i,y_j \rangle = -\langle y_j,x_i \rangle = \delta_{ij}$, and $\langle x_i',x_j' \rangle' = \langle y_i',y_j' \rangle' = 0$, $\langle x_i',y_j' \rangle' = -\langle y_j',x_i' \rangle' = \delta_{ij}$, $\langle .\,,. \rangle$ and $\langle .\,,. \rangle'$ being skew symmetric bilinear forms inducing $\xi$ and $\xi'$, respectively. Let $T$ be the linear isomorphism of $V$ onto itself defined by

$$T : \begin{cases} x_i \to x_i' \\ y_i \to y_i' \end{cases} \qquad (i = 1, 2, \cdots, N).$$

We then have, for all $x, y \in V$,

$$\langle Tx, Ty \rangle' = \langle x, y \rangle,$$

so that for any linear manifold $M \subseteq V$,

$$T^{-1}[\xi'(M)] = \xi(T^{-1}(M)).$$

This is just (25). This proves theorem 4.2 completely.

We now proceed to the analysis of nonisotropic polarities. Suppose $\theta$ is an anti-automorphism of $\mathbf{D}$ and $\langle \,.\,,\,.\, \rangle$ is a $\theta$-bilinear form on $V \times V$. We shall call $\langle \,.\,,\,.\, \rangle$ *symmetric* if

(27)                            $$\langle x, y \rangle^\theta = \langle y, x \rangle$$

for all $x, y \in V$. Notice that the symmetry is with respect to the particular anti-automorphism $\theta$ associated with $\langle \,.\,,\,.\, \rangle$.

**Lemma 4.3.** *Let* $\langle \,.\,,\,.\, \rangle$ *be a symmetric $\theta$-bilinear form such that for some $x, y$ in $V$, $\langle x, y \rangle \neq 0$. Then $\theta$ is involutive, i.e., $\theta^2 = 1$.*

**Proof.** Since $\langle ax, y \rangle = a \langle x, y \rangle$, it is clear that the set of elements of $\mathbf{D}$ of the form $\langle x, y \rangle$, with $x, y$ in $V$, is the whole of $\mathbf{D}$. If $x, y \in V$,

$$\{\langle x, y \rangle^\theta\}^\theta = \langle y, x \rangle^\theta$$
$$= \langle x, y \rangle.$$

Thus $c^{\theta^2} = c$ for all $c$ in $\mathbf{D}$.

**Lemma 4.4.** *Let $\theta$ be an anti-automorphism of $\mathbf{D}$ and $\langle \,.\,,\,.\, \rangle$ a nonsingular $\theta$-bilinear form on $V \times V$. Suppose $\dim V \geq 2$ and that (i) the duality induced by $\langle \,.\,,\,.\, \rangle$ is a polarity and (ii) there exists a nonzero $x \in V$ such that $\langle x, x \rangle \neq 0$ and $\langle x, x \rangle^\theta = \langle x, x \rangle$. Then $\theta$ is involutive, $\langle \,.\,,\,.\, \rangle$ is symmetric, and the induced polarity is nonisotropic.*

**Proof.** Let $\xi(M \to \xi(M))$ be the duality induced by $\langle \,.\,,\,.\, \rangle$. If $u$ and $v \in V$, $\langle u, v \rangle = 0$ if and only if $v \in \xi(\mathbf{D} \cdot u)$ and as $\xi$ is a polarity, this is equivalent to $u \in \xi(\mathbf{D} \cdot v)$ or $\langle v, u \rangle = 0$. Let now $c = \langle x, x \rangle$. Then $c \neq 0$ and $c^\theta = c$. Since, by (15), $\dim \xi(\mathbf{D} \cdot x) = n - 1$, and since $x \notin \xi(\mathbf{D} \cdot x)$, $V$ is the direct sum of $\mathbf{D} \cdot x$ and $\xi(\mathbf{D} \cdot x)$. If $u, v \in \xi(\mathbf{D} \cdot x)$, then

$$\langle \langle u, v \rangle x - u, \, x + cv \rangle = \langle u, v \rangle c - \langle u, cv \rangle$$
$$= \langle u, v \rangle c - \langle u, v \rangle c^\theta$$
$$= 0.$$

By the observation made earlier, $\langle x + cv, \langle u, v \rangle x - u \rangle = 0$. This gives, on computation, $\langle x, x \rangle \langle u, v \rangle^\theta - c \langle v, u \rangle = 0$ or $\langle u, v \rangle^\theta = \langle v, u \rangle$. Thus $\langle \,.\,,\,.\, \rangle$ is symmetric when restricted to $\xi(\mathbf{D} \cdot x) \times \xi(\mathbf{D} \cdot x)$. As $\langle \,.\,,\,.\, \rangle$ cannot vanish identically on $\xi(\mathbf{D} \cdot x) \times \xi(\mathbf{D} \cdot x)$, lemma 4.3 implies that $\theta$ is involutive.

We shall now prove that $\langle .\,,\,. \rangle$ is symmetric on $V \times V$. Let $y, z \in V$. Then, $y = ax + u$, $z = bx + v$, where $a, b \in \mathbf{D}$ and $u, v \in \xi(\mathbf{D} \cdot x)$. We therefore have

$$
\begin{aligned}
\langle y,z \rangle^\theta &= \langle ax + u, bx + v \rangle^\theta \\
&= (acb^\theta)^\theta + \langle v,u \rangle \\
&= bca^\theta + \langle v,u \rangle \\
&= \langle bx + v, ax + u \rangle \\
&= \langle z,y \rangle,
\end{aligned}
$$

which proves that $\langle .\,,\,. \rangle$ is symmetric. As $\langle x,x \rangle \neq 0$, $\xi$ cannot be isotropic. This completes the proof of lemma 4.4.

**Theorem 4.5.** *Let $\mathbf{D}$ be a division ring and $V$ a vector space of dimension $n(< \infty)$ over $\mathbf{D}$. Let $\theta$ be an involutive anti-automorphism of $\mathbf{D}$ and $\langle .\,,\,. \rangle$ a nonsingular symmetric $\theta$-bilinear form on $V \times V$. Then the duality of $\mathscr{L}(V,\mathbf{D})$ induced by $\langle .\,,\,. \rangle$ is a nonisotropic polarity unless $\mathbf{D}$ is a field of characteristic 2. Conversely, let $n \geq 3$ and let $\xi(M \to \xi(M))$ be a nonisotropic polarity of $\mathscr{L}(V,\mathbf{D})$. Then, there exists an involutive anti-automorphism $\theta$ of $\mathbf{D}$ and a nonsingular symmetric $\theta$-bilinear form $\langle .\,,\,. \rangle$ on $V \times V$, such that $\xi$ is induced by $\langle .\,,\,. \rangle$. If $\theta'$ is another involutive anti-automorphism of $\mathbf{D}$ and $\langle .\,,\,. \rangle'$ a nonsingular symmetric $\theta'$-bilinear form on $V \times V$, then $\xi$ is induced also by $\langle .\,,\,. \rangle'$ if and only if there exists a nonzero element $d \in \mathbf{D}$ such that*

$$
\begin{aligned}
\langle x,y \rangle' &= \langle x,y \rangle d & (x,y \in V), \\
c^{\theta'} &= d^{-1} c^\theta d & (c \in \mathbf{D}).
\end{aligned}
\tag{28}
$$

*In this case,*

$$
d^\theta = d.
\tag{29}
$$

**Proof.** Suppose that $\theta$ is an involutive anti-automorphism of $\mathbf{D}$ and $\langle .\,,\,. \rangle$ a nonsingular symmetric $\theta$-bilinear form. The induced duality is evidently a polarity. We claim that this polarity is not isotropic. If it were, then $\langle z,z \rangle = 0$ for all $z \in V$, from which we conclude, as in the proof of theorem 4.2, that $\langle x,y \rangle = -\langle y,x \rangle$ for all $x, y \in V$. Since $\langle .\,,\,. \rangle$ is symmetric, we conclude that $\langle x,y \rangle^\theta = -\langle x,y \rangle$ for all $x, y \in V$. This implies that $c^\theta = -c$ for all $c$ in $\mathbf{D}$. For $c = 1$, this implies $1 + 1 = 0$. From this it follows easily that $\mathbf{D}$ is a field and that $\mathbf{D}$ has characteristic 2.

Suppose now that $\xi$ is any nonisotropic polarity of $\mathscr{L}(V,\mathbf{D})$ where $\dim V = n \geq 3$. By theorem 4.1 we can select an anti-automorphism $\theta_0$ and a nonsingular $\theta_0$-bilinear form $\langle .\,,\,. \rangle_0$ on $V \times V$ which induces $\xi$. Since $\xi$ is not isotropic, there exists an $x \in V$ such that $\langle x,x \rangle_0 = c_0 \neq 0$. Write $\langle u,v \rangle = \langle u,v \rangle_0 c_0^{-1}$, $c^\theta = c_0 c^{\theta_0} c_0^{-1}$. Then $\theta$ is an anti-automorphism of $\mathbf{D}$ and $\langle u,v \rangle$ is a nonsingular $\theta$-bilinear form on $V \times V$ which also induces

$\xi$, by theorem 4.1. Moreover $\langle x,x \rangle = 1$. The conditions of lemma 4.4 are met and we conclude that $\theta$ is involutive and $\langle .\,,.\rangle$ is symmetric.

Suppose now that $\theta'$ is another involutive anti-automorphism of $\mathbf{D}$ and $\langle .\,,.\rangle'$ a nonsingular, symmetric, $\theta'$-bilinear form on $V \times V$. Then, by theorem 4.1, $\langle .\,,.\rangle'$ induces $\xi$ if and only if for some nonzero $d \in \mathbf{D}$, $\langle x,y \rangle' = \langle x,y \rangle d$ for all $x, y \in V$ and $c^{\theta'} = d^{-1} c^{\theta} d$ for all $c \in \mathbf{D}$. Select $x, y \in V$ such that $\langle x,y \rangle = 1$. Then $\langle y,x \rangle = 1$, $\langle x,y \rangle' = d$, and

(30a)
$$\{\langle x,y \rangle'\}^{\theta'} = \langle y,x \rangle'$$
$$= d,$$

while, at the same time,

(30b)
$$\{\langle x,y \rangle'\}^{\theta'} = d^{\theta'}$$
$$= d^{-1} d^{\theta} d.$$

From (30a) and (30b) we infer that $d = d^{\theta}$. This proves (29) and completes the proof of the entire theorem.

**Remark.** It is useful to notice that the form $\langle .\,,.\rangle$ which induces $\xi$ in the above proof has the property that $\langle w,w \rangle = 1$ for some $w$ in $V$.


## 3. ORTHOCOMPLEMENTATIONS AND HILBERT SPACE STRUCTURES

We now introduce the notion of an orthocomplementation in a projective geometry. An *orthocomplementation* in $\mathscr{L}(V,\mathbf{D})$ is a polarity $\xi(M \to \xi(M))$ such that, for all $M$,

$$M \cap \xi(M) = 0.$$

In other words, an orthocomplementation of $\mathscr{L}(V,\mathbf{D})$ is a mapping

$$\xi : M \to \xi(M)$$

of $\mathscr{L}(V,\mathbf{D})$ into itself such that

(31)
  (i) $\xi$ is one-one and onto,
  (ii) $M \subseteq N$ if and only if $\xi(N) \subseteq \xi(M)$,
  (iii) $M = \xi(\xi(M))$ for all $M$,
  (iv) $M \cap \xi(M) = 0$ for all $M$.

Notice that a polarity $\xi$ is an orthocomplementation if and only if for every $x$ in $V$ we have

(32)
$$(\mathbf{D} \cdot x) \cap (\xi(\mathbf{D} \cdot x)) = 0.$$

In fact, if this is satisfied for all $x$ in $V$ and if for some $M$ in $\mathscr{L}(V,\mathbf{D})$, $M \cap \xi(M) \neq 0$, then for any nonzero $x$ in $M \cap \xi(M)$, $\mathbf{D} \cdot x \subseteq \xi(\mathbf{D} \cdot x)$, which contradicts (32). Any orthocomplementation is a nonisotropic polarity. Theorem 4.5 and the equation (32) now lead to

**Theorem 4.6.** (*Birkhoff-von Neumann* [1]). *Let $\xi(M \to \xi(M))$ be an ortho-complementation of $\mathscr{L}(V,\mathbf{D})$, $V$ being a vector space of dimension $n(\geq 3)$ over the division ring $\mathbf{D}$. Then there exists an involutive anti-automorphism $\theta$ of $\mathbf{D}$ and a nonsingular symmetric $\theta$-bilinear form $\langle\,.\,,\,.\,\rangle$ such that*

(i) *for any $M$ in $\mathscr{L}(V,\mathbf{D})$,*
$$\xi(M) = \{u : \langle x,u\rangle = 0 \text{ for all } x \in M\},$$
(ii) *$\langle x,x\rangle = 0$ if and only if $x = 0$.*

*Moreover, $\theta$ and $\langle\,.\,,\,.\,\rangle$ can be chosen such that $\langle w,w\rangle = 1$ for any preassigned vector $w$ of $V$, and then they are uniquely determined.*

We shall now examine the nature of the forms which induce ortho-complementations. Let $\theta$ be any involutive anti-automorphism of $\mathbf{D}$. A symmetric $\theta$-bilinear form on $V \times V$ is called *definite* if

(33)
$$\begin{aligned}
&\text{(i) } \langle x,x\rangle = 0 \quad \text{if and only if} \quad x = 0, \\
&\text{(ii) } \langle w,w\rangle = 1 \quad \text{for some} \quad w \in V.
\end{aligned}$$

A definite form is necessarily nonsingular. We shall devote the rest of the section to showing that definite forms are associated with Hilbert space structures in general, in the case of real, complex, and quaternionic geometries.

Let $\mathbf{D}$ be one of $\mathbf{R}$, $\mathbf{C}$, $\mathbf{Q}$. For $c \in \mathbf{D}$, let $c^*$ be equal to $c$ if $\mathbf{D} = \mathbf{R}$, to the complex conjugate of $c$ if $\mathbf{D} = \mathbf{C}$, and to the canonical conjugate of $c$ if $\mathbf{D} = \mathbf{Q}$. Let $V$ be a vector space over $\mathbf{D}$, not necessarily finite dimensional. When $\mathbf{D} = \mathbf{C}$ we consider $\mathbf{R}$ as embedded in $\mathbf{C}$ in the usual way. When $\mathbf{D} = \mathbf{Q}$ we identify the center of $\mathbf{Q}$, which consists of elements of the form $cl$ ($c \in \mathbf{R}$), with $\mathbf{R}$, by the identification $cl \rightleftarrows c$. An *inner product for $V$* is a $*$-bilinear form on $V \times V$ such that (i) for any $x \in V$, $\langle x,x\rangle$ lies in the center of $\mathbf{D}$ and coincides with a nonnegative real number, and (ii) $\langle x,x\rangle = 0$ if and only if $x = 0$. If we write $\|x\| = +\langle x,x\rangle^{1/2}$ then $\|\cdot\|$ is a *norm* for $V$. $V$ is said to be a *Hilbert space over $\mathbf{D}$* if it is complete with respect to this norm. The basic facts of Hilbert space theory over $\mathbf{Q}$ are quite analogous to the theory over $\mathbf{R}$ and $\mathbf{C}$ (cf. Finkelstein, Jauch, and others [1]). It is easily shown using standard arguments that if dim $V < \infty$, the correspondence $M \to M^\perp$ is an orthocomplementation of $\mathscr{L}(V,\mathbf{D})$ where, we define as usual,

$$M^\perp = \{u : \langle x,u\rangle = 0 \quad \text{for all} \quad x \in M\}.$$

Our aim is to prove now that orthocomplementations in $\mathscr{L}(V,\mathbf{D})$ are associated with Hilbert space structures for $V$. We consider separately the three cases $\mathbf{D} = \mathbf{R}$, $\mathbf{C}$, and $\mathbf{Q}$.

(a) **R**, *the real number field*. In this case, $\theta$ is obviously the identity. Moreover, for any definite form $\langle\,.\,,\,.\,\rangle$ the function $x \to \langle x,x \rangle$ never vanishes for $x \neq 0$ in $V$. If dim $V \geq 2$, by *continuity* $\langle x,x \rangle$ is either $> 0$ or $< 0$ for all nonzero vectors $x$. However, since for some $w$, $\langle w,w \rangle = 1$, we have the latter alternative so that the definite forms are the usual positive definite quadratic forms on $V$.

(b) **C**, *the complex number field*. Let $\langle\,.\,,\,.\,\rangle$ be a definite form in an $n$-dimensional complex space $V$, with $n \geq 2$. Let $\theta$ be the associated automorphism of **C**, and $\langle\,.\,,\,.\,\rangle$ a nonsingular $\theta$-bilinear form on $V \times V$. We shall now show that if $\theta$ is the identity, then $\langle\,.\,,\,.\,\rangle$ cannot be definite, whereas if $\theta$ is the conjugation, we are obviously led to the usual Hermitian forms. We shall prove first that if $\langle\,.\,,\,.\,\rangle$ is a nonsingular symmetric *bilinear* form, then for some vector $x \neq 0$ of $V$, one has

$$\langle x,x \rangle = 0.$$

Let $v$ be a vector which is nonzero. If $\langle v,v \rangle = 0$, we are through. Otherwise we may assume by multiplying $v$ by a constant that $\langle v,v \rangle = 1$. Consequently, one has, as in the proof of lemma 4.4,

$$V = \mathbf{D} \cdot v \oplus \xi(\mathbf{D} \cdot v),$$

where $\xi$ is the polarity associated with $\langle\,.\,,\,.\,\rangle$. As $n \geq 2$, $\xi(\mathbf{D} \cdot v) \neq 0$. Therefore $\langle\,.\,,\,.\,\rangle$ is nonsingular on $\xi(\mathbf{D} \cdot v) \times \xi(\mathbf{D} \cdot v)$. Let $u$ be a nonzero vector in $\xi(\mathbf{D} \cdot v)$. If $\langle u,u \rangle \neq 0$, we may assume, exactly as we did before for $v$, that $\langle u,u \rangle = 1$. Thus, $\langle u,u \rangle = \langle v,v \rangle = 1$, $\langle u,v \rangle = 0$, and if we define the vector $x$ by the equation $(i^2 = -1)$

$$x = iu + v,$$

then $x \neq 0$ and

$$\langle x,x \rangle = 0.$$

(c) **Q**, *the quaternions*. Let $\theta$ be an anti-automorphism which is involutive and $\langle\,.\,,\,.\,\rangle$ a definite form over $V \times V$, $V$, an $n$-dimensional vector space over **Q** $(n \geq 2)$. Let $\mathbf{q} \to \mathbf{q}^*$ be the canonical conjugation of **Q**. Then $\mathbf{c} \to (\mathbf{c}^\theta)^*$ is an automorphism of **Q**. However, as any automorphism of **Q** is inner (cf. Chapter III), there exists a $\mathbf{q}_0 \in \mathbf{Q}$ with $|\mathbf{q}_0| = 1$, such that

(34) $$\mathbf{c}^\theta = \mathbf{q}_0 \mathbf{c}^* \mathbf{q}_0^{-1}$$

for all $\mathbf{c} \in \mathbf{Q}$. Now, $\theta$ is involutive and as $|\mathbf{q}_0| = 1$, $\mathbf{q}_0 \mathbf{q}_0^* = 1$. Consequently,

(35) $$\mathbf{c} = \mathbf{q}_0^2 \mathbf{c}(\mathbf{q}_0^2)^{-1}.$$

This means that $\mathbf{q}_0^2$ lies in the center of **Q** and hence we see that $\mathbf{q}_0^2$ is a real number. Since $\mathbf{q}_0$ has norm 1, one has

$$\mathbf{q}_0^2 = \pm 1.$$

We claim that the equation $q_0{}^2 = -1$ is not compatible with the definiteness of $\langle .\,,.\rangle$. Suppose, in fact, that $q_0{}^2 = -1$. Then, as $q_0 \in SU(2,\mathbf{C})$, we see that the eigenvalues of $q_0$ are $+i$ and $-i$, and, consequently, we may write $q_0$ as

$$q_0 = q_0'j_1q_0'^{-1}$$

for some unit quaternion $q_0'$. Let $v$ be a vector in $V$ with $\langle v,v\rangle \neq 0$. Since $\theta$ leaves the center $\mathbf{R}$ of $\mathbf{Q}$ invariant and since the only automorphism of $\mathbf{R}$ is the identity, $c^\theta = c$ for all $c \in \mathbf{R}$. Hence we may replace $v$ by $cv$ for a suitable real number $c$ to assume that $\langle v,v\rangle$ is a unit quaternion; i.e.,

$$\langle v,v\rangle = \mathbf{a} \qquad (\mathbf{a} \in \mathbf{Q}, \quad |\mathbf{a}| = 1).$$

As in lemma 4.4, we have

$$V = (\mathbf{Q}\cdot v) \oplus \xi(\mathbf{Q}\cdot v),$$

and hence, as $\dim V \geq 2$, there is a vector $u$ in $\xi(\mathbf{Q}\cdot v)$ such that $\langle u,u\rangle \neq 0$. Once again we may assume $\langle u,u\rangle = \mathbf{b}$, $|\mathbf{b}| = 1$. Since for any $\mathbf{c}$ in $\mathbf{Q}$, $\mathbf{c}^\theta = q_0\mathbf{c}^*q_0{}^{-1}$ and since $\langle .\,,.\rangle$ is symmetric,

$$\langle u,u\rangle^\theta = \langle u,u\rangle, \qquad \langle v,v\rangle^\theta = \langle v,v\rangle$$

so that

$$q_0\mathbf{a}^* = \mathbf{a}q_0, \qquad q_0\mathbf{b}^* = \mathbf{b}q_0.$$

Since $q_0 = q_0'j_1q_0'^{-1}$, the equation $q_0\mathbf{a}^* = \mathbf{a}q_0$ becomes

$$j_1(q_0'^{-1}\mathbf{a}q_0')^* = (q_0'^{-1}\mathbf{a}q_0')j_1.$$

Since

$$j_1 = \begin{pmatrix} i & 0 \\ 0 & -i \end{pmatrix},$$

this means that

$$q_0'^{-1}\mathbf{a}q_0' = \begin{pmatrix} c & r \\ -r^* & c \end{pmatrix},$$

where $c$ is real, $r$ is complex, $|c|^2 + |r|^2 = 1$, and $r^*$ is the complex conjugate of $r$. Thus

$$\mathrm{tr}(\mathbf{a}q_0) = \mathrm{tr}(\mathbf{a}q_0'j_1q_0'^{-1})$$
$$= \mathrm{tr}(q_0'^{-1}\mathbf{a}q_0'j_1)$$
$$= \mathrm{tr}\begin{pmatrix} ci & -ir \\ -ir^* & -ci \end{pmatrix}$$
$$= 0.$$

Similarly,

$$\mathrm{tr}(\mathbf{b}q_0) = 0.$$

Thus $\mathbf{aq}_0$ and $-\mathbf{bq}_0$ have the same trace. Since $|\mathbf{aq}_0|=|-\mathbf{bq}_0|=1$, it follows that $\mathbf{aq}_0$ and $-\mathbf{bq}_0$ are conjugate. Therefore, for some unit quaternion $\mathbf{q}_1$,

$$\mathbf{q}_1\mathbf{aq}_0\mathbf{q}_1{}^*+\mathbf{bq}_0 = 0,$$

i.e.,

$$\mathbf{q}_1\mathbf{aq}_0\mathbf{q}_1{}^*\mathbf{q}_0{}^{-1}+\mathbf{b} = 0.$$

Since $\langle u,u\rangle=\mathbf{b}$, $\langle v,v\rangle=\mathbf{a}$, $\langle u,v\rangle=0$, this means that

$$
\begin{aligned}
\langle \mathbf{q}_1v+u,\ \mathbf{q}_1v+u\rangle &= \mathbf{q}_1\langle v,v\rangle\mathbf{q}_1{}^\theta +\mathbf{b}\\
&= \mathbf{q}_1\mathbf{aq}_0\mathbf{q}_1{}^*\mathbf{q}_0{}^{-1}+\mathbf{b}\\
&= 0.
\end{aligned}
$$

Thus $\mathbf{q}_0{}^2 = -1$ leads to the existence of a nonzero vector $w$ with $\langle w,w\rangle=0$. We must have, therefore,

$$\mathbf{q}_0{}^2 = +1.$$

As $\mathbf{q}_0 \in SU(2,\mathbf{C})$, we conclude easily that

$$\mathbf{q}_0 = \pm 1$$

and hence that for all $\mathbf{c}$ in $\mathbf{Q}$,

$$\mathbf{c}^{\,\theta} = \mathbf{c}^*.$$

$\langle\,.\,,\,.\,\rangle$ is thus $*$-bilinear and satisfies the condition

$$\langle u,v\rangle^* = \langle v,u\rangle$$

for all $u,\ v \in V$. In particular, $\langle u,u\rangle$ is real for all $u \in V$.

$u \to \langle u,u\rangle$ is thus a real valued function which vanishes only when $u=0$. Since it is evidently continuous and for some $w$, $\langle w,w\rangle=1$, we see that $\langle u,u\rangle>0$ for all nonzero $u$.

In other words, if $V$ is an $n$-dimensional space over $\mathbf{Q}$ $(n\geq 3)$ with a given orthocomplementation in $\mathscr{L}(V,\mathbf{Q})$, there exists a nonsingular $*$-bilinear form $\langle\,.\,,\,.\,\rangle$ which induces the given orthocomplementation and which has, in addition, the properties:

 (i) $\langle x,y\rangle^* = \langle y,x\rangle$,
 (ii) $\langle x,x\rangle \geq 0$, $= 0$ if and only if $x = 0$.

Thus the orthocomplementation is the one associated with a Hilbert space structure over $\mathbf{Q}$. Combining all this we obtain the following theorem:

**Theorem 4.7.** *Let* $\mathbf{D}=\mathbf{R}$ *or* $\mathbf{Q}$ *and let* $V$ *be a vector space of dimension* $n(\geq 3)$ *over* $\mathbf{D}$. *If* $\xi$ *is any orthocomplementation of* $\mathscr{L}(V,\mathbf{D})$, *there exists an inner product* $\langle\,.\,,\,.\,\rangle$ *converting* $V$ *into a Hilbert space such that* $\xi$ *coincides* *with the orthocomplementation induced by* $\langle\,.\,,\,.\rangle$. $\langle\,.\,,\,.\rangle$ *is uniquely determined by* $\xi$ *up to a multiplicative positive real number. If* $\mathbf{D}=\mathbf{C}$ *and* $\xi$ *is regular in the sense that the anti-automorphism of* $\mathbf{C}$ *associated with* $\xi$ *is either the identity or the conjugation, then it is the conjugation and* $\xi$ *is induced by a Hermitian inner product* $\langle\,.\,,\,.\rangle$, *converting* $V$ *into a Hilbert space. Moreover,* $\langle\,.\,,\,.\rangle$ *is determined by* $\xi$ *up to multiplication by a positive real number.*

## 4. THE ORTHOGONAL AND UNITARY GROUPS

Our main result in this section is the description of all automorphisms of $\mathscr{L}(V,\mathbf{D})$ which preserve the orthocomplementation induced on it by an inner product for $V$, $\mathbf{D}$ being one of $\mathbf{R}$, $\mathbf{C}$, or $\mathbf{Q}$.

**Lemma 4.8.** *Let* $\mathbf{D}$ *be a division ring and let* $V$ *be a vector space of dimension* $n(\geq 3)$ *over* $\mathbf{D}$. *Let* $\varphi$ *be an automorphism of* $\mathbf{D}$ *and* $\theta$ *an involutive anti-automorphism of* $\mathbf{D}$. *Suppose* $\langle\,.\,,\,.\rangle$ *is a nonsingular, symmetric,* $\theta$-*bilinear form on* $V \times V$. *If* $L$ *is a* $\varphi$-*linear isomorphism of* $V$ *onto itself, such that the induced automorphism of* $\mathscr{L}(V,\mathbf{D})$ *preserves the polarity induced by* $\langle\,.\,,\,.\rangle$, *then there exists a* $d \neq 0$ *in* $\mathbf{D}$ *such that*

$$(36) \qquad \langle Lx,Ly\rangle = \langle x,y\rangle^{\varphi}d$$

*for all* $x, y \in V$.

**Proof.** Let $M \to M'$ be the polarity of $\mathscr{L}(V,\mathbf{D})$ induced by $\langle\,.\,,\,.\rangle$ and let $\xi_L$ be the automorphism of $\mathscr{L}(V,\mathbf{D})$ induced by $L$. If $x, y \in V$, then $\mathbf{D}\cdot x \subseteq (\mathbf{D}\cdot y)'$ if and only if $\mathbf{D}\cdot(Lx) \subseteq (\mathbf{D}\cdot(Ly))'$ as $\xi_L$ preserves the polarity $M \to M'$. Consequently, $\langle x,y\rangle=0$ if and only if $\langle Lx,Ly\rangle=0$. This shows that if we define $\langle x,y\rangle^{\sim} = \langle Lx,Ly\rangle^{(\varphi^{-1})}$, $(x, y \in V)$ and $\psi=\varphi^{-1}\theta\varphi$, then $\psi$ is an involutive anti-automorphism of $\mathbf{D}$, $\langle\,.\,,\,.\rangle^{\sim}$ is a nonsingular $\psi$-bilinear form on $V \times V$ and $\langle\,.\,,\,.\rangle^{\sim}$ induces the same polarity as $\langle\,.\,,\,.\rangle$. From theorem 4.1 we conclude that there is a $d \neq 0$ in $\mathbf{D}$ such that

$$\langle x,y\rangle^{\sim} = \langle x,y\rangle d^{(\varphi^{-1})}$$

for all $x, y \in V$. In other words,

$$\langle Lx,Ly\rangle^{(\varphi^{-1})} = \langle x,y\rangle d^{(\varphi^{-1})}$$

for all $x, y$ in $V$. Applying $\varphi$ to this we obtain (36).

**Theorem 4.9.** *Let* $\mathbf{D}$ *be one of* $\mathbf{R}$, $\mathbf{C}$, *or* $\mathbf{Q}$, *and* $V$ *a vector space of dimension* $n(\geq 3)$ *over* $\mathbf{D}$. *Let* $\langle\,.\,,\,.\rangle$ *be an inner product for* $V$ *which converts* $V$ *into a Hilbert space. If* $\xi$ *is any automorphism of* $\mathscr{L}(V,\mathbf{D})$ *which preserves the* *orthocomplementation induced by* $\langle\,.\,,\,.\,\rangle$, *then there exists a semilinear isomorphism* $L$ *of* $V$ *onto itself which induces* $\xi$ *such that*

(i) *for* $\mathbf{D} = \mathbf{R}$ *or* $\mathbf{Q}$, $L$ *is linear, whereas for* $\mathbf{D} = \mathbf{C}$, $L$ *is either linear or conjugate linear,*

(ii) *for all* $x, y \in V$,

$$(37) \qquad\qquad \langle Lx, Ly \rangle = \langle x,y \rangle$$

*if* $L$ *is linear, and*

$$(38) \qquad\qquad \langle Lx, Ly \rangle = \langle y,x \rangle$$

*if* $\mathbf{D} = \mathbf{C}$ *and* $L$ *is conjugate linear. In particular,* $L$ *is an isometry of* $V$.

**Proof.** Let us first consider the case when $\xi$ is a linear automorphism of $\mathscr{L}(V,\mathbf{D})$; i.e., there exists a linear isomorphism $L_1$ of $V$ onto itself such that $\xi$ is induced by $L_1$. By lemma 4.8 there is a $d \neq 0$ in $\mathbf{D}$ such that

$$(39) \qquad\qquad \langle L_1 x, L_1 y \rangle = \langle x,y \rangle d$$

for all $x, y \in V$. Since $\langle u,u \rangle$ is a positive real number for all $u$ in $V$, we deduce, by putting $y = x$ in (39), that $d$ is a positive real number. If we write $L_1 = d^{1/2} L$, then $L$ induces $\xi$ and

$$(40) \qquad\qquad \langle Lx, Ly \rangle = \langle x,y \rangle$$

for all $x, y \in V$.

If $\xi$ is not a linear automorphism of $\mathscr{L}(V,\mathbf{D})$, then it follows from theorem 3.16 that $\mathbf{D} = \mathbf{C}$. Let $\varphi$ be the automorphism of $\mathbf{C}$ corresponding to $\xi$ and let $L_1$ be a $\varphi$-linear isomorphism of $V$ onto itself which induces $\xi$. Since $\xi$ is not linear, $\varphi$ is not the identity. By lemma 4.8, there exists a nonzero $d$ in $\mathbf{C}$ such that $\langle L_1 x, L_1 y \rangle = \langle x,y \rangle^{\varphi} d$ for all $x, y \in V$. If $x_0 \in V$ and $\langle x_0, x_0 \rangle = 1$, then $\langle L_1 x_0, L_1 x_0 \rangle = d$, showing that $d$ is a positive real number. Since, for any $x$ in $V$, $\langle x,x \rangle^{\varphi} = d^{-1} \langle L_1 x, L_1 x \rangle$, $\langle x,x \rangle^{\varphi}$ is a real number $\geq 0$ and hence $r^{\varphi} \geq 0$ for all real numbers $r \geq 0$. This shows that $\varphi$ eaves the set $\mathbf{R}$ of real numbers invariant. Since any automorphism of $\mathbf{R}$ is the identity, $r^{\varphi} = r$ for all real numbers $r$. Evidently, as $\varphi$ is not the identity, $i^{\varphi} = -i$. Consequently, $c^{\varphi} = c^*$ for all $c \in \mathbf{C}$.

If we now define $L = d^{-1/2} L_1$, we have

$$(41) \qquad\qquad \langle Lx, Ly \rangle = \langle y,x \rangle$$

for all $x, y \in V$. This completes the proof of theorem 4.9.

When $\mathbf{D} = \mathbf{C}$ and $L$ is a conjugate linear isomorphism of $V$ such that $\langle Lx, Ly \rangle = \langle y,x \rangle$ for all $x, y \in V$, we call $L$ *anti-unitary*. If $L$ is a linear isomorphism of $V$ onto itself such that $\langle Lx, Ly \rangle = \langle x,y \rangle$ for all $x, y \in V$, we say that $L$ is *unitary*.

# CHAPTER V

# COORDINATIZATION OF GENERALIZED
# GEOMETRIES

## 1. GENERALIZED GEOMETRIES

We mentioned previously (cf. Chapter II) that the fundamental problem of geometry is to set up an isomorphism of an abstractly given geometry with the geometry of subspaces of a vector space. In this chapter we shall examine this problem. The classical result in this direction asserts that for a geometry of dimension $\geq 4$ there exists always an isomorphism with the projective geometry of a vector space, and that such an isomorphism can be constructed even when the dimension is 3, provided the geometry is what is known as Desarguesian. These are of course well known results.

It turns out that this theorem is somewhat inadequate to enable us to describe the structure of the logics of quantum mechanical systems, since the latter are seldom of finite dimension. It is therefore necessary to formulate and prove a generalization of the classical result so that one can handle the infinite case as well. For this purpose we introduce the concept of a generalized geometry (cf. Chapter II for the definition of a geometry). Let $\mathscr{L}$ be a partially ordered set with partial ordering $<$ and zero element 0. For elements $a,\, b \in \mathscr{L}$, such that $a < b$, $a \neq b$, we write

$$(1) \qquad \mathscr{L}[a,b] = \{x : x \in \mathscr{L}, a < x < b\}.$$

It is easy to see that $<$ induces a partial ordering in $\mathscr{L}[a,b]$ for which $a$ is the zero element and $b$ is the unit element. $\mathscr{L}$ is called a *generalized geometry* if the following conditions are satisfied:

$$(2)$$
    (i) for any finite subset $F$ of $\mathscr{L}$, $\bigvee_{a \in F} a$, $\bigwedge_{a \in F} a$ exist,
    (ii) if $a \in \mathscr{L}$ and $a \neq 0$, $\mathscr{L}[0,a]$ is a geometry.

*It is important to note that we do not require the existence of a unit element.* If $\mathscr{L}$ has a unit element, say 1, then by (ii) $\mathscr{L}$ itself is a geometry. For general $\mathscr{L}$, it follows from (ii) that $\mathscr{L}$ has points and that every element in $\mathscr{L}$ is a sum of points. Since any finite number of elements of $\mathscr{L}$ can, by virtue of (i) and (ii), be regarded as elements in geometry, it follows from theorem 2.8 that we may speak, for any $a \in \mathscr{L}$, of dim$(a)$, the dimension of $a$. It is most simply defined as the dimension of the unit element $a$ of the geometry $\mathscr{L}[0,a]$. Clearly, $\dim(a)$ is equal to the number of elements in any set of independent points whose lattice sum is $a$. The function $a \to \dim(a)$ has the properties:

(3)
$\quad$ (i) $\dim(0) = 0$, $0 < \dim(a) < \infty$ for all nonzero $a$,
$\quad$ (ii) if $a < b$ and $a \neq b$, then $\dim(a) < \dim(b)$,
$\quad$ (iii) $\dim(a) = 1$ if and only if $a$ is a point,
$\quad$ (iv) if $a, b \in \mathscr{L}$, then $\dim(a \vee b) + \dim(a \wedge b) = \dim(a) + \dim(b)$.

Unless $\mathscr{L}$ is itself a geometry, $\sup_a \dim(a)$ will be infinite. We shall call this supremum the *dimension of* $\mathscr{L}$, possibly infinite,

(4) $$\dim(\mathscr{L}) = \sup_{a \in \mathscr{L}} \dim(a).$$

Note that for $a, b, c \in \mathscr{L}$ with $c < a$, $a \wedge (b \vee c) = (a \wedge b) \vee c$ (since this identity is valid in the geometry $\mathscr{L}[0, a \vee b]$).

A typical example of a generalized geometry is obtained as follows. Let **D** be a division ring and $V$ a vector space over **D**, not necessarily finite dimensional. Let $\mathscr{L}$ be the set of all *finite dimensional* subspaces of $V$, partially ordered under inclusion. Then it is obvious that $\mathscr{L}$ is a generalized geometry (which is not a geometry, unless $\dim V < \infty$). The fundamental theorem of this chapter asserts that every generalized geometry $\mathscr{L}$, with $\dim(\mathscr{L}) \geq 4$, may be obtained in this manner.

Our solution to this problem follows the classical method. We first examine Desarguesian planes and prove that one can associate a division ring to any Desarguesian plane in a rather canonical manner. We then select a "hyperplane" in the generalized geometry and use this as a "hyperplane at infinity" to construct affine coordinates for points which do not lie at infinity. The introduction of *homogeneous* coordinates will then follow in the usual manner.

## 2. DIVISION RINGS ASSOCIATED WITH DESARGUESIAN PLANES

Let $\mathscr{L}$ be a generalized geometry with $\dim(\mathscr{L}) \geq 3$. Let $O$ be a point of $\mathscr{L}$ and $t_i$ $(i=1, 2, 3)$ be three distinct lines containing $O$. Let $A_i$, $A_i{}'$ be points on $t_i$ such that $O$, $A_i$ and $A_i{}'$ are distinct $(i=1, 2, 3)$. The ordered set $\Gamma = \{O; A_1, A_1{}'; A_2, A_2{}'; A_3, A_3{}'\}$ is called *pre-Desarguesian* if (i) $A_1$, $A_2$, and $A_3$ are independent, and (ii) $A_1{}'$, $A_2{}'$, and $A_3{}'$ are independent. Since $O = t_1 \wedge t_2$, the element $t_1 \vee t_2$ is a plane, and $A_1 \vee A_2$ and $A_1{}' \vee A_2{}'$ are two distinct lines in it. Therefore $X_3 = (A_1 \vee A_2) \wedge (A_1{}' \vee A_2{}')$, and similarly, $X_1 = (A_2 \vee A_3) \wedge (A_2{}' \vee A_3{}')$ and $X_2 = (A_3 \vee A_1) \wedge (A_3{}' \vee A_1{}')$ are points. It can be shown quite simply that $X_1$, $X_2$, and $X_3$ are distinct and also distinct from the seven points of $\Gamma$. Since $A_i$ as well as the $A_i{}'$ ($i=1, 2, 3$) are independent, the elements $b$ and $b'$, where

$$b = A_1 \vee A_2 \vee A_3,$$
$$b' = A_1{}' \vee A_2{}' \vee A_3{}',$$

are planes. Clearly, $X_i < b \wedge b'$, for $i=1, 2, 3$. Two cases arise.

*Case 1: $b \neq b'$.* In this case, $\dim(b \wedge b') \leq 2$ and as $X_1 \vee X_2 < b \wedge b'$, $\dim(b \wedge b') = 2$ and $X_1 \vee X_2 = b \wedge b'$; but then, as $X_3 < b \wedge b'$, we conclude that $X_1$, $X_2$, and $X_3$ are collinear.

*Case 2: $b = b'$.* In this case, $X_1$, $X_2$, and $X_3$ *need not* lie on a line.

The set $\Gamma$ is *Desarguesian* if $X_1$, $X_2$, and $X_3$ lie on a line, say $t$. $O$ is called the *center* of $\Gamma$ and $t$ the *axis* of $\Gamma$. If every pre-Desarguesian set is Desarguesian, we shall say that $\mathscr{L}$ is *Desarguesian*. If $\dim(\mathscr{L}) \geq 4$, then $\mathscr{L}$ is Desarguesian as we shall prove now. Note that $\Gamma$ is Desarguesian whenever the planes $A_1 \vee A_2 \vee A_3$ and $A_1{}' \vee A_2{}' \vee A_3{}'$ are distinct.

**Lemma 5.1.** *Let $\mathscr{L}$ be a generalized geometry with $\dim(\mathscr{L}) \geq 4$. Then $\mathscr{L}$ is Desarguesian.*

**Proof.** Let $\Gamma = \{O;\ A_1, A_1{}';\ A_2, A_2{}';\ A_3, A_3{}'\}$ be pre-Desarguesian. We may clearly assume that the planes $A_1 \vee A_2 \vee A_3$ and $A_1{}' \vee A_2{}' \vee A_3{}'$ are identical. Hence all the points of $\Gamma$ lie on a plane, say $b$. We use the notation of the preceding paragraph. We must prove that $X_1$, $X_2$, and $X_3$ lie on a line. Since $\dim(\mathscr{L}) \geq 4$, there exists a point $P$ such that $P \nleq b$.

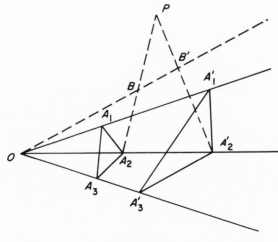

Fig. 1

We take such a $P$ and select, on the lines $P \vee A_2$ and $P \vee A_2'$, two points $B$ and $B'$ distinct from $P$, $A_2$, and $A_2'$ such that $O$, $B$, and $B'$ are collinear (see Fig. 1). $B$ and $B'$ therefore do not lie on $b$. Then it is easy to check that

$$\Gamma' = \{O;\ A_1, A_1';\ B, B';\ A_3, A_3'\}$$

is pre-Desarguesian. The planes $A_1 \vee B \vee A_3$ and $A_1' \vee B' \vee A_3'$ are distinct, as otherwise $B$ would lie on $b = A_1 \vee A_3 \vee A_3'$. $\Gamma'$ is thus Desarguesian. Let $t'$ be its axis. It is easy to see that $P \not< t'$. Indeed, if $P < t'$, then $P$ would lie in the plane $A_1 \vee B \vee A_3$ which would imply that $A_2$ lies in the plane $A_1 \vee B \vee A_3$, in turn leading to the conclusion that $B < b$. Since all the points in sight lie on $P \vee b$, $P \vee t'$ and $b$ are distinct planes both $< P \vee b$. Since $\dim(P \vee b) = 4$, it follows that

$$\dim\left((P \vee t') \wedge b\right) = \dim(P \vee t') + \dim(b) - \dim\left((P \vee t') \vee b\right) = 2.$$

Therefore $t = (P \vee t') \wedge b$ is a line. In order to prove that $\Gamma$ is Desarguesian, it suffices to prove that $X_i < t$ for $i = 1, 2, 3$. Since

$$X_2 = (A_1 \vee A_3) \wedge (A_1' \vee A_3'),$$

$X_2 < t'$ and hence $X_2 < t' \wedge b < t$. We shall now prove that $X_1 < t$. The planes $P \vee A_2 \vee A_3$ and $P \vee A_2' \vee A_3'$ are distinct and their lattice sum is obviously $P \vee b$. Hence their intersection $u$ is of dimension 2, i.e., a line. $P$ lies on this line $u$. Further, if $(A_3 \vee B) \wedge (A_3' \vee B') = X_1'$, $X_1' < t'$ and $X_1' < u$ also. As $P \neq X_1'$, $u = P \vee X_1'$ and hence $u < P \vee t'$. This shows that $u \wedge b < t$. Now $X_1 = (A_3 \vee A_2) \wedge (A_3' \vee A_2') < u \wedge b$ so that $X_1 < t$. A similar argument proves that $X_3 < t$. $\Gamma$ is thus Desarguesian.

If $\dim(\mathscr{L}) = 3$, the above argument is no longer valid. $\mathscr{L}$ is then a plane and it is a classical fact that there exist non-Desarguesian projective planes. Our analysis in this section will be concerned only with Desarguesian planes (cf. Seidenberg [1] for examples of non-Desarguesian planes).

Consider now a projective plane $\mathscr{L}$ and a line $n$ of $\mathscr{L}$. Let $P$ be a point not on $n$. Then any line containing $P$ meets $n$ in a unique point. Further, for any point $X$ on $n$, $P$ and $X$ are distinct so that $P \vee X$ is a well-defined line. If $X'$ is a second point on $n$ with $X \neq X'$, $P \vee X$ and $P \vee X'$ are distinct lines. Thus if there are exactly $k$ points on $n$, there are exactly $k$ lines through any point $P$, $P$ not on $n$. This is true even if $P$ lies on $n$. Suppose in fact that $P$ lies on $n$. Let now $n'$ be another line, $n \neq n'$ and $Q$ a point not on $n$, not on $n'$. (That such a point exists is easily seen.) For any point $X$ on $n$, $Q \neq X$ so that $Q \vee X$ is a well-defined line $\neq n'$. It meets $n'$ in a well-defined point $X'$. The map $X \rightarrow X'$ is one-one and onto between the set of points on $n$ and the set of those on $n'$. If thus there are exactly (at least) $k$ points on $n$, there are exactly (at least) $k$ points on $n'$. If now $P$ is a point on $n$, then the line $n'$ does not contain $P$, and on $n'$ there are exactly $k$ points so that, since $P$ is not on $n'$, we know from the preceding that containing $P$ there are exactly $k$ lines.

A plane $\mathscr{L}$ is called *trivial* if every line of $\mathscr{L}$ contains exactly 3 points. Then through every point exactly 3 lines pass and there are, as is easily seen, exactly 7 points and 7 lines of $\mathscr{L}$. An example of a trivial plane can be obtained as follows. Let $\mathbf{D}$ be the field consisting only of the two elements 0 and 1. It is of characteristic 2 so that $1 = -1$. Consider the three-dimensional coordinate vector space of vectors $(x_1, x_2, x_3)$ over $\mathbf{D}$. If $x$ is a nonzero vector, the only vectors on the ray joining $x$ to the origin are 0 and $x$. There are altogether 8 vectors including 0 and hence 7 rays through 0. These rays lie 3 each on 7 two-dimensional spaces, whose equations are $x_1 = 0$, $x_2 = 0$, $x_3 = 0$, $x_1 + x_2 = 0$, $x_2 + x_3 = 0$, $x_1 + x_3 = 0$, $x_1 + x_2 + x_3 = 0$. The lattice of subspaces of this vector space is a trivial geometry. It is more or less elementary to show that, up to a lattice isomorphism, there is only one plane geometry with exactly 3 points on each line. We shall assume in much of what follows that $\mathscr{L}$ is Desarguesian and nontrivial.

We shall now introduce the concept of an automorphism of a projective plane and, even more generally, an isomorphism of two generalized geometries. Let $\mathscr{L}_i$ $(i = 1, 2)$ be generalized geometries. An *isomorphism* of $\mathscr{L}_1$ onto $\mathscr{L}_2$ is a one-one order preserving map of $\mathscr{L}_1$ onto $\mathscr{L}_2$. If $\alpha(a \to \alpha(a))$ is any such isomorphism, then $\alpha(a)$ is a point if and only if $a$ is a point. $\alpha$ thus induces a one-one correspondence of the set of all points of $\mathscr{L}_1$, onto the set of all points of $\mathscr{L}_2$. Moreover, if $a_1$, $a_2$, $a_3$ are three points of $\mathscr{L}_1$, they are collinear if and only if the points $\alpha(a_1)$, $\alpha(a_2)$, and $\alpha(a_3)$ are collinear in $\mathscr{L}_2$. We shall now prove the useful lemma which asserts that any collinearity-preserving correspondence between points is induced by an isomorphism. We shall consequently refer to both of these kinds of mappings as isomorphisms. An isomorphism of $\mathscr{L}$ onto $\mathscr{L}$ is called an *automorphism*.

**Lemma 5.2.** *Let $\mathscr{L}_1$, $\mathscr{L}_2$ be two generalized geometries and*

$$\alpha : P \to \alpha(P) \tag{5}$$

*a one-one map of the set of all points of $\mathscr{L}_1$ onto the set of all points of $\mathscr{L}_2$. Suppose $\alpha$ is collinearity-preserving, i.e., points $P_i$ $(i = 1, 2, 3)$ of $\mathscr{L}_1$ are collinear if and only if the points $\alpha(P_i)$ $(i = 1, 2, 3)$ of $\mathscr{L}_2$ are collinear. Then there exists a unique isomorphism $\alpha^\sim$ of $\mathscr{L}_1$ onto $\mathscr{L}_2$ such that for any point $P$ of $\mathscr{L}_1$,*

$$\alpha^\sim(P) = \alpha(P). \tag{6}$$

**Proof.** For any $a \in \mathscr{L}_1$, there is a set $\{P_1, \cdots, P_t\}$ of points such that $a = \bigvee_{i=1}^{t} P_i$. We define

$$(7) \qquad\qquad \alpha^{\sim}(a) = \bigvee_{i=1}^{t} \alpha(P_i).$$

Clearly, if there exists an isomorphism extending $\alpha$, it is defined by (7) so that the uniqueness of $\alpha^{\sim}$ will follow automatically. We shall now prove, by induction on $t = \dim(a)$, that (7) defines $\alpha^{\sim}$ unambiguously. Suppose $a \in \mathscr{L}_1$ has dimension $t+1$ $(t \geq 1)$, and $\{P_i\}$, $\{Q_i\}$ are two sets of independent points with $a = \bigvee_{i=1}^{t+1} P_i = \bigvee_{i=1}^{t+1} Q_i$. We must prove that $\bigvee_{i=1}^{t+1} \alpha(P_i) = \bigvee_{i=1}^{t+1} \alpha(Q_i)$. It is enough, in view of the symmetry between the sets $\{P_i\}$ and $\{Q_i\}$, to prove that $\bigvee_{i=1}^{t+1} \alpha(Q_i) < \bigvee_{i=1}^{t+1} \alpha(P_i)$, i.e., to prove that $\alpha(Q_j) < b = \bigvee_{i=1}^{t+1} \alpha(P_i)$ for all $j \leq t+1$. Fix $j \leq t+1$. If $Q_j = P_{t+1}$, $\alpha(Q_j) < b$ trivially. If $Q_j \neq P_{t+1}$, $c = Q_j \vee P_{t+1}$ is a line and $c \vee (\bigvee_{i=1}^{t} P_i) = a$. We then conclude from the equation

$$\dim(c) + \dim\left(\bigvee_{i=1}^{t} P_i\right) = \dim(a) + \dim\left(c \wedge \left(\bigvee_{i=1}^{t} P_i\right)\right)$$

that

$$\dim\left(c \wedge \left(\bigvee_{i=1}^{t} P_i\right)\right) = 1.$$

Thus $R_1 = c \wedge (\bigvee_{i=1}^{t} P_i)$ is a point of $\bigvee_{i=1}^{t} P_i$. Let $R_2, \cdots, R_t$ be points chosen so that $\{R_1, \cdots, R_t\}$ is an independent set with lattice sum $\bigvee_{i=1}^{t} P_i$. From the induction hypothesis we know that

$$\bigvee_{i=1}^{t} \alpha(R_i) = \bigvee_{i=1}^{t} \alpha(P_i)$$

and hence

$$\alpha(R_1) < \bigvee_{i=1}^{t} \alpha(P_i).$$

Since $Q_j$, $P_{t+1}$, and $R_1$ are collinear, $\alpha(Q_j)$, $\alpha(P_{t+1})$, and $\alpha(R_1)$ are collinear. Consequently,

$$\alpha(Q_j) < \alpha(P_{t+1}) \vee \alpha(R_1)$$
$$< \bigvee_{i=1}^{t+1} \alpha(P_i),$$

which is what we wanted to prove.

Equation (7) thus defines $\alpha^{\sim}$ unambiguously. It now follows quite easily that $\alpha^{\sim}$ is an isomorphism of $\mathscr{L}_1$ onto $\mathscr{L}_2$ extending $\alpha$.

The set of all automorphisms of a generalized geometry is a group under composition. In the problem of constructing coordinates for a geometry an important role is played by certain subgroups of this group—subgroups of the group of projectivities. We shall now describe these. We begin with a lemma.

**Lemma 5.3.** *Let $\mathscr{L}$ be a generalized geometry and $a, b \in \mathscr{L}$. Suppose that* $\dim(a) = \dim(b) = s > 0$ *and that* $\dim(a \wedge b) = s - 1$. *Then there exist points* $X < a \vee b$ *such that $X$ lies neither on $a$ nor on $b$. For any such $X$, $X \vee a = X \vee b$, and*

$$(8) \qquad \alpha : c \to (X \vee c) \wedge b \qquad (c < a)$$

*is an isomorphism of $\mathscr{L}[0,a]$ onto $\mathscr{L}[0,b]$. Moreover,*

$$(9) \qquad \alpha(c) = c$$

*for all $c < a \wedge b$.*

**Proof.** Since $\dim(a \wedge b) = s - 1$, we see that

$$\dim(a \vee b) = \dim(a) + \dim(b) - \dim(a \wedge b) = s + 1.$$

If then $X < a \vee b$ is a point which lies neither on $a$ nor on $b$,

$$\dim(X \vee a) = \dim(X \vee b) = s + 1,$$

so that $X \vee a = X \vee b = a \vee b$. To see that such points exist, select a point $Y < a$ such that $Y \not< b$ and a point $Z < b$ such that $Z \not< a$. Then $Y \neq Z$ and any other point $X$ on the line $Y \vee Z$ is of the type required.

Suppose now $X$ is such a point. $\alpha$, as defined by (8), is obviously order-preserving. If $c < a$, $\dim(X \vee c) = \dim(c) + 1$ and as $X \vee c \vee b = a \vee b$,

$$\dim(\alpha(c)) = \dim(X \vee c) + \dim(b) - \dim(a \vee b) = \dim(c).$$

Thus $\alpha$ is also dimension-preserving. $\alpha$ is thus one-one. If $d < b$ and we write $c = (X \vee d) \wedge a$, an interchange of $a$ and $b$ in the above argument shows that $\dim(c) = \dim(d)$. Since $(X \vee c) \wedge b < (X \vee d) \wedge b = d$ (modularity) $\alpha(c) < d$ and hence $\alpha(c) = d$ as $\dim(\alpha(c)) = \dim(c) = \dim(d)$. $\alpha$ is thus a one-one order-preserving map of $\mathscr{L}[0,a]$ onto $\mathscr{L}[0,b]$. Evidently, for $c < a \wedge b$, $\alpha(c) = c$. This proves the lemma.

We shall say that $\alpha$ is a *perspectivity of $a$ on $b$ with center $X$* and denote it by

$$(10) \qquad \alpha = \pi(X; a,b).$$

Suppose now that $\mathscr{L}$ is a projective plane, and $a$ and $b$ are distinct lines in $\mathscr{L}$. Then the hypotheses of the above lemma are met as

$$\dim(a \vee b) = 3, \qquad \dim(a \wedge b) = 1.$$

The isomorphism is then illustrated by Fig. 2.

We are now in a position to introduce the notion of a projectivity in a projective plane $\mathscr{L}$. Let $n_0, n_1, \cdots, n_s$ be lines in $\mathscr{L}$ such that for $0 \le i \le s - 1$, $n_i \neq n_{i+1}$. Let $X_1, \cdots, X_s$ be points such that $X_j$ is not on either $n_{j-1}$ or $n_j$. Then we have for each $j$, a perspectivity $t_j$ of $n_{j-1}$ onto

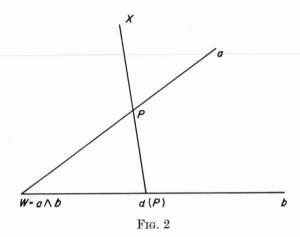

Fig. 2

$n_j$ with center $X_j$. The product $t_s t_{s-1} \cdots t_1$ of these transformations gives us a transformation of the set of points lying on $n_0$ onto the set of those lying on $n_s$. We shall call this a *projectivity of $n_0$ onto $n_s$*. Given $n_0$ and $n_s$, a projectivity of $n_0$ onto $n_s$ is obtained by specifying the $n_j$'s and $X_j$'s for the intermediate $j$. It is perfectly possible that the same projectivity of $n_0$ onto $n_s$ may be obtained in many different ways as a product of perspectivities.

Let $n$ be a line of a projective plane $\mathscr{L}$. The set $\mathfrak{P}(n)$ of all projectivities of $n$ onto itself is evidently a group under composition. The elements of $\mathfrak{P}(n)$ which can be expressed as products of at most $k$ perspectivities form a subset of $\mathfrak{P}(n)$, denoted by $\mathfrak{P}_k(n)$. Clearly, $\mathfrak{P}_r(n)\mathfrak{P}_s(n) \subseteq \mathfrak{P}_{r+s}(n)$. We shall be mainly concerned with $\mathfrak{P}_2(n)$ and certain of its subsets.

*From now on, until the end of this section, $\mathscr{L}$ denotes an arbitrary, but fixed, nontrivial Desarguesian plane.* Let $n$, $m$ be two distinct lines and $X$, $Y$ two distinct points such that neither of $X$ or $Y$ lies on either of $n$ or $m$ (such $n$, $m$, $X$, $Y$ exist, as $\mathscr{L}$ is not trivial). Then the projectivity $r(Y,X; n,m)$ given by

$$(11) \qquad r(Y,X; n,m) = \pi(X; m,n)\pi(Y; n,m)$$

is an element of $\mathfrak{P}_2(n)$.

We shall call $Y$ the *first center of perspectivity* of this projectivity and $X$ its *second center of perspectivity*. Let $W$ be the point where $n$ and $m$ meet. We shall call this projectivity *special* if $W$ lies on the line $X \vee Y$ (Fig. 3(b)); otherwise we shall call it *general*. In the general case, the point $W$ is left fixed by the projectivity as also the point $O$ where the line $X \vee Y$ meets $n$ (Fig. 3(a)). We shall call these the *canonical fixed points* of

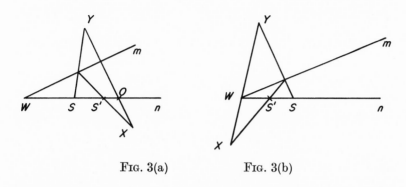

FIG. 3(a)          FIG. 3(b)

the projectivity. We use the symbol $p(Y,X; n,m)$ to denote always a special projectivity of $n$ onto itself. The general projectivities are always denoted by $q(Y,X; n,m)$. Note that the symbols $p(Y,X; n,m)$ and $q(Y,X; n,m)$ are defined only when (i) $Y \neq X$ and neither $X$ nor $Y$ lies on either $m$ or $n$, (ii) $m \neq n$. If $Y \vee X$ does not contain $W = n \wedge m$, $O$ is called the *first* canonical fixed point of $q(Y,X; n,m)$ and $W$, the *second*. Note that $q(Y,X; n,m)$ has no fixed points other than $O$ and $W$ while $p(Y,X; n,m)$ has $W$ as its only fixed point.

We shall prove first that any *special* projectivity $p(Y,X; n,m)$ is uniquely determined by its action on any given point $O$ of $n$ with $O \neq W$. In other words, we have

**Lemma 5.4.** *Let $n$ be any line of $\mathscr{L}$ and $O$, $W$ two distinct points of $n$. If $p = p(Y,X; n,m)$ and $p' = p(Y',X'; n,m')$ are two special projectivities of $n$ belonging to $\mathfrak{P}_2(n)$, having $W$ as their canonical fixed point, such that $pO = p'O$, then $p = p'$.*

**Proof.** We are given that $O \neq W$ and that $pO = p'O = B$. Obviously, $O \neq B \neq W$. Define, for any $M$ distinct from $O$ and $W$,

(12) $$M' = pM.$$

We must prove that $M' = p'M$ also.

First we consider the case $m = m'$. To prove that $M' = p'M$, it suffices to show that $M'$ lies on the line joining $X'$ to the point $(M \vee Y') \wedge m$. This will be proved if we show that the lines $M' \vee X'$ and $M \vee Y'$ meet at a point on $m$. Let us assume that (i) the lines $Y \vee X$ and $Y' \vee X'$ are distinct, (ii) $O$, $Y$, $Y'$ are not collinear. Therefore, $B$, $X$, $X'$ are not collinear. Let $M_0$ be the point $(Y \vee Y') \wedge n$. Then $M_0 \neq O$ (Fig. 4). An easy check reveals that $\Gamma = \{W; O,B; Y,X; Y',X'\}$ is pre-Desarguesian with center $W$. $\Gamma$ is thus Desarguesian. Since $R = (O \vee Y) \wedge (B \vee X)$, and

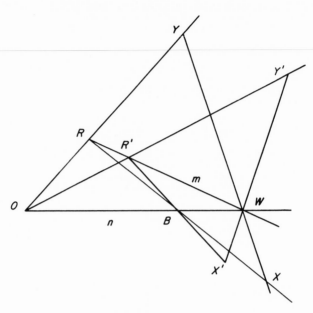

FIG. 4

$R' = (O \vee Y') \wedge (B \vee X')$ are distinct points on $m$, it follows that the axis of $\Gamma$ must be $m$. Hence $Y \vee Y'$ and $X \vee X'$ meet on $m$. Thus

$$pM_0 = p'M_0 = (X \vee X') \wedge n.$$

If $M \neq M_0$, $\Gamma_1 = \{W;\ M,M';\ Y,X;\ Y',X'\}$ is Desarguesian and hence the lines $M' \vee X'$ and $M \vee Y'$ meet on the axis of $\Gamma_1$. Now $(Y \vee Y') \wedge (X \vee X')$ is on $m$ by what we just saw, while $(M' \vee X) \wedge (M \vee Y)$ is on $m$ because $M' = pM$. Thus $m$ is the axis of $\Gamma_1$, proving what we wanted.

The case when $O$, $Y$, $Y'$ are collinear now remains. However, now $M_0 = O$ and as $B = pM_0 = p'M_0$, $B$, $X$, $X'$ are collinear. This means that $Y \vee Y'$ and $X \vee X'$ meet on $m$. If $M \neq O$, and $\neq W$, then $\{W;\ M,M';\ Y,X;\ Y',X'\}$ is Desarguesian and the proof proceeds as before.

Suppose finally that the line $Y' \vee X'$ is the same as the line $Y \vee X$. Since $\mathscr{L}$ is nontrivial, $\mathscr{L}$ has at least 4 lines through every point. We then take a line through $W$ which is distinct from $n$, $m$ and $X \vee Y$. Let us take $Y''$ and $X''$ on this line such that $p(Y'',X'';\ n,m)$ is defined and takes $O$ to $B$. Then by what we have just proved, $p(Y,X;\ n,m) = p(Y'',X'';n,m)$ and $p(Y',X';\ n,m) = p(Y'',X'';\ n,m)$. Thus $p(Y,X;\ n,m) = p(Y',X';\ n,m)$.

We now pass on to the case when $m \neq m'$. We assume first that $m'$ does not pass through either $X$ or $Y$, i.e., $n$, $m'$, $m$ and $Y \vee X$ are distinct lines (see Fig. 5). Then $R' = (O \vee Y) \wedge m'$ is distinct from $R = (O \vee Y) \wedge m$.

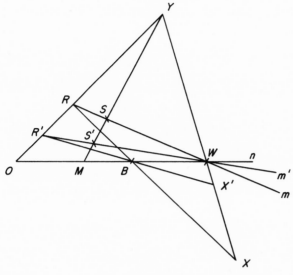

FIG. 5

Let $(R' \vee B) \wedge (Y \vee X) = X''$. Then $X''$ and $Y$ do not lie either on $m'$ or $n$, and $p(Y,X''; n,m')$ is well defined. Clearly, $p(Y,X''; n,m')O = B$. We shall first prove that $p(Y,X''; n,m') = p(Y,X; n,m)$. Let $M$ be any point of $n$, $M \neq O$, $M \neq W$, and let $M' = p(Y,X; n,m)M$. It is enough to prove that $M'$ lies on the line joining $X''$ to the point $(M \vee Y) \wedge m' = S'$ say, i.e., to prove that $X''$, $S'$, and $M'$ all lie on one line. Let $S = (Y \vee M) \wedge m$. Then

$$\{R; S,W; Y,R'; X,B\}$$

is Desarguesian and hence posseses an axis. This axis contains the points $(S \vee Y) \wedge (W \vee R') = S'$, $(Y \vee X) \wedge (R' \vee B) = X''$ and

$$(X \vee S) \wedge (B \vee W) = p(Y,X; n,m)M = M'.$$

This proves our assertion. Since $p(Y',X'; n,m') = p(Y,X''; n,m')$ by what we have seen earlier, we conclude that $p(Y,X; n,m) = p(Y',X'; n,m')$. We next consider the case when $m'$ contains $X$ or $Y$. Then $m' = X \vee Y$. In this case (as $\mathscr{L}$ is nontrivial) we take a line $m''$ through $W$, distinct from $m$, $m'$ and $n$, and points $Y_1$ and $X_1$ on $m''$ such that (i) $Y_1$ and $X_1$ do not lie on $n$ or $m$ and (ii) $p(Y_1,X_1; n,m'')O = B$. Using the result proved, we conclude that (a) as $m''$ does not contain $X$ or $Y$, so

$$p(Y,X; n,m) = p(Y_1,X_1; n,m''),$$

and (b) as $m'$ does not contain $X_1$ or $Y_1$, so

$$p(Y_1, X_1; n, m'') = p(Y', X'; n, m').$$

This completes the proof of the lemma.

Let $\mathfrak{A} = \mathfrak{A}(n; W)$ be the set consisting of the identity mapping and the special projectivities of $n$ onto itself which are of the form $p(Y, X; n, m)$ (where the lines $Y \vee X$, $n$, and $m$ meet at $W$).

**Lemma 5.5.** $\mathfrak{A}$ *is an abelian group of transformations of the set of points lying on $n$.*

**Proof.** We shall first prove that $\mathfrak{A}$ is a group. We must show that for any two elements $\sigma_1$ and $\sigma_2$ in $\mathfrak{A}$, $\sigma_1 \sigma_2$ and $\sigma_1^{-1}$ belong to $\mathfrak{A}$. If $\sigma_1$ is not the identity, write $\sigma_1 = p(Y, X; n, m)$. That $\sigma_1^{-1} \in \mathfrak{A}$ follows at once from the fact that $p(X, Y; n, m)$ is the inverse of $p(Y, X; n, m)$. Consider now $\sigma_1 \sigma_2$. We may assume that $\sigma_1$ is not the inverse of $\sigma_2$ and that neither $\sigma_1$ nor $\sigma_2$ is the identity. Let $\sigma_2 O = B$, $\sigma_1 B = C$, where $O$ is an arbitrary point $\neq W$ of the line $n$. In view of the assumption on $\sigma_1$ and $\sigma_2$, $O$, $B$, $C$ are distinct among themselves and from $W$. Let $Y$, $X$, and $m$ be chosen so that

$$\sigma_2 = p(Y, X; n, m).$$

We can then evidently find a $Z$ on the line $Y \vee X$ such that

$$C = p(X, Z; n, m) B.$$

In view of lemma 5.4 we must have:

$$\sigma_1 = p(X, Z; n, m),$$

since both are elements of $\mathfrak{A}$ and move $B$ into $C$. It follows immediately that $\sigma_1 \sigma_2 = p(Y, Z; n, m)$, showing that $\sigma_1 \sigma_2 \in \mathfrak{A}$.

It remains to prove that $\mathfrak{A}$ is abelian. It is obviously enough to prove that $\sigma_1 \sigma_2 O = \sigma_2 \sigma_1 O$. Let $\sigma_1 O = A$ and $\sigma_2 O = B$. We must show that $\sigma_2 A = \sigma_1 B$. Choose $Y$, $X$, $n$, and $m$ in such a way that $\sigma_1 = p(Y, X; n, m)$ and choose the line $m'$ such that $p(Y, X; n, m') = \sigma_2$. This is clearly possible. If $B = A$, then lemma 5.4 implies that $\sigma_2 = \sigma_1$ and hence $\sigma_1 \sigma_2 = \sigma_2 \sigma_1$. We may thus assume that $O$, $B$, $A$, and $W$ are distinct points. As $\sigma_1 \neq \sigma_2$, $m \neq m'$. To prove that $\sigma_1 \sigma_2 = \sigma_2 \sigma_1$, it is enough to prove that $\sigma_1 B = \sigma_2 A$. As $A \neq O$, $\sigma_2 A \neq B = \sigma_2 O$. If $\sigma_2 A = O$ or $A$, it follows that $\sigma_2$ is $\sigma_1^{-1}$, or the identity, respectively. We may thus assume that $\sigma_2 A (= T)$, $O$, $A$, $B$, and $W$ are distinct (see Fig. 6).

Let $R = (O \vee Y) \wedge m$ and $R' = (O \vee Y) \wedge m'$. Let $V$ be the point where $X \vee T$ and $A \vee Y$ meet. As $\sigma_2 A = T$, $V$ lies on $m'$. Let $U$ be the point

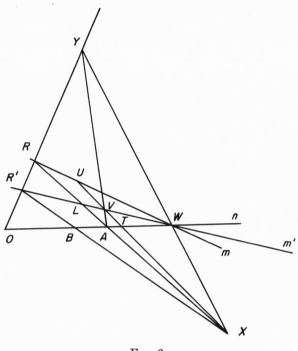

FIG. 6

$(X \vee T) \wedge m$. In order to prove that $\sigma_1 B = T$, it is enough to prove that $B$, $U$, and $Y$ lie on a line. It is easily checked that

$$\Gamma = \{Y; R, R'; A, V; W, X\}$$

is Desarguesian. Let $t$ be the axis of $\Gamma$. Then the points

$$K = (R \vee W) \wedge (R' \vee X), \qquad L = (R \vee A) \wedge (R' \vee V),$$

and $T = (A \vee W) \wedge (V \vee X)$ lie on $t$. Consequently,

$$\Gamma' = \{K; L, T; X, B; W, U\}$$

is Desarguesian. Let $t'$ be its axis. Then the points $(B \vee U) \wedge (X \vee W)$, $A = (L \vee X) \wedge (T \vee B)$, and $V = (L \vee W) \wedge (T \vee U)$ lie on $t'$. In other words, the lines $B \vee U$, $X \vee W$, and $A \vee V$ meet in a point which is obviously $Y$. Thus $B$, $U$, $Y$ are collinear. As we mentioned at the outset, this completes the proof of the lemma.

**Lemma 5.6.** *Let $n$ be any line of $\mathscr{L}$ and $O$, $W$, $E$ three distinct points on it. If $q$, $q'$ are two general elements of $\mathfrak{P}_2(n)$ with $O$ and $W$, respectively, as their first and second canonical fixed points, then $q = q'$ as soon as $qE = q'E$.*

**Proof.** Assume that $q = q(Y,X; n,m)$ and $q' = q(Y',X'; n,m')$. The proof is similar to that of lemma 5.4. We first consider the case when $m = m'$, but the lines $Y \vee X$ and $Y' \vee X'$ are distinct. Since both $q$ and $q'$ take $E$ to $B$, it follows that both the points $(E \vee Y) \wedge (B \vee X)$ and $(E \vee Y') \wedge (B \vee X')$ lie on $m$. From this it easily follows that the triples $\{E,Y,Y'\}$ and $\{B,X,X'\}$ are either both collinear or both noncollinear (i.e., independent). In the first case, $Y \vee Y'$ and $X \vee X'$ meet at a point, say, $R$, on the line $m$. On the other hand, if both of them are independent,

$$\Gamma = \{W; E,B; Y,X; Y',X'\}$$

is Desarguesian. Evidently, the axis of $\Gamma$ is $m$. Thus $Y \vee Y'$ and $X \vee X'$ meet on $m$, in either case.

Suppose now $M_0 = (Y \vee Y') \wedge n$. Then it is obvious that

$$qM_0 = q'M_0 = (X \vee X') \wedge n.$$

Let now $M$ be a point of $n$, different from all of $O$, $E$, $W$ and $M_0$. Let $M' = qM$. Then $M' \neq qM_0$, and hence the triples $\{M,Y,Y'\}$ and $\{M',X,X'\}$ are both independent. Consequently, $\Gamma' = \{W; M,M'; Y,X; Y',X'\}$ is Desarguesian. Once again, the axis of $\Gamma'$ is $m$ as both $(Y \vee Y') \wedge (X \vee X')$ and $(M \vee Y) \wedge (M' \vee X)$ lie on $m$: the former because of our earlier reasoning and the latter because of the assumption $M' = qM$. Thus

$$(M' \vee X') \wedge (M \vee Y') < m$$

showing that $M' = q'M$ also.

Let us now consider the case when $m$ is still equal to $m'$ but the lines $Y \vee X$ and $Y' \vee X'$ are the same. In this case, let us take a line through $W$ distinct from $n$ and $Y \vee X$, and on it take points $Y''$ and $X''$ such that the equation

$$q(Y'',X''; n,m)E = B$$

is satisfied. Using what we proved just now, we infer that

$$q(Y,X; n,m) = q(Y'',X''; n,m)$$

and

$$q(Y',X'; n,m) = q(Y'',X''; n,m).$$

Thus $q = q'$.

It remains to discuss the case when $m \neq m'$. We remark first that the entire lemma is trivial when there are at most 5 points on every line. Hence we may assume that there are at least 6 points on every line and hence at least 6 lines through every point. Suppose first that $m'$ does not pass through $X$ or $Y$. Let $X''$ be a point on $Y \vee X$ such that the equation $q(Y,X''; n,m')E = B$ is satisfied (Fig. 7). To prove that

$$q(Y,X; n,m) = q(Y',X'; n,m'),$$

it is enough to prove that $q(Y,X; n,m) = q(Y,X''; n,m')$, since we know from our discussion in the previous paragraph that

$$q(Y',X'; n,m') = q(Y,X''; n,m').$$

Let $M$ be a point on $n$, distinct from $O$, $E$, and $W$. Write

$$M' = q(Y,X; n,m)M.$$

We want to prove that $M' = q(Y,X''; n,m')M$ also.

To prove this we introduce the point $S = (M \vee Y) \wedge m$. Clearly $M' = (X \vee S) \wedge n$. Obviously it suffices to prove that the points $M'$, $X''$, and $(M \vee Y) \wedge m'$ lie on a line.

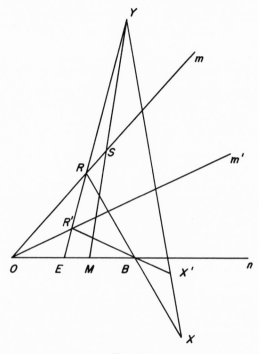

Fɪɢ. 7

However, $\Gamma = \{R; R',Y; B,X; O,S\}$ is Desarguesian. Therefore the points $X'' = (R' \vee B) \wedge (Y \vee X)$, $M' = (O \vee B) \wedge (S \vee X)$, and

$$(O \vee R') \wedge (S \vee Y)$$

lie on a line. Thus

$$q(Y,X; n,m) = q(Y,X''; n,m').$$

As we remarked earlier, this proves that $q(Y,X; n,m) = q(Y',X'; n,m')$.

The case when $m \neq m'$ but $X$ or $Y < m'$ still remains to be described. Since there are at least 6 lines through $O$, we can take a line $\ell$ through $O$ such that $\ell$ is distinct from the lines $O \vee X$, $O \vee Y$, $O \vee X'$, $O \vee Y'$, and $n$. Choose points $X_1$ and $Y_1$ on $\ell$ such that $q(Y_1, X_1; n, \ell)E = B$. By the result in the preceding case we know that $q(Y, X; n, m) = q(Y_1, X_1; n, \ell)$ and $q(Y', X'; n, m') = q(Y_1, X_1; n, \ell)$ as $\ell$ does not pass through any one of $X$, $Y$, $X'$, and $Y'$. Therefore we can conclude finally that

$$q(Y, X; n, m) = q(Y', X'; n, m')$$

in this case also. The proof of the lemma is thus complete.

We write $\mathfrak{M} = \mathfrak{M}(n; O, W)$ for the set consisting of the identity mapping and the general elements of $\mathfrak{P}_2(n)$ which have $O$ and $W$ as their first and second canonical fixed points, respectively. We observe that $q(X, Y; n, m)$ is the inverse of $q(Y, X; n, m)$ and that

$$q(X, Z; n, m)q(Y, X; n, m) = q(Y, Z; n, m).$$

We may then proceed to argue exactly as we did in the proof that $\mathfrak{A}$ is a group (lemma 5.4), and arrive at the following result. We omit the proof as there are no changes in any detail.

**Lemma 5.7.** $\mathfrak{M}$ *is a group of transformations of the set of points lying on* $n$ *onto itself.*

**Lemma 5.8.** *Let $C$ be a point and $t$ and $t'$ two distinct lines containing $C$. Let $A$ and $A'$ be two points on $t'$ such that $C$, $A$, and $A'$ are distinct. Then there exists a unique automorphism $\alpha$ of $\mathscr{L}$ such that (i) $\alpha(P) = P$ for any point $P$ on $t$; (ii) if $X$ is a point not on $t$, $\alpha(X)$ lies on the line $C \vee X$; and (iii) $\alpha(A) = A'$.*

**Proof.** Let $u$ be a line containing $C$ and distinct from $t$. Let $X$, $X'$ be points on $u$ such that $C$, $X$, and $X'$ are distinct. Let $\Gamma(u)$ be the set of all points of $\mathscr{L}$ which do not lie on $u$. We shall define a mapping $\theta_{X,X'}$ which maps $\Gamma(u)$ into itself in the following manner. For any point $B$ in $\Gamma(u)$, the line $B \vee X$ and the point $K = (B \vee X) \wedge t$ are well defined. The line $K \vee X'$ and the point $B' = (K \vee X') \wedge (C \vee B)$ are then well defined. We put (see Fig. 8)

$$(13) \qquad\qquad \theta_{X,X'}(B) = B'.$$

Note that for any $B \in \Gamma(u)$, $C$, $B$, and $\theta_{X,X'}(B)$ lie on a line. It is clear that if $P \in \Gamma(u)$, $\theta_{X,X'}(P) = P$ if and only if $P$ lies on $t$. It is also easy to see that $\theta_{X,X'}$ is one-one and maps $\Gamma(u)$ onto itself. Suppose now that $B$ and $B'$ are related by (13) ($B \in \Gamma(u)$) and that $B$ does not lie on the line $t$.

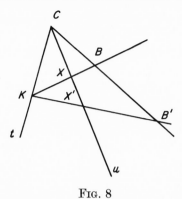

Fɪɢ. 8

Then $v = B \vee B'$ is a well-defined line distinct from $t$ and $u$, and $\theta_{B,B'}$ is, a well-defined mapping of $\Gamma(v)$. We claim that

(14) $\qquad \theta_{X,X'}(D) = \theta_{B,B'}(D) \qquad (D \in \Gamma(v) \cap \Gamma(u)).$

(14) is trivial if $D$ lies on $t$. Let $D$ be a point which lies on none of $t$, $u$, $v$. If $D$ lies on the line $X \vee B$, then

$$\theta_{X,X'}(D) = \theta_{B,B'}(D) = (C \vee D) \wedge (B' \vee X').$$

If $D$ does not lie on the line $X \vee B$ and $D' = \theta_{X,X'}(D)$, then $D'$ does not lie on the line $X' \vee B'$. $\Gamma = \{C; X,X'; B,B'; D,D'\}$ is then Desarguesian. Therefore the points $K = (X \vee B) \wedge (X' \vee B')$, $L = (B \vee D) \wedge (B' \vee D')$, and $M = (X \vee D) \wedge (X' \vee D')$ are distinct and lie on a line. As $\theta_{X,X'}(D) = D'$, $M$ lies on $t$. Thus $L$ lies on $t$ also, which proves that $\theta_{B,B'}(D) = D'$. (14) is thus proved. Note also that $\theta_{B,B'}(X) = X'$.

We now define $\alpha$ as follows. For any point $P$ lying on $t$, we put $\alpha(P) = P$. If $P$ does not lie on $t$ or $t'$, we write $\alpha(P) = \theta_{A,A'}(P)$. If $P$ lies on $t'$, then we take $X$ and $X'$ lying neither on $t$ nor on $t'$ such that $\theta_{A,A'}(X) = X'$, and define $\alpha(P) = \theta_{X,X'}(P)$. We first assert that $\alpha$ is well defined. This is trivial if the plane $\mathscr{L}$ is trivial. Let us assume that $\mathscr{L}$ is nontrivial. Let $X_1$, $X_1'$ be points lying neither on $t$ nor on $t'$ such that $\theta_{A,A'}(X_1) = X_1'$. We want to prove that for $P < t'$, $\theta_{X,X'}(P) = \theta_{X_1,X_1'}(P)$. Suppose that the lines $X \vee X'$ and $X_1 \vee X_1'$ are distinct. Then, we conclude first from (14) that

$$\theta_{A,A'}(X_1) = \theta_{X,X'}(X_1),$$

so that $X_1' = \theta_{X,X'}(X_1)$. We then use (14) once again to conclude that $\theta_{X_1,X_1'}(P) = \theta_{X,X'}(P)$ for $P < t'$. On the other hand, suppose that the lines $X \vee X'$ and $X_1 \vee X_1'$ coincide. We then take a line through $C$ different from $t$, $t'$ and $X \vee X'$, and distinct points $X_2$, $X_2'$ on it different from $C$ such that $\theta_{A,A'}(X_2) = X_2'$. By our earlier result we have

$$\theta_{X,X'}(P) = \theta_{X_2,X_2'}(P) = \theta_{X_1,X_1'}(P).$$

$\alpha$ is therefore well defined. Clearly, $\alpha(A) = A'$. (i) and (ii) are also obvious.

We claim that $\alpha$ is an automorphism of $\mathscr{L}$. $\alpha$ is clearly a one-one map of the set of all points of $\mathscr{L}$ onto itself. We shall prove that $\alpha$ preserves collinearity. Note that by (iii) above, $\alpha$ leaves any line through $C$ invariant. Hence it is enough to prove that the image, under $\alpha$, of any line $k$ not containing $C$ is also a line. Let $k \wedge t = K$, $k \wedge t' = Z$. Let $Z' = \alpha(Z)$. Let $k'$ be the line $K \vee Z'$. We assert that $U < k$ if and only if $\alpha(U) < k'$; this will prove that $k'$ is the image of $k$ under $\alpha$. Suppose $U < k$ and that $U$ is different from $K$ and $Z$. Let $U' = \alpha(U) = \theta_{A,A'}(U)$. Then $Z' = \theta_{U,U'}(Z)$, and hence $U \vee Z$ and $U' \vee Z'$ meet on $t$. In other words, $U' < k'$. If $U' < k'$ is different from $K$ and $Z'$ and we define $U$ by the equation $\alpha(U) = U'$, the same argument shows that $U < k$. The cases $U = K$ or $Z$ being trivial, this completes the argument that $\alpha$ maps $k$ onto $k'$. $\alpha$ is thus an automorphism.

Suppose that $\beta$ is another automorphism of $\mathscr{L}$ satisfying (i) through (iii). It is obvious that $\beta = \alpha = \theta_{A,A'}$ on $\Gamma(t')$. However, then (14) shows that $\beta$ coincides with $\alpha$ on $t'$ also. This completes the proof of the lemma.

We denote the automorphism $\alpha$ by $\alpha(C,t; A,A')$.

**Lemma 5.9.** *Let $m_1$ and $m_2$ be two lines not necessarily distinct. Let $p$ be a projectivity of $m_1$ onto $m_2$. Then there exists an automorphism of $\mathscr{L}$ such that $pX = \alpha(X)$ for all points $X$ lying on $m_1$.*

**Proof.** It is obviously sufficient to prove this when $p$ is a perspectivity and $m_1 \neq m_2$. Let $O = m_1 \wedge m_2$ and let $C$ be the center of perspectivity of $p$. Let $t$ denote the line $C \vee O$. Let $X \neq O$ be a point of $m_1$. Define

$$X' = (C \vee X) \wedge m_2$$

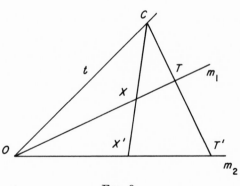

FIG. 9

(see Fig. 9). Let us define $\alpha$ to be the automorphism $\alpha(C,t; X,X')$ whose existence is assured by the preceding lemma. It is clear then that for any point $T$ on $m_1$, $\alpha(T) = T'$, where $T'$ is the point at which $C \vee T$ meets $m_2$.

In other words, α coincides with the perspectivity $p$ on the line $m_1$. This proves the lemma.

**Lemma 5.10.** *Let* $m$ *and* $m'$ *be two lines in* $\mathscr{L}$. *Let* $O$, $E$, $W$ *be three distinct points on* $m$, *and* $O'$, $E'$, $W'$ *three distinct points on* $m'$. *Then there exists an automorphism* α *of* $\mathscr{L}$ *such that* $\alpha(O)=O'$, $\alpha(E)=E'$, *and* $\alpha(W)=W'$.

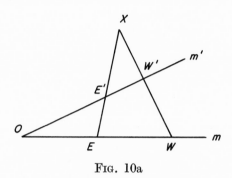

FIG. 10a

**Proof.** In view of lemma 5.9, it is enough to prove the existence of a projectivity of $m$ onto $m'$ which takes $O$, $E$, and $W$ to $O'$, $E'$, and $W'$, respectively. Consider the case $m \neq m'$ first. If the two triples $\{O,E,W\}$ and $\{O',E',W'\}$ have a common element, we may assume, by a renaming, that it is $O=O'$. If then $O=O'$, we define $X=(E \vee E') \wedge (W \vee W')$. The perspectivity of $m$ onto $m'$ with center $X$ takes $O$, $E$, and $W$ to $O'$, $E'$, and $W'$, respectively. On the other hand, if the triples $O$, $E$, $W$ and $O'$, $E'$, $W'$ have no common element, then consider the line $m''=O' \vee W$ (Fig. 10b).

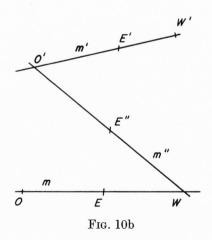

FIG. 10b

By what we have said just now there is a perspectivity of $m$ onto $m''$, which leaves $W$ fixed and takes $E$ to $E''$, and $O$ to $O'$, where $E''$ is some point on the line $m''$, distinct from $O'$ and $W$. Once again there is a perspectivity of $m''$ to $m'$ which leaves $O'$ fixed and takes $W$ to $W'$ and $E''$ to $E'$. If we apply these two perspectivities in succession, we get a projectivity which takes $O$ to $O'$, $E$ to $E'$, and $W$ to $W'$. This finishes the proof of the lemma when $m \neq m'$. The case when $m = m'$ follows by taking a line $m'' \neq m$ and three points $O''$, $E''$, $W''$ on it and constructing in succession projectivities $m \to m'$ and $m'' \to m' = m$.

Suppose now that $\mathscr{L}$ is a Desarguesian plane. Let $n$ be a line of $\mathscr{L}$, and $O$, $E$, $W$ three distinct points on $n$. If $\mathscr{L}$ is trivial, these are the only points on $n$ and we define $\mathbf{D} = \{O, E\}$. We then convert $\mathbf{D}$ into a division ring trivially with $O$ as its zero and $E$ as its unit. Suppose next that $\mathscr{L}$ is nontrivial. For any point $B$ on the line $n$ distinct from $O$ and $W$, we write $p_B$ for the unique element of $\mathfrak{A} = \mathfrak{A}(n, W)$ with $p_B O = B$, i.e., $p_B$ is the unique special projectivity with $W$ as its canonical fixed point and such that $p_B O = B$. Similarly, if $B \neq E$, $O$, or $W$, we write $q_B$ for the unique general projectivity of $\mathfrak{P}_2(n)$, with $O$ and $W$, respectively, as its first and second canonical fixed points and such that $q_B E = B$. We put $p_O = I = q_E$, $I$ denoting the identity map of the set of points of $n$ onto itself.

Let

(15) $$\mathbf{D} = \{X : X \quad \text{a point on } n, X \neq W\}.$$

For $A$, $B$ in $\mathbf{D}$ we write

$$A + B = p_B A,$$

(16)
$$A \cdot B = \begin{cases} O & \text{if } B = O, \\ q_B A & \text{if } B \neq O. \end{cases}$$

Note that $O \cdot B = O$ for all $B \in \mathbf{D}$.

**Theorem 5.11.** $\mathbf{D}$ *is a division ring with* $+$ *as addition,* $\cdot$ *as multiplication.* $O$ *as its zero, and* $E$ *as its unit.*

**Proof.** From lemma 5.4 it follows that the map

$$\gamma : B \to p_B$$

is one-one and maps $\mathbf{D}$ onto $\mathfrak{A}$. Moreover, for $C$, $B \in \mathbf{D}$,

$$p_C p_B(O) = p_C(B)$$
$$= B + C$$
$$= p_{B+C}(O).$$

From lemma 5.4 we know that $p_C p_B \in \mathfrak{A}$ and moreover that $p_C p_B = p_{B+C}$. Since $\mathfrak{A}$ is abelian, we conclude that $+$ converts $\mathbf{D}$ into an abelian group.

$O$ is clearly the identity element of this additive group. On the other hand, using lemmas 5.6 and 5.7 we find that the map

$$\gamma' : B \to q_B$$

is one-one and maps $\mathbf{D} - \{O\}$ onto the group $\mathfrak{M}$ and takes $B \cdot C$ into $q_C q_B$. Consequently, $\cdot$ converts $\mathbf{D} - \{O\}$ into a multiplicative group (not necessarily abelian) with $E$ as its unit.

It remains to establish the distributivity laws, i.e., for any three elements $A$, $B$, and $X \in \mathbf{D}$, we have to prove the relations

$$X \cdot (A + B) = X \cdot A + X \cdot B,$$
$$(A + B) \cdot X = A \cdot X + B \cdot X.$$

These are trivial if $X = O$ or $X = E$. Let us assume therefore that $X \in \mathbf{D} - \{O\}$ but $X \neq E$. We define the mappings $\ell(X)$ and $r(X)$ of the set of points of $n$ onto itself by

$$\ell(X) : A \to X \cdot A, \qquad \ell(W) = W,$$
$$r(X) : A \to A \cdot X, \qquad r(W) = W.$$

Evidently, $\ell(X)$ and $r(X)$ are one-one and onto. $r(X) = q_X$ and is therefore a projectivity of $n$ onto itself. We claim that $\ell(X)$ is also a projectivity of $n$ onto itself. To prove this we proceed as follows. We take a line through $W$ distinct from $n$ and two points $X'$, $Y'$ on it such that $X'$, $Y'$, and $W$ are distinct. Let $a$ be the line $E \vee Y'$, $b$ the line $X \vee Y'$. Let $p$ be the projectivity of $n$ onto itself defined by

$$p = \pi(X'; b,n)\pi(O; a,b)\pi(X'; n,a)$$

(see Fig. 11); here the $\pi$'s denote perspectivities (cf. (10)). Clearly $pO = O$, $pW = W$, and $pE = X$. Suppose now that $A$ is a point of $n$ distinct from $O$, $E$, and $W$. Let $R = \pi(X'; n,a)A$, $S = \pi(O; a,b)R$, and $T = \pi(X'; b,n)S'$. Let $m$ be the line $O \vee R$. Then it is easily seen from Fig. 11 that $T = q(Y',X'; n,m)X$ and $A = q(Y',X'; n,m)E$. Thus $T = X \cdot A$. However, $T = pA$ so that $pA = \ell(X)A$. This proves that $p = \ell(X)$ and hence that $\ell(X)$ is a projectivity of $n$ onto itself. In order to prove the distributivity laws it is therefore enough to show that for any projectivity $\varphi$ of the line $n$ onto itself which fixes $O$ and $W$, the equation

$$\varphi(A + B) = \varphi(A) + \varphi(B) \qquad (A, B \in \mathbf{D})$$

holds. Suppose then $\varphi$ is a projectivity of the line $n$ onto itself which leaves $O$ and $W$ fixed. In view of lemma 5.8 there exists an automorphism $\varphi^{\sim}$ of $\mathscr{L}$ such that $\varphi^{\sim}$ leaves the line $n$ invariant and on it its action coincides with that of $\varphi$. It is obvious that

$$\varphi^{\sim} \cdot p(Y,X; n,m) \cdot \varphi^{\sim -1} = p(\varphi^{\sim}(Y), \varphi^{\sim}(X); n, \varphi^{\sim}(m)).$$

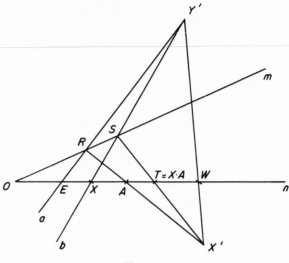

As $\varphi^\sim(O) = O$ and $\varphi^\sim(W) = W$, we conclude from this and the equations (15) and (16) that

$$\varphi^\sim(A + B) = \varphi^\sim(A) + \varphi^\sim(B).$$

This completes the proof that **D** is a division ring with $O$ as its zero and $E$ as its unit and finishes the proof of the theorem.

**Remark.** It can be shown that the division ring is, up to an isomorphism, determined uniquely by $\mathscr{L}$ (cf. lemma 5.13). A proof of this can be given using an argument similar to the one given in the proof of lemma 5.13.

## 3. AFFINE COORDINATES

In this section we shall introduce coordinates for all the points of $\mathscr{L}$ except those which "lie at infinity." If $\mathscr{L}$ is a geometry, an arbitrary hyperplane in $\mathscr{L}$ is chosen and the points on it will be called points at infinity. The construction we use is a simple modification of this procedure; this modification is necessary since we are dealing with a generalized geometry of possibly infinite dimension. The method we use for obtaining the coordinates is based on simple geometrical notions. The reader who desires to have an intuitive picture of what is going on will have to interpret incidences at infinity in terms of parallellism; for instance, lines meeting at infinity would have to be interpreted as being parallel lines. If this is done, he will find that our method of introducing coordinates is nothing but an adaptation, to the present setup, of the construction of the coordinates of a point in ordinary Euclidean space.

It might seem to the reader that we are needlessly complicating the entire scheme by considering generalized geometries and not geometries. The point is that for one of the main theorems of Chapter VII (Piron's characterization of the lattice of closed linear manifolds of a Hilbert space) we need to know the structure of arbitrary generalized geometries since the finite dimensional subspaces of an infinite dimensional Hilbert space form a generalized geometry and not a geometry. Coordinatization theorems which work only for geometries are thus inadequate for our purpose.

Throughout this section $\mathscr{L}$ will denote a fixed generalized geometry whose dimension (possibly infinite) is $\geq 4$. Let $t$ be any line in $\mathscr{L}$, and $a$, a plane of $\mathscr{L}$, such that $t < a$. We know from lemma 5.1 that $\mathscr{L}[0,a]$ is Desarguesian. Therefore on taking three distinct points $O$, $E$, and $W$ on $t$, we may convert the set of all points, which lie on $t$ and are different from $W$, into a division ring, by means of the definitions (15) and (16). This division ring evidently depends, in addition to $t$, $O$, $E$, $W$, on the choice of $a$. We denote it by $\mathbf{D}^a$ and call it the division ring *associated with* $t$, $O$, $E$, $W$, and $a$.

**Lemma 5.12.** *Let $t$ be a line, $O$, $E$, $W$ three distinct points of $t$, and $a$, $b$ two planes containing $t$. Then the identity mapping $P \to P$ is an isomorphism of $\mathbf{D}^a$ onto $\mathbf{D}^b$.*

**Proof.** If $a = b$, there is nothing to prove. Suppose $a \neq b$. Then $\dim(a \wedge b) = 2$ so that $\dim(a \vee b) = 4$. By lemma 5.3 there exists a point $X < a \vee b$ which lies neither on $a$ nor on $b$. We consider the map

$$\alpha : c \to (X \vee c) \wedge b \qquad (c < a)$$

of $\mathscr{L}[0,a]$ into $\mathscr{L}[0,b]$. We know from lemma 5.3 that $\alpha$ is an isomorphism which fixes all the points of the line $t$. Since $\alpha$ transforms projectivities in $\mathscr{L}[0,a]$ into projectivities in $\mathscr{L}[0,b]$, and since it leaves invariant every point of $t$, lemma 5.12 follows at once if we note that (15) and (16) depend only on the lattice structure of the geometry involved.

In view of lemma 5.12 we are entitled to speak of *the division ring associated with* $t$, $O$, $E$, $W$. The same argument leads to the following lemma.

**Lemma 5.13.** *Let $t_i$ be a line and let $O_i$, $E_i$, $W_i$ be three distinct points on $t_i$ $(i = 1, 2)$. Let $\mathbf{D}^i$ be the division ring associated with $t_i$, $O_i$, $E_i$, $W_i$. Suppose that $a = t_1 \vee t_2$ is a plane. If $\alpha$ is any projectivity of $t_1$ onto $t_2$ in the plane $a$ carrying $O_1$, $E_1$, $W_1$ to $O_2$, $E_2$, $W_2$, respectively, then $P \to \alpha(P)$ is an isomorphism of $\mathbf{D}^1$ onto $\mathbf{D}^2$. In particular, $\mathbf{D}^1$ and $\mathbf{D}^2$ are isomorphic.*

**Proof.** The first statement follows from the fact (cf. lemma 5.9) that there exists an automorphism of $\mathscr{L}[0,a]$ which extends $\alpha$. The second statement follows from lemma 5.10 and the first statement.

A set of points of $\mathscr{L}$ is called *independent* if every finite subset of it is independent (cf. Chapter II).

**Lemma 5.14.** *Let $\{P_j\}$ $(j \in J)$ be an independent set of points. For any finite subset $K \subseteq J$, let $u(K)=0$, if $K = \varnothing$ and if $K \neq \varnothing$, let*

$$(17) \qquad u(K) = \bigvee_{j \in K} P_j.$$

*Then the map $K \to u(K)$ has the properties:*

$$(18) \qquad \begin{aligned} u(K \cup K') &= u(K) \vee u(K'), \\ u(K \cap K') &= u(K) \wedge u(K'). \end{aligned}$$

**Proof.** The first equation is obvious. For proving the second, write $K'' = K - (K \cap K')$. Then, as the set $\{P_j\}$ is independent, $u(K') \wedge u(K'')=0$. Consequently,

$$u(K) \wedge u(K') = \{u(K'') \vee u(K \cap K')\} \wedge u(K')$$

$$= u(K \cap K') \qquad \text{(modularity)}.$$

Let $C$ be any independent set of points. We shall say that $C$ is a *basis for* $\mathscr{L}$ if it is maximal. A simple argument using Zorn's lemma shows that $\mathscr{L}$ has a basis. If $C$ is a basis for $\mathscr{L}$ and $P$ any point of $\mathscr{L}$, then there exists a finite set $D \subseteq C$ such that $P < \bigvee_{Q \in D} Q$ (cf. (17)); for if not, the set $\{P\} \cup C$ will be larger and independent. Clearly, if $a \in \mathscr{L}$ is arbitrary, there is a finite set $D \subseteq C$ such that $a < \bigvee_{Q \in D} Q$. Let $O$ be any point of $\mathscr{L}$. By a *frame at* $O$ we mean a pair $(O, \{P_j\}_{j \in J})$ such that $\{O, \{P_j\}_{j \in J}\}$ is a basis for $\mathscr{L}$. Given any point $O$ of $\mathscr{L}$, there exist frames at $O$.

*From now on we shall fix a point $O$ and a frame $(O, \{P_j\}_{j \in J})$ at $O$.* We use the definitions (17) for $u(K)$.

We are now ready to introduce the concept of elements at infinity in $\mathscr{L}$. An element $a \in \mathscr{L}$ is said to *lie (be) at infinity* if there exists a finite set $K \subseteq J$ such that $a < u(K)$. It is to be noted that the notion of being at infinity is relative to a frame in $\mathscr{L}$. The equations (18) show that the subset $\mathscr{L}_\infty$, of all elements of $\mathscr{L}$ which lie at infinity, is closed under the operations $\vee$ and $\wedge$. Moreover, if $a \in \mathscr{L}_\infty$, and $b < a$, then $b \in \mathscr{L}_\infty$. $\mathscr{L}_\infty$ is thus a generalized geometry under the partial ordering induced by $\mathscr{L}$; $\vee$ and $\wedge$ in $\mathscr{L}_\infty$ are the same as in $\mathscr{L}$.

**Lemma 5.15.** *Let* $a \in \mathscr{L}$, $\dim(a) > 0$. *Suppose* $a \notin \mathscr{L}_\infty$. *Then, there exists an element* $a_\infty < a$ *such that*

(19)
  (i) $\dim(a_\infty) = \dim(a) - 1$,
  (ii) $a_\infty \in \mathscr{L}_\infty$,
  (iii) *if* $b \in \mathscr{L}_\infty$ *and* $b < a$, *then* $b < a_\infty$.

$a_\infty$ *is uniquely determined by* (ii) *and* (iii).

**Proof.** There exists a finite set $K \subseteq J$ such that $a < O \vee u(K)$. Since $a \notin \mathscr{L}_\infty$, $a \not< u(K)$. Hence $\dim(a \vee u(K)) > \dim u(K)$ and, consequently, $a \vee u(K) = O \vee u(K)$. Let $a_\infty = a \wedge u(K)$. We then obtain the equation

$$\dim(a_\infty) = \dim(a) + \dim(u(K)) - \dim(O \vee u(K))$$
$$= \dim(a) - 1.$$

Since $a_\infty < u(K)$, $a_\infty \in \mathscr{L}_\infty$. Suppose now that $b \in \mathscr{L}_\infty$ and that $b < a$. If $b \not< a_\infty$, $\dim(b \vee a_\infty) > \dim(a_\infty)$, and hence $\dim(b \vee a_\infty) = \dim(a)$. This implies that $a = b \vee a_\infty \in \mathscr{L}_\infty$, a contradiction. Finally, it is obvious that (ii) and (iii) determine $a_\infty$ uniquely.

**Corollary 5.16.** *If* $P$ *is a point* $\notin \mathscr{L}_\infty$, $K$ *is a finite subset of* $J$, *and* $a = P \vee u(K)$, *then*

(20) $$a_\infty = u(K).$$

Given any $a \in \mathscr{L}$ which does not lie at infinity, it is customary to call $a_\infty$ as the *hyperplane at infinity* on $a$. If $a$ is a line, then $a_\infty$ is a point. It is called the *point at infinity* on $a$. $l = \bigvee_{j \in J} P_j$ is the *hyperplane at infinity of* $\mathscr{L}$, in case $\mathscr{L}$ is a geometry.

The lines $m_j = O \vee P_j$ ($j \in J$) are called the *axes* of the frame $(O, \{P_j\}_{j \in J})$. $P_j$ is obviously the point at infinity on $m_j$. Let $E_j$ be a point on $m_j$, distinct from $O$ and $P_j$. *We choose such* $E_j$ *for each* $j \in J$ *and fix them through the rest of the present section.* Let $\mathbf{D}_j$ be the division ring associated with $m_j$, $O$, $E_j$, $P_j$. The elements of $\mathbf{D}_j$ are the points of $m_j$ which do not lie at infinity. $O$ is the zero and $E_j$ the unit element of $\mathbf{D}_j$. The operations $+$ and $\cdot$ are defined (cf. lemma 5.12) using (15) and (16) in any plane containing $m_j$.

Since it is necessary to work with a single division ring for purposes of coordinatization, we shall now introduce certain isomorphisms between the division rings $\mathbf{D}_j$. Let $j$, $k$ be indices in $J$, $j \neq k$. The lines $E_j \vee E_k$ and $P_j \vee P_k$ are distinct and lie on the plane $O \vee P_j \vee P_k$. Moreover, $P_j \vee P_k$ is at infinity. Therefore they meet at a point, say $P_{jk}$, which is at infinity. The map $X \to \theta_{jk}(X)$, where

(21) $$\theta_{jk}(X) = (X \vee P_{jk}) \wedge m_j \qquad (X < m_k),$$

is a perspectivity of the line $m_k$ onto the line $m_j$ taking $P_k$ to $P_j$. By lemma 5.9 there exists an automorphism $\alpha$ of the plane $O \vee P_j \vee P_k$ such that $\alpha(X) = \theta_{jk}(X)$ for all points $X < m_k$. From (21) it follows that

$\theta_{jk}(O) = O$ and $\theta_{jk}(E_k) = E_j$. From lemma 5.13 we deduce that $\theta_{jk}$ is an isomorphism of the divison ring $\mathbf{D}_k$ onto the division ring $\mathbf{D}_j$.

Note that for $j \neq k$, $P_{jk} = P_{kj}$ and that $P_{jk}$, $P_j$, and $P_k$ are distinct. From (19) it follows that $P_{jk}$ is the point at infinity on the line $E_j \vee E_k$. For $j \in J$ we write $\theta_{jj}$ for the identity automorphism of $\mathbf{D}_j$.

**Lemma 5.17.†** *If $j$, $k$, $r \in J$, then*

(22)
$$\theta_{rj} \circ \theta_{jk} = \theta_{rk}.$$

**Proof.** From (21) it follows at once that $\theta_{jk} \circ \theta_{kj}$ is the identity map of $\mathbf{D}_j$. Hence, in order to prove (22), it may be assumed that $j$, $k$, and $r$ are distinct indices. Let $X \in \mathbf{D}_k$, $Y = \theta_{jk}(X)$, and $Z = \theta_{rj}(Y)$. We must prove that $Z = \theta_{rk}(X)$. If $X = E_k$, then $Y = E_j$ and $Z = E_r$ so that there is nothing more to prove. We may therefore assume that $X \neq O$, $\neq E_k$. Then $Y \neq O$, $\neq E_j$, $Z \neq O$, $\neq E_r$. If $X$, $Y$, and $Z$ were on a line, $O \vee X \vee Y \vee Z$ would be a plane containing $P_j$, $P_k$, and $P_r$ and $O$, which is not possible. $\{X, Y, Z\}$ is thus an independent set. Similarly $\{E_j, E_k, E_r\}$ is independent. Therefore, $\Gamma = \{O; X, E_k; Y, E_j; Z, E_r\}$ is Desarguesian. Let $t$ be the axis of $\Gamma$. By our construction of $\theta_{jk}$, $(E_j \vee E_k) \wedge (Y \vee X) = P_{jk}$, since $Y = \theta_{jk}(X)$. For a similar reason, $P_{rj} = (E_r \vee E_j) \wedge (Z \vee Y)$. Therefore $t = P_{jk} \vee P_{rj}$. We conclude from this that (i) $t$ lies at infinity and (ii) $Z \vee X$ and $E_r \vee E_k$ meet on $t$. As $P_{rk}$ is the point at infinity on $E_r \vee E_k$, we may conclude that $P_{rk} < Z \vee X$. This proves however that $\theta_{rk}(X) = Z$.

The equation (22) shows that there exists a division ring $\mathbf{D}$ and isomorphisms $\varphi_j$ of $\mathbf{D}$ onto $\mathbf{D}_j$ such that the following diagrams are commutative:

(23)

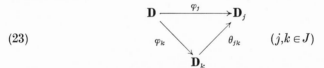

$(j, k \in J)$

† The main thrust of the lemmas from now on is toward a proof of theorem 5.26., the central result of this chapter. If $\mathscr{L}$ is a geometry (thus of finite dimension) then the methods of the preceding section lead to the proof that $\mathscr{L}$ is isomorphic to a suitable projective geometry $\mathscr{L}(V, \mathbf{D})$. It would then appear to be possible to deduce theorem 5.26 for an arbitrary generalized geometry by using the above result for each $\mathscr{L}[0, a]$ $(a \in \mathscr{L})$ and exploiting the fact that $\mathscr{L}$ is an "inductive limit" of the $\mathscr{L}[0, a]$. However, there are difficulties in such an approach. The point is that given $a \in \mathscr{L}$, the division ring associated with $\mathscr{L}[0, a]$ depends on many arbitrary choices; although its isomorphism class depends only on $a$, one cannot define it depending "functorially" on $a$. Careful selections of representatives in these isomorphism classes (of division rings) must therefore be made. But then it turns out that all of this can be achieved in a much simpler and neater fashion if we use the result on $\mathscr{L}[0, a]$ only when $a$ is a plane and attack the problem of "coordinatizing" $\mathscr{L}$ directly, without passing through the intermediate step of considering the case when $\mathscr{L}$ is a geometry. Lemma 5.17 is then the main formal device of ensuring that the division rings are selected with "matching" isomorphisms.

In order to construct $\mathbf{D}$ and the $\varphi_j$, all we have to do is to choose some index $j_0 \in J$ and define $\mathbf{D} = \mathbf{D}_{j_0}$ and $\varphi_j = \theta_{jj_0}$; the equation (22) implies the commutativity of the diagram (23). For that which follows, it does not matter how the $\mathbf{D}$ and $\varphi_j$ are chosen. *We shall fix, for the rest of this section, a division ring* $\mathbf{D}$ *and isomorphisms* $\varphi_j$ *of* $\mathbf{D}$ *onto* $\mathbf{D}_j$ $(j \in J)$ *such that the diagrams* (23) *commute.* We write $O$ for the zero element of $\mathbf{D}$ and $E$ for the unit element of $\mathbf{D}$. Obviously, $\varphi_j(O) = O$ and $\varphi_j(E) = E_j$.

Let $\mathfrak{P}$ be the set of *points* of $\mathscr{L}$ which do not lie at infinity. We shall introduce "coordinates" for each point of $\mathfrak{P}$. Let us denote by $\mathbf{W}$ the space of all functions with finite supports defined on $J$ with values in $\mathbf{D}$. $\mathbf{W}$ becomes a (left) vector space over $\mathbf{D}$ if addition and scalar multiplication (from the left) are defined in the standard fashion. The dimension of $\mathbf{W}$ is precisely the cardinal number of $J$. Suppose now that $P$ is a point from $\mathfrak{P}$. Then there exists a finite set $K \subseteq J$ such that $P < O \vee u(K)$. For any $j \in K$, $(P \vee u(K - \{j\})) \vee (O \vee P_j) = O \vee u(K)$. Since $P \in \mathfrak{P}$, $P \not\leq u(K - \{j\})$ so that $\dim(P \vee u(K - \{j\})) = \dim (u(K))$. Consequently,

$$(24) \qquad \dim\{(P \vee u(K - \{j\})) \wedge m_j\} = 1.$$

$(P \vee u(K - \{j\})) \wedge m_j$ is thus a well-defined point of the line $m_j$. We write

$$(25) \qquad M_j^P = (P \vee u(K - \{j\})) \wedge m_j.$$

If $j \notin K$, we write

$$(26) \qquad M_j^P = O.$$

Finally, if $P = O$, we define, for all $j \in J$,

$$(27) \qquad M_j^O = O \qquad (j \in J).$$

We should have actually written $M_{j,K}^P$ for $M_j^P$, since (25) and (26) involve the set $K$. The next lemma shows that there is no need to do so.

**Lemma 5.18.** *If* $P \in \mathfrak{P}$ *and* $K$ *and* $L$ *are two finite subsets of* $J$ *such that* $P < O \vee u(K)$ *and* $P < O \vee u(L)$, *then* $M_{j,K}^P = M_{j,L}^P$ *for all* $j \in J$.

**Proof.** From (18) it follows that

$$P < (O \vee u(K)) \wedge (O \vee u(L)) = O \vee u(K \cap L).$$

If $j \notin K \cup L$, then $M_{j,K}^P = M_{j,L}^P = O$ by definition. Suppose $j \in K - K \cap L$. Then $M_{j,L}^P = O$ by definition. On the other hand, as

$$P < O \vee u(K \cap L) < O \vee u(K - \{j\}), \qquad O < P \vee u(K - \{j\}),$$

and hence

$$O < (P \vee u(K - \{j\})) \wedge m_j.$$

(24) and (25) now imply that $M_{j,K}^P = O$. A similar argument shows that for $j \in L - K \cap L$, $M_{j,L}^P = M_{j,K}^P = O$. Suppose finally that $j \in K \cap L$. Then

$M_{j,K\cap L}^{P} < m_j \wedge (O \vee u(K \cap (L-\{j\}))) < m_j \wedge (O \vee u(K-\{j\}))$, so that we conclude from (24) and (25) once again that $M_{j,K\cap L}^{P} = M_{j,K}^{P}$. Similarly, $M_{j,L}^{P} = M_{j,K\cap L}^{P}$.

**Lemma 5.19.** $M_j^{P} \in \mathbf{D}_j$ *for any* $P \in \mathfrak{P}$ *and any* $j \in J$.

**Proof.** Let $K$ be a finite set $\subseteq J$ such that $P < O \vee u(K)$. If $M_j^{P} \notin \mathbf{D}_j$, then $M_j^{P} = P_j$ and (26) implies that $j \in K$. However, then

$$P_j < O \vee u(K-\{j\})$$

which leads to the relation $O < P_j \vee u(K-\{j\}) = u(K)$, a contradiction.

Since $M_j^{P} \in \mathbf{D}_j$, $\varphi_j^{-1}(M_j^{P})$ is an element of $\mathbf{D}$ for all $j \in J$. Let $\mathbf{f}_P$ be the function from $J$ to $\mathbf{D}$ defined by

$$(28) \qquad \mathbf{f}_P(j) = \varphi_j^{-1}(M_j^{P}) \qquad (j \in J).$$

Clearly $\mathbf{f}_P$ is an element of the vector space $\mathbf{W}$. Let $\mathbf{0}$ be the origin of $\mathbf{W}$, i.e., the function identically equal to $O$.

**Lemma 5.20.** $\mathbf{f}_O = \mathbf{0}$ *and*

$$(29) \qquad \mathbf{f} : P \to \mathbf{f}_P$$

*is a one-one map of the set* $\mathfrak{P}$ *onto* $\mathbf{W}$.

**Proof.** From (27) we conclude at once that $\mathbf{f}_O = \mathbf{0}$. We now consider points different from $O$. Let $\mathbf{g} \in \mathbf{W}$ be an element such that $\mathbf{g} \neq \mathbf{0}$. Let $J' = \{j_1, \cdots, j_s\}$ be the nonempty finite subset of $J$ such that $\mathbf{g}(j) = O$ if and only if $j \in J - J'$. The element $\varphi_{j_r}(\mathbf{g}(j_r))$ lies in $\mathbf{D}_{j_r}$. Write

$$(30) \qquad Q_r = \varphi_{j_r}(\mathbf{g}(j_r)) \qquad (r = 1, 2, \cdots, s).$$

Then $Q_r$ lies on the line $m_{j_r}$, $Q_r \neq O$, $Q_r \neq P_{j_r}$. Define

$$a_r = Q_r \vee u(J' - \{j_r\}) \qquad (1 \leq r \leq s),$$

$$P = \bigwedge_{r=1}^{s} a_r.$$

We shall prove that $b_t = \bigwedge_{r=1}^{t} a_r$ has dimension $s - t + 1$. Obviously, $b_1 \,(=a_1)$ has dimension $s$ as $Q_r \in \mathfrak{P}$. It is enough to show that

$$\dim(b_{t+1}) + 1 = \dim(b_t)$$

for $1 \leq t \leq s-1$. The sum $b_t \vee a_{t+1}$ contains $P_{j_1}, \cdots, P_{j_s}$ and $Q_{t+1}$ and hence has dimension $s+1$.† Consequently,

$$\dim(b_{t+1}) = \dim(b_t) + \dim(a_{t+1}) - (s+1) = \dim(b_t) - 1.$$

---

† $a_{t+1} \vee b_t < O \vee u(J')$, hence has dimension $\leq s+1$.

This proves that $P$ is a point. We claim that $P \in \mathfrak{P}$. If not, $P$ lies at infinity and, as $P < a_r = Q_r \vee u(J'-\{j_r\})$, we can conclude from (20) that $P < u(J'-\{j_r\})$. Since this is valid for $r = 1, 2, \cdots, s$, and since

$$\bigwedge_{r=1}^{s} u(J'-\{j_r\}) = 0$$

by (18), we have a contradiction. Now, $a_r = Q_r \vee u(J'-\{j_r\})$ and $P < a_r$ so that $P < Q_r \vee u(J'-\{j_r\})$. This implies that $Q_r < P \vee u(J'-\{j_r\})$. On the other hand, $Q_r < m_{j_r}$, so that

$$Q_r < (P \vee u(J'-\{j_r\})) \wedge m_{j_r},$$

from which, we conclude, using (24) and (25), that $M_j^P = Q_j$ for all $j \in J'$. For $j \in J - J'$, $M_j^P = \mathbf{g}(j) = O$ any way, proving that $\mathbf{f}_P = \mathbf{g}$. It now remains to show that $P$ is the only element of $\mathfrak{P}$ whose image under $\mathbf{f}$ is $\mathbf{g}$. If $P'$ is another such point, then $Q_r = M_{j_r}^{P'} < P' \vee u(J'-\{j_r\})$ for $r = 1, 2, \cdots, s$ so that $P' < a_r$ for all $r$. Hence $P' < P = \bigwedge_{r=1}^{s} a_r$, which proves that $P' = P$. This completes the proof of the lemma.

We shall now describe a few properties of the points $M_j^P$ ($j \in J$) associated with $P$. Suppose $K$ and $L$ are finite subsets of $J$ such that $P < O \vee u(K)$ and $P < O \vee u(L)$. Then $P < O \vee u(K \cap L)$. From this observation it follows easily that there exists a unique smallest finite set $K_P$ such that $P < O \vee u(K_P)$. It is obvious that $P < O \vee u(K) \Leftrightarrow K_P \subseteq K$; $K_P = \varnothing$ if and only if $P = O$. Next we consider the case when $K_P$ consists of a single element, say $j$. In this case, $P < O \vee P_j$, and we conclude that $P = M_j^P < m_j$. Since $\{j\} = K_P$, $P \neq O$. Conversely, if $P \in \mathfrak{P}$ lies on $m_{j_0}$ and is different from $O$, $K_P = \{j_0\}$. If $K_P$ has at least two elements, $P$ does not lie on any of the axes $m_j$ of our frame. Note also that for $j \in K_P$, $\mathbf{f}_P(j) \neq O$; for, if $\mathbf{f}_P(j) = O$,

$$O < P \vee u(K_P - \{j\}),$$

implying

$$P < O \vee u(K_P - \{j\});$$

and this contradicts minimality of $K_P$.

**Lemma 5.21.** *Let $P \in \mathfrak{P}$ be different from $O$ and let $R$ denote the point at infinity on the line $O \vee P$. Suppose $j \in J$ is some index such that $P \neq M_j^P$ (i.e., $P \nless m_j$). Then, for any point $Q \in \mathfrak{P}$ on the line $O \vee P$ which is different from $O$, one has $Q \neq M_j^Q$. Moreover, the points at infinity on the lines $P \vee M_j^P$ and $Q \vee M_j^Q$ are the same, say $S$, and this point $S$ is given by*

$$(31) \qquad S = (R \vee P_j) \wedge u(K-\{j\}),$$

*where $K$ is any finite subset of $J$ such that $P < O \vee u(K)$. In particular, $S < u(K-\{j\})$.*

**Proof.** If $Q < O \vee P$ with $Q \neq O$ is such that $Q = M_j^Q$, then $Q < m_j$. This would imply that $P < m_j$, which is a contradiction, since $P \neq M_j^P$. Let $R$

be the point at infinity on $P \vee O$ and let $j \in J$ be such that $P \neq M_j^P$. Let $S$ be the point at infinity on $P \vee M_j^P$. Then, as $P \vee M_j^P < P \vee u(K - \{j\})$ ($K$ being a finite set such that $P < O \vee u(K)$), $S < u(K - \{j\})$. On the other hand, $S$ is a point at infinity on the plane $O \vee P \vee M_j^P$ whose line at infinity is $R \vee P_j$. Thus $S < R \vee P_j$. Consequently,

$$S < (R \vee P_j) \wedge u(K - \{j\}).$$

The right side of this relation is an element of dimension $\leq 2$; if it is of dimension 2, $P_j < u(K - \{j\})$ which is not possible. This proves (31). We now notice that $R$ is also the point at infinity on $O \vee Q$, and as $Q < O \vee u(K)$, we conclude, using the same argument as for $P$, that the point at infinity on $Q \vee M_j^Q$ is given by the right side of (31). Thus $S$ is also the point at infinity on $Q \vee M_j^Q$.

**Lemma 5.22.** *Let $P \in \mathfrak{P}$ and $O \neq P$. Then for a point $Q \in \mathfrak{P}$ to lie on the line $O \vee P$, it is necessary and sufficient that there exist an $M \in \mathbf{D}$ such that*

$$(32) \qquad\qquad \mathbf{f}_Q = M \cdot \mathbf{f}_P.$$

*Given $P$, $M$ is uniquely determined by $Q$, and $M = O$ if and only if $Q = O$.*

**Proof.** Let $P \in \mathfrak{P}$, $O \neq P$. Let $K = K_P$ be the smallest finite set $\subseteq J$ such that $P < O \vee u(K)$. Suppose $Q < O \vee P$, $Q \in \mathfrak{P}$. If $Q = O$, $\mathbf{f}_Q = \mathbf{0}$ and we may take $M = O$ in (32). Let $Q \neq O$. Since $Q < O \vee u(K)$, $\mathbf{f}_Q(j)$ vanishes for $j \in J - K$, and hence the existence of $M$ satisfying (32) is trivial if $K$ consists of only one element. We may therefore assume that $K$ has at least two elements. As $K_Q = K$, obviously, $\mathbf{f}_Q(j) \neq O$ for all $j \in K$. Hence, for each $j \in K$, there exists a unique nonzero $M_j \in \mathbf{D}_j$ such that

$$(33) \qquad\qquad M_j^Q = M_j \cdot M_j^P \qquad (j \in K).$$

As $K$ has at least two elements, $P$ does not lie on any $m_j$, so that $P \neq M_j^P$ for any $j \in K$. The existence of $M \in \mathbf{D}$ satisfying (32) would follow if we are able to show that for any two distinct indices $j, k \in K$,

$$(34) \qquad\qquad \theta_{jk}(M_k) = M_j;$$

for, if this be the case, the commutativity of the diagrams (23) would ensure the existence of $M \in \mathbf{D}$ such that $\varphi_j(M) = M_j$ for all $j \in K$; since $M_j^P = M_j^Q = O$ for $j \in J - K$, $M$ would satisfy (32).

We now proceed to the proof of (34). We consider two cases.

*Case 1:* For some $j \in K$, $M_j^Q = M_j^P$. Since $P \neq M_j^P$ and since the points at infinity on the lines $P \vee M_j^P$ and $Q \vee M_j^Q$ are identical, it follows that $P$, $Q$, and $M_j^P$ lie on a line. If $P \neq Q$, this would mean that $M_j^P < O \vee P$, an impossibility. Thus $P = Q$ so that $M_k = E_k$, the identity of $\mathbf{D}_k$ for all $k \in K$.

*Case 2:* For each $j \in K$, $O$, $M_j{}^P$, and $M_j{}^Q$ are distinct. Let now $j$, $k \in K$ be two distinct indices. We observe that $P$, $M_j{}^P$, and $M_k{}^P$ are independent. Otherwise, $P < O \vee P_j \vee P_k$ so that $K = \{j,k\}$, and then (31) would imply that the point at infinity on $P \vee M_j{}^P$ is just $P_k$. This would then lead to the relation $M_k{}^P < P \vee P_k$ or $P < m_k$, which is absurd. The same argument applied to $Q$ shows that $M_j{}^Q$, $M_k{}^Q$, and $Q$ are independent. Consequently, $\Gamma = \{O \; ; \; P,Q; \; M_j{}^P, M_j{}^Q; \; M_k{}^P, M_k{}^Q\}$ is Desarguesian. By lemma 5.21, the lines $P \vee M_j{}^P$ and $Q \vee M_j{}^Q$ have the same point at infinity, and hence they meet at infinity. Similarly, $Q \vee M_k{}^Q$ and $P \vee M_k{}^P$ meet at infinity. The axis of $\Gamma$ thus lies at infinity. This means that

$$(M_j{}^P \vee M_k{}^P) \wedge (M_j{}^Q \vee M_k{}^Q) = T$$

is a point at infinity. Since $T < O \vee P_j \vee P_k$, $T$ lies on the line $P_j \vee P_k$. If $\pi$ denotes, in the plane $O \vee P_j \vee P_k$, the perspectivity $\pi(T; m_j, m_k)$, $\pi(M_j{}^P) = M_k{}^P$, and $\pi(M_j{}^Q) = M_k{}^Q$. Therefore, from the definition (21) of $\theta_{jk}$, $\theta_{jk} \circ \pi$ is a *general* element of $\mathfrak{P}_2(m_j)$ having $O$ and $P_j$ as its first and second canonical fixed points. By the definition of multiplication in $\mathbf{D}_j$, this means that there exists a nonzero $N_j \in \mathbf{D}_j$ such that $\theta_{jk} \circ \pi$ is *right multiplication* by $N_j$. Thus $\theta_{jk}(M_k{}^Q) = M_j{}^Q N_j$ and $\theta_{jk}(M_k{}^P) = M_j{}^P N_j$. This proves that $\theta_{jk}(M_k) = M_j$. Equations (34) and (32) are now proved.

We now come to the converse. The cases $M = O$ or $E$ are trivial. Let $P$, $Q \in \mathfrak{P}$ be distinct points different from $O$ and let $M \in \mathbf{D}$ be a nonzero element such that

$$\mathbf{f}_Q = M \cdot \mathbf{f}_P.$$

We want to show that $Q$ lies on the line $O \vee P$. Let $K = K_P$ be the smallest subset of $J$ such that $\mathbf{f}_P(j) = 0$ for $j \notin K$. Then $\mathbf{f}_Q(j)$ and $\mathbf{f}_P(j)$ are both nonzero for $j \in K$. If $K$ consists of only one index, say $k$, then $Q$ and $P$ both lie on the line $m_k$. We may therefore assume that $K$ has at least two elements. Then for any $j \in K$, $P \neq M_j{}^P$ and $Q \neq M_j{}^Q$. Choose a $j_0 \in K$. Let $S$ be the point at infinity on the line $P \vee M_{j_0}{}^P$. Since $S$, $M_{j_0}{}^Q$, and $P$ are distinct points in the plane $O \vee P \vee M_{j_0}{}^P$, it is clear that the lines $S \vee M_{j_0}{}^Q$ and $O \vee P$ have a point in common, say $Q'$. $Q'$ lies on $O \vee P$ and is obviously different from $P$ and $S$. Since $S$ is the point at infinity on $M_{j_0}{}^Q \vee S$, $Q' \in \mathfrak{P}$. Now $Q' \vee M_{j_0}{}^{Q'}$ has also $S$ as its point at infinity (cf. lemma 5.21), and so, $M_{j_0}{}^{Q'} = M_{j_0}{}^Q$. As $Q' < O \vee P$, there exists, by the first half of the lemma, an $M' \in \mathbf{D}$ such that $\mathbf{f}_{Q'} = M' \cdot \mathbf{f}_P$. Since $M_{j_0}{}^{Q'} = M_{j_0}{}^Q$ we may conclude that $\varphi_{j_0}(M') = \varphi_{j_0}(M)$ and hence that $M' = M$. This proves that $Q' = Q$. The uniqueness of $M$ follows from lemma 5.20. The proof is complete.

**Lemma 5.23.** *Let* $O' \in \mathfrak{P}$ *be a point different from* $O$, *and* $t'$ *a line through* $O'$ *not containing* $O$. *Let* $U$, $R$ *be the points at infinity on the lines* $O \vee O'$

*and $t'$, respectively, and let $t$ be the line $O \vee R$. If $P$ is any point of $\mathfrak{P}$ lying on the line $t$, and*

$$(35) \qquad\qquad P' = (U \vee P) \wedge t',$$

*then*

$$(36) \qquad\qquad \mathbf{f}_{P'} = \mathbf{f}_P + \mathbf{f}_{O'}.$$

*Conversely, suppose that for some $\mathbf{g} \in \mathbf{W}$, $\mathbf{f}_{P'} = \mathbf{g} + \mathbf{f}_{O'}$ for some point $P' \in \mathfrak{P}$ on the line $t'$. Then $\mathbf{g} = \mathbf{f}_P$ for some $P \in \mathfrak{P}$ lying on $t$, and $P$ and $P'$ are related as in (35).*

**Proof.** Let $P$ be a point of $\mathfrak{P}$ lying on $t$. The lines $U \vee P$ and $t'$ are distinct and lie on the plane $O \vee U \vee R$. Hence they meet in the point $P'$, given by (35). We shall prove (36). It suffices to prove that

$$(37) \qquad\qquad M_j{}^{P'} = M_j{}^{O'} + M_j{}^{P}$$

for all $j \in J$. Let $K$ be a finite subset of $J$ such that $O'$, $P$, and $P'$ are all $< O \vee u(K)$. For $j \notin K$, (37) is trivial as all three terms are equal to $O$. Let $j \in K$. We shall consider three cases.

*Case 1:* $O' < O \vee u(K - \{j\})$. Then $O < O' \vee u(K - \{j\})$. From (20) we conclude that the point $U$ at infinity on $O \vee O'$ satisfies the relation $U < u(K - \{j\})$. Consequently, as $P' < P \vee U$,

$$P' \vee u(K - \{j\}) < P \vee U \vee u(K - \{j\})$$
$$< P \vee u(K - \{j\}),$$

from which we conclude that $M_j{}^{P'} < M_j{}^{P}$. Hence $M_j{}^{P'} = M_j{}^{P}$. However, as $O < O' \vee u(K - \{j\})$, $M_j{}^{O'} = O$. Therefore (37) is proved in this case.

*Case 2:* $R < O \vee u(K - \{j\})$. Since $R$ lies at infinity, $R < u(K - \{j\})$. Hence $O < P \vee R < P \vee u(K - \{j\})$, which shows that $M_j{}^{P} = O$. However,

$$O' \vee u(K - \{j\}) < P' \vee R \vee u(K - \{j\})$$
$$< P' \vee u(K - \{j\}),$$

from which we deduce as before that $M_j{}^{O'} = M_j{}^{P'}$. This proves (37) in this case.

*Case 3:* Neither $O'$ nor $R$ lies in $O \vee u(K - \{j\})$. Since $R$ is on $t'$, this means that $t' \not< O \vee u(K - \{j\})$. As $t' < O \vee u(K)$, $t' \wedge (O \vee u(K - \{j\}))$ is a point, say $O''$. Clearly, $O''$ is different from $O$ and $R$; in particular, $O'' \in \mathfrak{P}$ (see Fig. 12). Let $U'$ be the point at infinity on $O \vee O''$, and $P''$ and $O_1$ be, respectively, the points on the line $O \vee R$ where $U' \vee P'$ and $U' \vee O'$ meet it. From case 1 we know, as $O'' < O \vee u(K - \{j\})$, that

$$(38) \qquad\qquad M_j{}^{P'} = M_j{}^{P''}, \qquad M_j{}^{O'} = M_j{}^{O_1}.$$

In the plane $O \vee U \vee U'$ (which contains all the points in sight), the special projectivity $p(U, U'; t, t')$ transforms $O$ to $O_1$ and $P$ to $P''$. If the line $t$

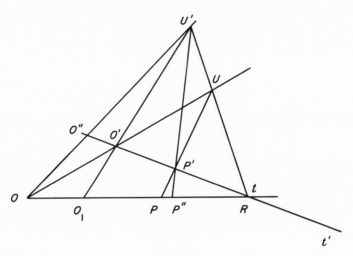

FIG. 12

coincides with the line $m_j$, then (16) already proves that $M_j^{P''} = M_j^P + M_j^{O_1}$ and (37) follows from (38). If $t \neq m_j$, then the points $O_1$, $P$, and $P''$ are different from $M_j^{O_1}$, $M_j^P$, and $M_j^{P''}$, respectively. Let us now consider the plane $t \vee m_j$. The points at infinity on $O_1 \vee M_j^{O_1}$, $P \vee M_j^P$, and $P'' \vee M_j^{P''}$ are, by lemma 5.21, all the same, say $T$. Then, the perspectivity of $t$ to $m_j$, in $t \vee m_j$, with center $T$, takes $O_1$, $P$, and $P''$ to $M_j^{O_1}$, $M_j^P$, and $M_j^{P''}$, respectively. Lemma 5.13 now implies that

$$(39) \qquad M_j^{P''} = M_j^P + M_j^{O_1}.$$

(39) and (38) imply (37).

We now come to the converse. Let $\mathbf{g} \in \mathbf{W}$ be such that $\mathbf{f}_{P'} = \mathbf{g} + \mathbf{f}_{O'}$, where $P' \in \mathfrak{P}$ lies on $t'$. Define $P$ by $(U \vee P') \wedge t$. Then $P$ and $P'$ are related by (35) and by the first half of this lemma, $\mathbf{f}_P = \mathbf{f}_{P'} - \mathbf{f}_{O'} = \mathbf{g}$. This proves everything.

**Corollary 5.24.** *Let $P_1'$, $P_2'$, $P_3'$ be three distinct points in $\mathfrak{P}$. Then they are collinear if and only if for some nonzero $A \in \mathbf{D}$,*

$$(40) \qquad \mathbf{f}_{P_3'} = A \cdot \mathbf{f}_{P_1'} + (E - A) \cdot \mathbf{f}_{P_2'},$$

*$E$ being the unit of $\mathbf{D}$.*

**Proof.** Assume first that the $P_i'$ lie on a line $t'$. If $t'$ contains $O$, then it follows from lemma 5.22 that for suitable $A_i \in \mathbf{D}$ (with $P_3' \neq O$; the case $P_3' = O$ is trivial),

$$\mathbf{f}_{P_i'} = A_i \cdot \mathbf{f}_{P_3'} \qquad (i = 1, 2).$$

Since $P_1'$, $P_2'$, and $P_3'$ are distinct, $E$, $A_1$, and $A_2$ are distinct elements of **D**. Clearly, (40) is satisfied with $A = (E - A_2) \cdot (A_1 - A_2)^{-1}$. We may thus assume that $O \not< t'$ and apply lemma 5.23 with $O' = P_2'$, using the same notation. If $P_1$ and $P_3$ are the points on $O \vee R$ corresponding to $P_1'$ and $P_3'$, we have

$$\mathbf{f}_{P_3'} = \mathbf{f}_{P_2'} + \mathbf{f}_{P_3} \quad \text{and} \quad \mathbf{f}_{P_1'} = \mathbf{f}_{P_2'} + \mathbf{f}_{P_1}.$$

By lemma 5.22 there is a nonzero $A \in \mathbf{D}$ such that

$$\mathbf{f}_{P_3} = A \cdot \mathbf{f}_{P_1}.$$

From this it is trivial to obtain (40). To prove the converse, let (40) be satisfied and let $t'$ be the line $P_1' \vee P_2'$. The case when $O < t'$ is trivial and so we consider the case $O \not< t'$. Write $O' = P_2'$ and define $P_1$ corresponding to $P_1'$. If $P_3$ is the point on the line $O \vee P_1$ such that $\mathbf{f}_{P_3} = A \cdot \mathbf{f}_{P_1}$, it follows that $\mathbf{f}_{P_3'} = \mathbf{f}_{P_2'} + \mathbf{f}_{P_3}$. Lemma 5.23 now implies that $P_3' < t'$.

## 4. HOMOGENEOUS COORDINATES

The detailed analysis of the set of points which do not lie at infinity, carried out in the previous section, enables one to introduce the so-called homogeneous coordinates for all the points of $\mathscr{L}$. Let $I$ be an index set containing $J$ and exactly one more element, denoted by $\infty$. Let **V** be the left vector space of all **D**-valued functions on $I$ with finite supports. We denote by $\mathscr{L}'$ the generalized geometry of all finite dimensional subspaces of **V**. Our aim in this section is to set up an isomorphism of $\mathscr{L}$ with $\mathscr{L}'$.

Consider a point $P \in \mathfrak{P}$. We define the function $\mathbf{g}_P$ on $I$ as follows:

$$(41) \qquad \mathbf{g}_P(j) = \begin{cases} \mathbf{f}_P(j), & j \in J, \\ E, & j = \infty \end{cases}.$$

Let

$$(42) \qquad \gamma(P) = \mathbf{D} \cdot \mathbf{g}_P.$$

$\gamma(P)$ is then a ray in **V** and is therefore a point of $\mathscr{L}'$. Suppose next that $P$ is a point of $\mathscr{L}$ lying at infinity. Let $Q$ be a point on the line $O \vee P$ such that $Q \in \mathfrak{P}$, $Q \neq O$. We write

$$(43) \qquad \mathbf{g}_{P,Q}(j) = \begin{cases} \mathbf{f}_Q(j), & j \in J \\ 0, & j = \infty \end{cases}$$

and define

$$(44) \qquad \gamma(P) = \mathbf{D} \cdot \mathbf{g}_{P,Q}.$$

If $Q' \in \mathfrak{P}$ is another point of the line $O \vee P$ which is different from $O$, it is clear that $\mathbf{g}_{P,Q'} = M \cdot \mathbf{g}_{P,Q}$ for some nonzero $M \in \mathbf{D}$ (lemma 5.22). This shows that $\gamma(P)$ is well defined by (44) and depends only on $P$. Equations

(41) through (44) show that, for a point $P$ to lie in $\mathfrak{P}$, it is necessary and sufficient that the ray $\gamma(P)$ not contain nonzero functions vanishing at $\infty$.

**Lemma 5.25.** $P \to \gamma(P)$ *is a one-one collinearity preserving map of the set of all points of $\mathscr{L}$ onto the set of all points of $\mathscr{L}'$.*

**Proof.** We show first that $\gamma$ is one-one and onto. Suppose that $\mathbf{g} \in \mathbf{V}$ is nonzero. Let $\xi$ be the point $\mathbf{D} \cdot \mathbf{g}$ of $\mathscr{L}'$. Assume first that $\mathbf{g}(\infty) \neq O$. Then, replacing $\mathbf{g}$ by $(\mathbf{g}(\infty))^{-1} \cdot \mathbf{g}$ we may assume that $\mathbf{g}(\infty) = E$. Since $\mathbf{f}$, as defined by (29), maps $\mathfrak{P}$ onto $\mathbf{W}$, there exists a point $P \in \mathfrak{P}$ such that $\mathbf{f}_P(j) = \mathbf{g}(j)$ for all $j \in J$. Clearly, $\mathbf{g}_P = \mathbf{g}$ and therefore $\gamma(P) = \xi$. The uniqueness of $P$ is obvious in this case. On the other hand, suppose that $\mathbf{g}(\infty) = O$. Let $Q$ be the point of $\mathfrak{P}$ such that $\mathbf{f}_Q(j) = \mathbf{g}(j)$ for all $j \in J$. Since $\mathbf{g}$ is nonzero, $Q \neq O$ and hence the line $O \vee Q$ is well defined. Let $P$ be the point at infinity on $O \vee Q$. It is obvious that $\gamma(P) = \xi$. Suppose $P'$ is another point of $\mathscr{L}$ such that $\gamma(P') = \xi$. Since $\mathbf{g}(\infty) = O$, $P'$ lies at infinity. Let $Q'$ be a point of $\mathfrak{P}$ different from $O$ lying on $O \vee P'$. Then $\mathbf{f}_{Q'}$ is a multiple of $\mathbf{f}_Q$ and hence $Q < O \vee Q' < O \vee P'$. Thus $P' < O \vee Q$ and therefore coincides with $P$.

We shall complete the proof of the lemma by showing that $\gamma$ preserves collinearity. Let $P_1$, $P_2$, $P_3$ be three distinct points of $\mathscr{L}$. We must prove that they are collinear if and only if the $\gamma(P_i)$ are collinear in $\mathscr{L}'$. Three cases arise.

*Case 1:* $P_i \in \mathfrak{P}$ for all $i$. In this case, the desired result follows from corollary 5.24. In fact, that corollary, taken with (41), implies that the $P_i$ are collinear in $\mathscr{L}$ if and only if for some nonzero $A \in \mathbf{D}$, $\mathbf{g}_{P_3} = A \cdot \mathbf{g}_{P_1} + (E - A) \cdot \mathbf{g}_{P_2}$. It is easy to verify that this is also the condition that $\gamma(P_1)$, $\gamma(P_2)$, and $\gamma(P_3)$ are collinear in $\mathscr{L}'$.

*Case 2:* Exactly one of the $P_i$, say $P_3$, lies at infinity. Let $\mathbf{g}_i \in \mathbf{V}$ be such that (i) $\mathbf{g}_i(\infty) = E$ and (ii) $\gamma(P_i) = \mathbf{D} \cdot \mathbf{g}_i$ ($i = 1, 2$). Let $Q$ be a point on $O \vee P_3$ different from $O$ and $P_3$ and let $\mathbf{g}_3 = \mathbf{g}_{P_3, Q}$ (cf. (43)). Then $\gamma(P_3) = \mathbf{D} \cdot \mathbf{g}_3$. It is trivial to show that $\gamma(P_1)$, $\gamma(P_2)$, and $\gamma(P_3)$ are collinear if and only if there exists an $M \in \mathbf{D}$ such that

$$\mathbf{f}_Q = M \cdot (\mathbf{f}_{P_2} - \mathbf{f}_{P_1}).$$

From lemma 5.23 we easily conclude that this is precisely the condition for $Q$ to lie on the line joining $O$ to the point at infinity on $P_1 \vee P_2$, i.e., for $P_3$ to lie on $P_1 \vee P_2$.

*Case 3:* $P_2$ and $P_3$ are both points at infinity. Suppose $P_1$, $P_2$, $P_3$ are collinear. Then $P_1$ is also at infinity. We can choose points $Q_i \neq O$ in $\mathfrak{P}$ such that (i) $Q_1 < O \vee P_1$, $Q_2 < O \vee P_2$ and (ii) $Q_1$, $Q_2$, and $P_3$ are collinear. Let $Q_3 \neq O$ be a point of $O \vee P_3$ such that $Q_3 \in \mathfrak{P}$. By lemma 5.23,

$$(45) \qquad\qquad \mathbf{f}_{Q_3} = M \cdot (\mathbf{f}_{Q_2} - \mathbf{f}_{Q_1})$$

for some $M \in \mathbf{D}$. (45) and (43) show now that $\gamma(P_1)$, $\gamma(P_2)$, and $\gamma(P_3)$ are collinear. Conversely, let $\gamma(P_1)$, $\gamma(P_2)$, and $\gamma(P_3)$ be collinear. Let $Q_i \in \mathfrak{P}$, $Q_i \neq O$ be a point on $O \vee P_i$ ($i = 1, 2, 3$). Then for some $M$, $N \neq O$ in $\mathbf{D}$,

$$\mathbf{f}_{Q_3} = M \cdot \mathbf{f}_{Q_1} + N \cdot \mathbf{f}_{Q_2}.$$

By lemma 5.22 there exists a point $Q_j' \in \mathfrak{P}$ ($j = 1, 2$) on the line $O \vee Q_j$, $Q_j' \neq O$ such that

$$\mathbf{f}_{Q_1'} = -M \cdot \mathbf{f}_{Q_1},$$
$$\mathbf{f}_{Q_2'} = +N \cdot \mathbf{f}_{Q_2}.$$

Then

$$\mathbf{f}_{Q_3} = \mathbf{f}_{Q_2'} - \mathbf{f}_{Q_1'}.$$

If $X$ is the point at infinity on $Q_1' \vee Q_2'$, lemma 5.23 and this last equation tell us that $Q_3$ has on $O \vee X$. Thus $X = P_3$. This implies that $P_1$, $P_2$, $P_3$ are collinear and completes the proof of the lemma.

Lemmas 5.2 and 5.25 imply the fundamental theorem of this chapter:

**Theorem 5.26.** *Let $\mathscr{L}$ be a generalized geometry whose dimension (possibly infinite) is at least 4. Then there exists a division ring $\mathbf{D}$ and a vector space $\mathbf{V}$ over $\mathbf{D}$ such that $\mathscr{L}$ is isomorphic to the generalized geometry of all finite dimensional subspaces of $\mathbf{V}$.*

# PART TWO

# THE LOGIC OF QUANTUM MECHANICS

# CHAPTER VI

# THE LOGIC OF A QUANTUM MECHANICAL SYSTEM

## 1. LOGICS

Let $\mathfrak{S}$ be any quantum mechanical system. We have seen that one can associate with $\mathfrak{S}$ the partially ordered set $\mathscr{L}(\mathfrak{S})$ of all experimentally verifiable propositions concerning $\mathfrak{S}$. The partial ordering is that induced by the implication relation. Moreover, the map, which associates with any element of $\mathscr{L}(\mathfrak{S})$ its negation, behaves very much like an ortho-complementation. This leads one to introduce axiomatically a class of partially ordered sets and to study their properties. We call these systems *logics*. The basic assumption of modern quantum theory can then be described (if we anticipate some terminology) by saying that $\mathscr{L}(\mathfrak{S})$ is a standard logic.

Let $\mathscr{L}$ be a lattice under a partial ordering $<$. By an *orthocomplementation* of $\mathscr{L}$ we mean a mapping

$$(\perp) : a \to a^\perp$$

of $\mathscr{L}$ into itself such that

(1)

    (i)   $\perp$ is one-one and maps $\mathscr{L}$ onto itself,
    (ii)  $a < b$ implies $b^\perp < a^\perp$,
    (iii) $a^{\perp\perp} = a$   for all $a$,
    (iv) $a \wedge a^\perp = 0$   for all $a$,
    (v)  $a \vee a^\perp = 1$   for all $a$.

We note that the relations $0^\perp = 1$ and $1^\perp = 0$ are easy consequences of (ii). Moreover it follows easily from (iii) that $\perp$ is one-one and onto, so that (iii) $\Rightarrow$ (i). Finally, we observe that (ii), (iii), and (iv) imply (v). In fact, let $a \in \mathscr{L}$ and $b = a \vee a^\perp$. Since both $a$ and $a^\perp$ are $<b$ and $a^{\perp\perp} = a$, (ii) implies that $b^\perp < a$ and $b^\perp < a^\perp$. Hence $b^\perp < a \wedge a^\perp = 0$ or $b = b^{\perp\perp} = 1$. A lattice $\mathscr{L}$, with an orthocomplementation $\perp (a \to a^\perp)$, is said to be a *logic* if

(2)

    (i)   for any countably infinite sequence $a_1, a_2, \cdots$ of elements of $\mathscr{L}$, $\bigvee_n a_n$ and $\bigwedge_n a_n$ exist in $\mathscr{L}$,
    (ii)  if $a_1, a_2 \in \mathscr{L}$ and $a_1 < a_2$, there exists an element $b \in \mathscr{L}$ such that $b < a_1^\perp$ and $b \vee a_1 = a_2$.

Before proceeding further we make the observation that if $a_1 < a_2$, the element $b$ whose existence is postulated in (ii) of (2) is unique and is in fact equal to $a_1^\perp \wedge a_2$. To see this, let us write $b_1 = a_1^\perp \wedge a_2$. Since $b < a_1^\perp$ and $b < a_2$, we have $b < b_1$. Therefore, using (ii) of (2) again, we find a $d \in \mathscr{L}$ such that $d < b^\perp$ and $d \vee b = b_1$. Since $d < b^\perp$, $b < d^\perp$. Further, $d < b_1 < a_1^\perp$ so that $a_1 < d^\perp$. Therefore, $a_1 \vee b = a_2 < d^\perp$ which implies that $d < a_2^\perp$. Moreover, $d < b_1 < a_2$ also. Consequently, $d < a_2 \wedge a_2^\perp = 0$ which means that $b_1 = b \vee d = b$.

The element $b = a_1^\perp \wedge a_2$ of (ii) of (2) will often be written as $a_2 - a_1$. For any $a \in \mathscr{L}$, we call $a^\perp$ the *orthogonal complement* of $a$ in $\mathscr{L}$. If $a < b^\perp$, then $b < a^\perp$; we shall then say that $a$ and $b$ are *orthogonal* and write $a \perp b$. Suppose $a, b \in \mathscr{L}$ are two elements such that $a < b$, $a \neq b$. As in Chapter V, we write

(3)            $\mathscr{L}[a,b] = \{c : c \in \mathscr{L}, \quad a < c < b\}.$

Then under the partial ordering inherited from $\mathscr{L}$, $\mathscr{L}[0,b]$ becomes a lattice, in which countable unions and intersections exist and whose zero element is $0$ and unit element is $b$. If we define, for any $x$ in $\mathscr{L}[0,b]$, its orthogonal complement $x'$ by $x' = x^\perp \wedge b$, then it can be shown that $\mathscr{L}[0,b]$ equipped with the orthocomplementation $x \to x'$ is a logic (cf. corollary 6.3).

The central assumption that one makes in any quantum mechanical application is that *the set of experimentally verifiable propositions is a logic.* The only thing that may be open to serious question in this is assumption (i) of (2) which forces any two elements of $\mathscr{L}$ to have a lattice sum, the others may be regarded as technical necessities. We can offer no really convincing phenomenological argument to support this (cf. Birkhoff-von Neumann [1]). If we omit the assumption that $\mathscr{L}$ is a lattice the axioms become so weak that it is very difficult to avoid pathology in any mathematical discussion. We point out also that every calculation in quantum mechanics is based on assumptions which not only imply that the set of experimentally verifiable propositions is a logic but in fact a very special one.

We shall now make a few general remarks. If $\mathscr{L}_1$ and $\mathscr{L}_2$ are two logics, an *injection* of $\mathscr{L}_1$ into $\mathscr{L}_2$ is a map $f(a \to f(a))$ of $\mathscr{L}_1$ into $\mathscr{L}_2$ such that (i) $f$ is one-one, $f(0) = 0$, $f(1) = 1$; (ii) if $a_1, a_2, \cdots$ is any at most countable sequence of elements of $\mathscr{L}_1$, $f(\bigvee_n a_n) = \bigvee_n f(a_n)$ and $f(\bigwedge_n a_n) = \bigwedge f(a_n)$; (iii) $f(a^\perp) = f(a)^\perp$ for all $a \in \mathscr{L}_1$. An *isomorphism* of $\mathscr{L}_1$ on $\mathscr{L}_2$ is an injection which maps $\mathscr{L}_1$ onto $\mathscr{L}_2$. If $\mathscr{L}_1 = \mathscr{L}_2$, isomorphisms are called *automorphisms.* The set of all automorphisms of a logic $\mathscr{L}$ is a group under composition; we denote it by $\mathrm{Aut}(\mathscr{L})$. If $\mathscr{L}_1$ and $\mathscr{L}$ are two logics, we say that $\mathscr{L}_1$ is a *sublogic* of $\mathscr{L}$ if (i) $\mathscr{L}_1 \subseteq \mathscr{L}$ and (ii) the identity map of $\mathscr{L}_1$ into $\mathscr{L}$ is an injection.

Any Boolean $\sigma$-algebra is a logic provided we define, for any element $a$, $a^\perp$ to be the complement of $a$. These logics are of course not very interesting from the point of view of quantum mechanics. To obtain a more typical example, let us consider a Hilbert space $\mathscr{H}$ over the real, complex or quaternionic division rings. We denote by $\mathscr{L}(\mathscr{H})$ the collection of all *closed* linear manifolds of $\mathscr{H}$. If we now define $<$ to mean set inclusion, and $\perp$ to mean the usual operation of orthogonal complementation in $\mathscr{L}(\mathscr{H})$, then it can easily be verified that $\mathscr{L}(\mathscr{H})$ is a logic. The isomorphism class of $\mathscr{L}(\mathscr{H})$ depends only on the field $\mathbf{D}$ of definition of $\mathscr{H}$ and the dimension of $\mathscr{H}$. A logic $\mathscr{L}$ is said to be *standard* if it is isomorphic to the logic $\mathscr{L}(\mathscr{H})$ of a separable infinite dimensional Hilbert space over one of the three division rings $\mathbf{R}$, $\mathbf{C}$, or $\mathbf{Q}$. Modern quantum theory works with the assumption that the logic of any atomic system is, if not standard, at least a sublogic of a standard logic. We shall make a deep study of standard logics in Chapter VII. We shall also describe there a number of logics that are sublogics of standard logics, but are not standard themselves.

We shall now proceed to derive a few simple consequences of the axioms (i) to (iii) defining a logic.

**Lemma 6.1.** *Let $\mathscr{L}$ be a logic and $a_1, a_2, \cdots$ a sequence of elements of $\mathscr{L}$. If $b \in \mathscr{L}$ and $b \perp a_n$ for all $n$, then $b \perp \bigvee_n a_n$. Moreover we have the identities:*

(4)
$$\left( \bigvee_n a_n \right)^\perp = \bigwedge_n a_n^\perp,$$
$$\left( \bigwedge_n a_n \right)^\perp = \bigvee_n a_n^\perp.$$

*Finally, if $a_1 < a_2$, $c < a_2$, and $c \perp a_1$, then $c < a_2 - a_1$.*

**Proof.** Since $b < a_n^\perp$, $a_n < b^\perp$ for all $n$. Hence $\bigvee_n a_n < b^\perp$ or $b < (\bigvee_n a_n)^\perp$. This proves that $b \perp \bigvee_n a_n$. We now prove the first equation of (4). For any $m$, $a_m < \bigvee_n a_n$, so that $(\bigvee_n a_n)^\perp < a_m^\perp$. Consequently, $(\bigvee_n a_n)^\perp < \bigwedge_m a_m^\perp$. On the other hand, $\bigwedge_m a_m^\perp < a_n^\perp$ for any $n$ and hence $a_n < (\bigwedge_m a_m^\perp)^\perp$. This leads to the relation $\bigvee_n a_n < (\bigwedge_m a_m^\perp)^\perp$ or $(\bigwedge_m a_m^\perp) < (\bigvee_n a_n)^\perp$. This proves the first relation in (4). The second is obtained from the first by replacing $a_n$ by $a_n^\perp$ for all $n$ and taking the orthogonal complements of the relation obtained. Finally, let $a_1 < a_2$, $c < a_2$, and $c \perp a_1$. Write $a_3 = a_1 \vee c$. $a_3 < a_2$ and hence there is a $d \in \mathscr{L}$ such that $d \perp a_3$ and $a_3 \vee d = a_2$. Since $d \perp a_1$ and $c \perp a_1$, $a_1 \perp (c \vee d)$. Moreover, $a_1 \vee (c \vee d) = a_2$. Hence $c \vee d = a_1^\perp \wedge a_2$, which proves that $c < a_2 - a_1$.

**Lemma 6.2.** *Let $a$, $b$, $c$ be three elements of a logic such that $a \perp b$ and $b < c$. Then*

(5)
$$(a \vee b) \wedge c = (a \wedge c) \vee b.$$

**Proof.** Write $d = (a \wedge c) \vee b$ and $e = (a \vee b) \wedge c$. It is obvious that $d < e$. Hence, by (ii) of (2), there exists an element $g$ of $\mathscr{L}$ such that $d \perp g$, and

$d \vee g = e$. Since $a \perp b$ and the element $g$ satisfies the relations $g < a \vee b$, $g \perp b$, it follows from the last statement of lemma 6.1 that $g < a$. Hence, as $g < e < c$, $g < a \wedge c < d$. However, since $g \perp d$, $g < d^\perp$ also. Therefore $g = 0$. This proves that $e = d \vee g = d$.

**Corollary 6.3.** *Let b be a nonzero element of* $\mathscr{L}$. *Then* $\mathscr{L}[0,b]$ *equipped with the orthocomplementation* $x \rightarrow x'$ *defined above is a logic.*

**Proof.** We must verify (ii), (iii), (iv) of (1) and (ii) of (2). (ii), (iv) of (1) are obvious. We shall now prove (iii) of (1). Let $x < b$. Since $x' \perp x$ and $x' \perp b^\perp$, one has $x' \perp x \vee b^\perp$, while $x' \vee x \vee b^\perp = 1$. Thus, we may conclude that $x'^\perp = x \vee b^\perp$. But then $x'' = x'^\perp \wedge b = (x \vee b^\perp) \wedge b = x$ from (5). We come finally to (ii) of (2). Let $x < y < b$. As $\mathscr{L}$ is a logic, there is a $z \in \mathscr{L}$ such that $z \perp x$ and $z \vee x = y$. Since $z < b$, $z = z \wedge b$ so that $z < x'$. This proves (2) in $\mathscr{L}[0,b]$.

**Remark.** It might be observed that (5) is a special case of the usual modular law. We may therefore regard any logic weakly modular since the modular law (5) is valid, not for all $a$ and $b$, but only for $a$, $b$ with $a \perp b$. The standard logics are the only ones which have had any significant measure of success as a framework for the precise formulation and solution of quantum mechanical problems. Since these are *not* modular, it is too restrictive to demand in the definition of a logic that it be modular. This explains why we have rejected modularity as a property of a logic and also why at the same time we have inserted the very much weaker condition (ii) of (2) which leads to (5). On the other hand, if a logic is modular, and separable in a natural sense, then it follows from a general result of Kaplansky [1] that it is a *continuous geometry* in the sense of von Neumann. Whether the logic of any atomic system may be assumed to be an orthocomplemented continuous geometry is still somewhat of an open question. The point is that, unlike a standard logic, a continuous geometry does not have points; this circumstance makes the description of the states of the logic very difficult. In particular, it is not clear whether such a logic can possess pure states (cf. section 7).

## 2. OBSERVABLES

We shall introduce in this section the concept of an observable associated with a logic. The formal definition is given in the next paragraph, but we shall first try to motivate the definition. Suppose that $\mathfrak{S}$ is a physical system, $\mathscr{L}(\mathfrak{S})$ its logic, and $\xi$ a physical quantity or observable. Then in any experiment which an observer performs, the statements that can be made concerning $\xi$ are of the type which asserts that the value of $\xi$ lies in some set $E$ of real numbers. It is natural and harmless to require that the sets $E$ be Borel. If we denote by $x(E)$ the statement that the value of $\xi$ lies in the Borel set $E \subseteq R^1$, then one has a mapping

$$x : E \to x(E)$$

of $\mathscr{B}(R^1)$ into $\mathscr{L}(\mathfrak{S})$. We shall regard two observables as "identical" if and only if the corresponding mappings are the same. If $f$ is a real valued Borel function of a real variable, then we mean by $f \circ \xi$ the observable whose value is $f(r)$ whenever $\xi$ takes the value $r$; to this observable clearly corresponds the mapping $E \to x(f^{-1}(E))$ (cf. Chapter I, sections 2 and 4).

Motivated by these remarks we introduce the following definitions. Let $\mathscr{L}$ be a logic. An *observable associated with* $\mathscr{L}$ is a mapping

$$x : E \to x(E)$$

of the $\sigma$-algebra $\mathscr{B}(R^1)$ of Borel sets of the real line into $\mathscr{L}$ such that

(6)
  (i) $x(\varnothing) = 0, x(R^1) = 1$,
  (ii) if $E, F \in \mathscr{B}(R^1)$ and $E \cap F = \varnothing$, $x(E) \perp x(F)$,
  (iii) if $E_1, E_2, \cdots$ is a sequence of mutually disjoint Borel sets in $R^1$,
$$x\left(\bigcup_n E_n\right) = \bigvee_n x(E_n).$$

We write $\mathcal{O}$ or $\mathcal{O}(\mathscr{L})$ for the set of all observables associated with $\mathscr{L}$. We remark that the properties (i) through (iii) are natural if we want to interpret $x(E)$ as the statement that the value of the observable $\xi$ lies in $E$.

If $X$ is any set and $\mathscr{L}$ is an arbitrary $\sigma$-algebra of subsets of $X$, then $\mathscr{L}$ is obviously a logic provided we define $<$ to be set inclusion and $\perp$ to be set complementation. Theorem 1.4 asserts that the set of observables is in canonical one-one correspondence with the algebra of all real valued $\mathscr{L}$-measurable functions on $X$; if $x(E \to x(E))$ is any observable, then the corresponding function $f$ on $X$ is the unique $\mathscr{L}$-measurable one such that $f^{-1}(E) = x(E)$ for all $E \in \mathscr{B}(R^1)$.

Suppose that $x$ is an observable and $f$ a real valued Borel function of a real variable. Then

(7) $$f \circ x : E \to x(f^{-1}(E))$$

is also an observable.

**Lemma 6.4.** *Let $\mathscr{L}$ be a logic and $x$ an observable associated with $\mathscr{L}$. Then for any sequence $E_1, E_2, \cdots$ of Borel sets*

(8)
$$x\left(\bigcup_n E_n\right) = \bigvee_n x(E_n),$$
$$x\left(\bigcap_n E_n\right) = \bigwedge_n x(E_n).$$

*Suppose further that $f_1$ and $f_2$ are two real valued Borel functions of a real variable t. Let $f_1 \circ f_2$ denote the function $t \to f_1(f_2(t))$. Then*

$$(9) \qquad (f_1 \circ f_2) \circ x = f_1 \circ (f_2 \circ x).$$

**Proof.** Since $x(E_n) \perp x(R^1 - E_n)$ and $x(E_n) \vee x(R^1 - E_n) = 1$, it follows that $x(R^1 - E_n) = x(E_n)^{\perp}$. Consequently, in view of the equation (4), the second equation in (8) will follow if we prove the first. To prove the first, we begin by observing that if $A \subseteq B$, then $x(A) < x(B)$; in fact,

$$x(B) = x(A) \vee x(B - A).$$

This said, let $E = \bigcup_n E_n$. Then $x(E_n) < x(E)$ for all $n$ so that $\bigvee_n x(E_n) < x(E)$. On the other hand, let $F_1 = E_1$ and for $n > 1$, let $F_n = E_n - \bigcup_{j < n} E_j$. The $F_n$ are then mutually disjoint, $F_n \subseteq E_n$ and $\bigcup_n F_n = E$. Therefore,

$$x(E) = \bigvee_n x(F_n) < \bigvee_n x(E_n).$$

This completes the proof of (8). Equation (9) is trivial.

Let $x$ be an observable associated with $\mathscr{L}$. A real number $\lambda$ is said to be a *strict* value of $x$ if $x(\{\lambda\}) \neq 0$. $x$ is said to be *discrete* if there exists a countable set $C = \{c_1, c_2, \cdots\}$ of real numbers such that $x(C) = 1$. $x$ is said to be *constant* if there exists a real number $a$ such that $x(\{a\}) = 1$; we shall then write $x = a$. $x$ is said to be *bounded* if there exists a compact set $K$ such that $x(K) = 1$. If we define $\sigma(x)$ by

$$(10) \qquad \sigma(x) = \bigcap_{C \text{ closed, } x(C) = 1} C,$$

then $\sigma(x)$ is a closed set called the *spectrum* of $x$. Since the topology of $R^1$ satisfies the second countability axiom, there exists a *sequence* of closed sets $C_1, C_2, \cdots$ such that $x(C_n) = 1$ for all $n$ and $\sigma(x) = \bigcap_n C_n$. Since $x(R^1 - C_n) = 0$ for all $n$,

$$x(R^1 - \sigma(x)) = x\left(\bigcup_n (R^1 - C_n)\right)$$
$$= \bigvee_n x(R^1 - C_n)$$
$$= 0,$$

which proves that $x(\sigma(x)) = 1$. $\sigma(x)$ is thus the *smallest closed set $C$* such that $x(C) = 1$. The numbers $\lambda \in \sigma(x)$ are called the *spectral values* of $x$. A strict value is a spectral value but the converse is not true in general. $x$ is bounded if and only if $\sigma(x)$ is a compact set. $\lambda \in \sigma(x)$ if and only if for any open set $U$ containing $\lambda$, $x(U) \neq 0$.

Since the defining axioms of a logic are somewhat weak, it is not reasonable to hope for any incisive description of the set of all observables associated with $\mathscr{L}$. In the next chapter we shall examine this question for logics which are associated with Hilbert spaces. For the moment we confine ourselves to a remark on discrete observables. Suppose $\mathscr{L}$ is an arbitrary logic. Let $x$ be a discrete observable and $\{c_1, c_2, \cdots\}$ the set of its strict values. Then $x(\{c_i\})$ and $x(\{c_j\})$ are orthogonal whenever $i \neq j$ and

$$\bigvee_i x(\{c_i\}) = 1.$$

Conversely, let $\{c_i\}_{i \in D}$ be an at most countably infinite set of distinct real numbers and $\{a_i\}_{i \in D}$ a family of mutually orthogonal elements of $\mathscr{L}$ (with the same indexing set $D$) such that

$$\bigvee_{i \in D} a_i = 1.$$

Then there exists a unique discrete observable $x$ associated with $\mathscr{L}$ such that $x(\{c_i\}) = a_i$ for all $i \in D$. In fact, we have only to define, for $E \in \mathscr{B}(R^1)$,

$$x(E) = \bigvee_{i:c_i \in E} a_i.$$

It is easy to verify that $x$ is an observable. It is clear that $x(\{c_i\}) = a_i$ for all $i \in D$ and that $x$ is discrete. The uniqueness of $x$ is obvious.

Even though many interesting and important observables are discrete, there are quantum observables which are not discrete. The construction of observables which are not discrete is, however, quite complicated. We shall indicate how it can be done in the next chapter for logics which are associated with Hilbert spaces. If $\mathscr{L}$ is an orthocomplemented geometry of finite dimension $N$, then it is easy to see that every observable associated with $\mathscr{L}$ is discrete and has at most $N$ values. Clearly, such logics are not suitable models to represent the experimentally verifiable propositions of complicated atomic systems.

## 3. STATES

If $\mathfrak{S}$ is a classical mechanical system, the concept of a *state* of $\mathfrak{S}$ is so defined (cf. Chapter I) that if $\mathfrak{S}$ is in a state $p$, and $\xi$ is any observable, then $\xi$ has a value in $p$. This leads one to postulate that the states are points of the phase space and observables are real valued functions on it.

In quantum theory this has been rejected as irreconcilable with the available experimental facts regarding the behavior of atomic systems when subjected to refined microscopic observations (cf. von Neumann [1], Heisenberg [1]). The modern approach to atomic physics is based on the principle that *in a given state of the system, an observable has only a probability distribution of values and in general no sharply defined value; and no matter how carefully the state is prepared, there will be some observables whose values are distributed according to probability distributions having arbitrarily high variance.* Accordingly, if $\mathfrak{S}$ is in a state $\sigma$, one can associate, with each observable $x$, a probability distribution, say $P_x{}^\sigma$, on the line, which will be interpreted as the *probability distribution of the values of $x$ when the system is in the state $\sigma$.* If $x$ is a discrete observable, and $c_1, c_2, \cdots$ are its possible values, then $P_x{}^\sigma$ would have mass concentrated on the set $\{c_1, c_2, \cdots\}$; the probability mass which is then assigned by $P_x{}^\sigma$ to the point $c_n$ will be the probability that an experiment on $\mathfrak{S}$, *designed to yield an exact value of $x$,* gives the value $c_n$, when $\mathfrak{S}$ is in the state $\sigma$. If $f$ is any real valued function of a real variable $t$, then, for the observable $f \circ x$, we would have the equation:

$$\text{Prob}\{f \circ x = a, \text{ when } \mathfrak{S} \text{ is in the state } \sigma\}$$

$$(11) \qquad = \sum_{n : f(c_n) = a} P_x{}^\sigma(\{c_n\}).$$

With these remarks serving as our motivation we proceed to the formal definitions. Let $\mathscr{L}$ be any logic and $\mathcal{O}$ the set of all observables of $\mathscr{L}$. A *state function* of $\mathscr{L}$ is a map

$$(12) \qquad\qquad P : x \to P_x \qquad (x \in \mathcal{O})$$

which assigns to each observable $x \in \mathcal{O}$ a probability distribution $P_x$ on $\mathscr{B}(R^1)$ such that for any real valued Borel function $f$ on $R^1$ and any observable $x$,

$$(13) \qquad\qquad P_{f \circ x}(E) = P_x(f^{-1}(E)).$$

Equation (13) has an interesting consequence. We claim first that if $0$ is the zero observable, then $P_0$ is the probability measure whose entire mass is concentrated at the origin. In fact, if $g$ is the function identically zero, then $g \circ 0 = 0$; since $g^{-1}(E) = R^1$ or $\varnothing$ according as $0 \in E$ or $0 \notin E$, we have, by (13), $P_0(E) = P_0(g^{-1}(E)) = 1$ or $0$ according as $0 \in E$ or $0 \notin E$. We next observe that if $x$ is any observable and $E$ is a Borel set such that $x(E) = 0$, then $P_x(E) = 0$. In fact, if $x(E) = 0$, then, for the function $f$ whose value is $1$ on $E$ and $0$ on $R^1 - E$, it is obvious that $y = f \circ x$ is the zero observable and hence $P_y$ is the measure concentrated at the origin. As $E = \{t : f(t) = 1\}$, we have $P_x(E) = P_y(\{1\}) = 0$. In other words,

$$(14) \qquad\qquad P_x(E) = 0 \qquad (E \in \mathscr{B}(R^1), \quad x(E) = 0).$$

(14) implies that if $x$ is discrete, the mass of $P_x$ is concentrated on the set of strict values of $x$.

In turns out to be possible to construct all the state functions of $\mathscr{L}$ in a particularly simple manner. In order to describe this construction we introduce, with Mackey [1], the notion of a *question*. An observable $x$

is said to be a *question* if $x(\{0,1\}) = 1$; $x$ is then discrete. If $a = x(\{1\})$, it is clear that $x$ is the only question such that $x(\{1\}) = a$. We shall call it the *question associated with a* and denote it by $q_a$.

Suppose now that $x$ is an observable associated with the logic $\mathscr{L}$ and $E$ any Borel set $\subseteq R^1$. If $\chi_E$ is the function which takes the value 1 on $E$ and 0 on $R^1 - E$, then $\chi_E \circ x$ is the question associated with $x(E)$, i.e.,

$$(15) \qquad\qquad \chi_E \circ x = q_{x(E)}.$$

In fact, since $\chi_E$ takes only the values 0 and 1, it is clear that $\chi_E \circ x$ is discrete and $(\chi_E \circ x)(\{0,1\}) = 1$. $\chi_E \circ x$ is therefore a question, and, as $E$ is the set where $\chi_E$ takes the value 1,

$$(\chi_E \circ x)(\{1\}) = x(E).$$

The description of all state functions can now be given in terms of the concept of a measure on $\mathscr{L}$. A *measure* on $\mathscr{L}$ is a function

$$(16) \qquad\qquad p : a \to p(a) \qquad (a \in \mathscr{L})$$

such that

(17)
   (i)   $p$ is real valued and $0 \le p(a) \le 1$ for all $a \in \mathscr{L}$,
   (ii)  $p(0) = 0$, $p(1) = 1$,
   (iii) if $a_1, a_2, \cdots$ is a sequence of mutually orthogonal elements of $\mathscr{L}$ and $a = \bigvee_n a_n$, then $p(a) = \sum_n p(a_n)$.

Notice that if $a_1, a_2 \in \mathscr{L}$ and $a_1 < a_2$, then there exists, by (ii) of (2), $b \in \mathscr{L}$ such that $a_1 \perp b$ and $a_2 = a_1 \vee b$. Therefore, $p(a_1) + p(b) = p(a_2)$. In particular,

$$(18) \qquad\qquad p(a_1) \le p(a_2) \qquad (a_1 < a_2).$$

The concept of a measure on $\mathscr{L}$ is a generalization of the well known concept when $\mathscr{L}$ is a Boolean $\sigma$-algebra. However $\mathscr{L}$ need not be distributive and hence the structure of a measure on $\mathscr{L}$ is much more complex than that of a measure on a Boolean $\sigma$-algebra.

**Theorem 6.5.** *Let $\mathscr{L}$ be a logic and $\mathcal{O}$ the set of all observables associated with $\mathscr{L}$. Let $p$ be a measure on $\mathscr{L}$. If we define, for any observable $x \in \mathcal{O}$ and any Borel set $E \subseteq R^1$,*

$$(19) \qquad\qquad P_x{}^p(E) = p(x(E)),$$

*then $P_x{}^p$ is a probability measure on $\mathscr{B}(R^1)$ and*

$$(20) \qquad\qquad P^p : x \to P_x{}^p$$

*is a state function of $\mathscr{L}$. Conversely, if $P(x \to P_x)$ is an arbitrary state* *function of $\mathscr{L}$, there exists one and only one measure $p$ on $\mathscr{L}$ such that* $P_x(E) = p(x(E))$ *for all $x$.*

**Proof.** Suppose that $p$ is a measure on $\mathscr{L}$. If $E_1, E_2, \cdots$ are mutually disjoint Borel sets of $R^1$ with union $E$, then $x(E_1), x(E_2), \cdots$ are mutually orthogonal elements of $\mathscr{L}$ with $x(E) = \bigvee_n x(E_n)$; moreover,

$$P_x^{\,p}(E) = \sum_n P_x^{\,p}(E_n).$$

Since $P_x^{\,p}(R^1) = p(1) = 1$, we see that $P_x^{\,p}$ is a probability measure on $\mathscr{B}(R^1)$. If $f$ is a real valued Borel function of a real variable, then

$$\begin{aligned} P_{f \circ x}^p(E) &= p((f \circ x)(E)) \\ &= p(x(f^{-1}(E))) \\ &= P_x^{\,p}(f^{-1}(E)). \end{aligned}$$

This proves that $x \to P_x^{\,p}$ is a state function of $\mathscr{L}$.

Conversely, let $P(x \to P_x)$ be a state function of $\mathscr{L}$. If $a \in \mathscr{L}$, $P_{q_a}$ is a probability distribution on the real line and as $q_a$ is a question, (14) ensures that $P_{q_a}(\{0,1\}) = 1$. Define

(21)                  $p(a) = P_{q_a}(\{1\}).$

$p(a \to p(a))$ is clearly a well-defined, real valued function on $\mathscr{L}$ and $0 \le p(a) \le 1$ for all $a$. We shall now prove that $p$ is a measure on $\mathscr{L}$. Since $q_0$ is the question with $q_0(\{1\}) = 0$, it follows from (14) that $P_{q_0}(\{1\}) = 0$. This proves that $p(0) = 0$. Similarly, we prove that $p(1) = 1$. Let $\{a_n\}_{n \ge 1}$ be a sequence of mutually orthogonal elements of $\mathscr{L}$ and let $a = \bigvee_n a_n$. Let $x$ be a discrete observable such that $x(\{0\}) = a^\perp$ and $x(\{n\}) = a_n$, $n = 1, 2, \cdots$. Let $f_n$ be the function on $R^1$ whose value is 1 for the point $n$ and 0 otherwise. Then $f_n \circ x$ is the question $q_{a_n}$ and we have, by (21) and (13),

$$p(a_n) = P_x(\{n\}).$$

Since $P_x$ is a probability measure, it follows that

$$\sum_{n=1}^{\infty} p(a_n) = P_x(Z),$$

where $Z$ is the set $\{1, 2, \cdots\}$. If $f$ denotes the function whose value is 1 on $Z$ and 0 on $R^1 - Z$, $f \circ x$ is the question $q_a$ and hence, exactly as before, $p(a) = P_x(Z)$, so that

(22)                  $p(a) = \sum_{n=1}^{\infty} p(a_n).$

$p$ is thus a measure on $\mathscr{L}$. If $x$ is any observable and $E \in \mathscr{B}(R^1)$, we have, on writing $g$ for the function whose value is 1 on $E$ and 0 on $R^1 - E$,

$$
\begin{aligned}
P_x(E) &= P_{g \circ x}(\{1\}) \\
&= P_{q_{x(E)}}(\{1\}) \\
&= p(x(E)).
\end{aligned}
$$

Finally, equation (21) implies easily that $p$ is unique. This completes the proof of the theorem.

In view of the theorem we proved just now, it is natural to define a *state* of a logic to be a measure on $\mathscr{L}$. The set of all states of $\mathscr{L}$ will be denoted by $\mathscr{S}$. If $p(a \rightarrow p(a))$ is a state of $\mathscr{L}$ and $x(E \rightarrow x(E))$ any observable, $E \rightarrow p(x(E))$ is a probability measure on $\mathscr{B}(R^1)$. It is called the *probability distribution of $x$ in the state $p$* and is denoted by $P_x^p$.

Using the probability distribution $P_x^p$, we may define the concepts of *moments* of an observable. The *(mean) expected value* $\mathscr{E}(x|p)$ of an observable $x$ in a state $p$ is defined by

$$
(23) \qquad \mathscr{E}(x|p) = \int_{-\infty}^{\infty} t\, dP_x^p(t).
$$

The *variance* of $x$ in the state $p$ is defined when $\mathscr{E}(x^2|p) < \infty$; in this case,

$$
(24) \qquad \mathrm{var}(x|p) = \mathscr{E}(x^2|p) - [\mathscr{E}(x|p)]^2.
$$

Clearly $\mathrm{var}(x|p) \geq 0$ and is $=0$ if and only if $P_x^p$ is concentrated at the single point $t_0 = \mathscr{E}(x|p)$, and then it is natural to say that, in the state $p$, $x$ has a *sharply defined value*, namely $t_0$.

## 4. PURE STATES. SUPERPOSITION PRINCIPLE

Let $\mathscr{L}$ be a logic and $\mathscr{S}$ the set of all states of $\mathscr{L}$. If $p_1, p_2, \cdots$ is a sequence of elements of $\mathscr{S}$ and $c_1, c_2, \cdots$ is a sequence of constants such that $c_n \geq 0$ for $n = 1, 2, \cdots$ and $c_1 + c_2 + \cdots = 1$, then the function $p(a \rightarrow p(a))$ defined by

$$
(25) \qquad p(a) = \sum_{n \geq 1} c_n p_n(a)
$$

is easily verified to be a state of $\mathscr{L}$. We shall write

$$
(26) \qquad p = \sum_{n \geq 1} c_n p_n.
$$

$\mathscr{S}$ is therefore a *convex set*. If $x$ is any observable, it follows at once from (26) that

$$(27) \qquad P_x{}^p = \sum_{n \geq 1} c_n P_x{}^{p_n}.$$

The equation (27) may be given the following interpretation. Suppose that one knows that the state of a system is one of $p_1, p_2, \cdots$ with probabilities $c_1, c_2, \cdots$, respectively. Then, for any bounded observable $x$, the expectation value of $x$ is $\sum_{n \geq 1} c_n \mathscr{E}(x|p_n)$ which is equal to $\mathscr{E}(x|p)$. In other words, assuming that the system is in the state $p$ is, statistically speaking, equivalent to assuming that its state is one of $p_1, p_2, \cdots$ with respective probabilities $c_1, c_2, \cdots$. It is customary to say that the state $p$ is a *classical superposition* of the states $p_n (n \geq 1)$.

In view of the probability interpretation of (26) and (27), interest centers around states for which no representation of the form (26) is possible. A state $p$ is said to be *pure* if the equation

$$(28) \qquad p = cp_1 + (1-c)p_2 \qquad (0 \leq c \leq 1, \quad p_1, p_2 \in \mathscr{S})$$

implies that $p = p_1 = p_2$. We write $\mathscr{P}$ for the set of all pure states of $\mathscr{L}$. $\mathscr{P}$ is the set of *extreme points* of the convex set $\mathscr{S}$.

We may now introduce the notion of superposition. Let $\mathscr{D}$ be a set of states and $p_0$ an arbitrary state. We say that $p_0$ is a *superposition of states in $\mathscr{D}$* if the following property is satisfied:

$$(29) \qquad a \in \mathscr{L}, \quad p(a) = 0 \quad \text{for all} \quad p \in \mathscr{D} \Rightarrow p_0(a) = 0.$$

If $p = c_1 p_1 + c_2 p_2 + \cdots$ where $c_1, c_2 \cdots \geq 0$, and $c_1 + c_2 + \cdots = 1$, then $p$ is a superposition of the states in the set $\{p_1, p_2, \cdots\}$. As we shall presently see, if $\mathscr{L}$ is a Boolean $\sigma$-algebra, this is, roughly speaking, the only kind of superposition possible, in particular, no pure state can be a superposition of other pure states distinct from it. This is in contradistinction to quantum mechanics, where the structure of $\mathscr{L}$, namely the fact that it is standard, forces the concept of superposition to be nontrivial *even among pure states*.

**Theorem 6.6.** *Let $\mathscr{L}$ be a Boolean $\sigma$-algebra of subsets of a space $X$ such that* (i) *$\mathscr{L}$ is separable (cf. Chapter I) and* (ii) *$\{a\} \in \mathscr{L}$ for all $a \in X$. For any $a \in X$ let $\delta_a$ be the state defined by*

$$(30) \qquad \delta_a(A) = \begin{cases} 1 & \text{if} \quad a \in A \\ 0 & \text{if} \quad a \notin A \end{cases}$$

*Then $\{\delta_a : a \in X\}$ is precisely the set of all pure states of $\mathscr{L}$. If $\mathscr{D}$ is any set of pure states, and $p_0$ an arbitrary pure state, $p_0$ is a superposition of states of $\mathscr{D}$ if and only if $p_0 \in \mathscr{D}$.*

**Proof.** Let $\{A_1, A_2, \cdots\}$ generate $\mathscr{L}$. That $\delta_a$ is pure is trivially verified. Suppose that $p$ is a pure state. If for some $A_0 \in \mathscr{L}$, $0 < p(A_0) < 1$, then, on putting

$$p_1(A) = (p(A_0))^{-1}p(A \cap A_0),$$
$$p_2(A) = (1 - p(A_0))^{-1}p(A \cap (X - A_0)),$$

we would obtain the decomposition

$$p = p(A_0) \cdot p_1 + (1 - p(A_0)) \cdot p_2;$$

$p_1 \neq p_2$ as $p_1(A_0) = 1$ and $p_2(A_0) = 0$. This is not possible as $p$ is pure by assumption. Therefore we may conclude for any $A \in \mathscr{L}$, that $p(A) = 0$ or $1$. By replacing $A_n$ by $X - A_n$ if necessary, we may assume that $p(A_n) = 1$ for all $n$, where $\{A_1, A_2, \cdots\}$ generates $\mathscr{L}$. Let

$$B = \bigcap_n A_n.$$

Then $p(B) = 1$. In particular, $B$ is nonempty. We assert that $B$ cannot contain more than a single point. In fact, the collection of all sets $C \in \mathscr{L}$ with the property that either $B \subseteq C$ or $B \cap C = \varnothing$, is a $\sigma$-algebra which contains all the $A_n$. Hence it coincides with $\mathscr{L}$. Therefore, as $\{x\} \in \mathscr{L}$, this is possible only if $B = \{a\}$ for some $a \in X$. But then $p = \delta_a$. Finally, let $p_0$ be a superposition of the states of $\mathscr{D}$ where each element of $\mathscr{D}$ is pure. If $p_0 = \delta_{a_0}$, but $p_0 \notin \mathscr{D}$, then $p(\{a_0\}) = 0$ for all $p \in \mathscr{D}$ but $p_0(\{a_0\}) = 1$; a contradiction. The theorem is completely proved.

Let $\mathscr{L}$ be an arbitrary logic and $\mathscr{P}$ the set of all pure states of $\mathscr{L}$. For any subset $S \subseteq \mathscr{P}$, we write $\bar{S}$ for the set of all $p \in \mathscr{P}$ such that $p$ is a superposition of the states of $S$. Let us now consider $\mathscr{M}$, the collection of all $S \subseteq \mathscr{P}$ with the property that $S = \bar{S}$. Under set inclusion, $\mathscr{M}$ becomes a partially ordered set. If $\mathscr{L}$ satisfies the assumptions of theorem 6.6 for example, then $\mathscr{M}$ is the class of all subsets of $\mathscr{P}$ and is therefore a Boolean algebra. However, in the case of more complex $\mathscr{L}$, $\mathscr{M}$ is not a Boolean algebra. In general, the geometric structure of $\mathscr{M}$ seems somewhat hard to determine. For the so-called *standard* logics to be introduced in the next chapter, this can be done and it becomes possible to determine the structure of $\mathscr{M}$ completely. For standard $\mathscr{L}$, $\mathscr{M}$ then becomes *isomorphic* to $\mathscr{L}$. It is this fact which confers on the set of pure states of a standard logic a geometric structure characteristic of quantum theory. In the physical literature (cf. Dirac [1]) this is elevated to a physical principle, the so-called *superposition principle*. From our point of view, the geometry of pure states will appear as a *consequence* of the structure of the logic $\mathscr{L}$.

## 5. SIMULTANEOUS OBSERVABILITY

One of the features which sets apart quantum mechanics from classical mechanics is the existence of observables whose values cannot always be simultaneously measured. We shall now introduce this idea formally. We begin with the elements of $\mathscr{L}$ themselves. Let $a, b \in \mathscr{L}$. We shall say that $a$ and $b$ are *simultaneously verifiable, $a \leftrightarrow b$* in symbols, if there are elements $a_1, b_1,$ and $c \in \mathscr{L}$ such that

(31)      (i) $a_1, b_1,$ and $c$ are mutually orthogonal,
          (ii) $a = a_1 \vee c, \quad b = b_1 \vee c.$

If $x$ and $y$ are two observables, they are said to be *simultaneously observable* if for any two Borel subsets $E$ and $F$ of $R^1$, $x(E) \leftrightarrow y(F)$; we shall write $x \leftrightarrow y$. If $A$ and $B$ are two subsets of $\mathscr{L}$, we write $A \leftrightarrow B$ when $a \leftrightarrow b$ for all $a \in A$ and $b \in B$.

The analysis of these concepts depends on a study of Boolean sub-algebras of $\mathscr{L}$. A subset $\mathscr{A} \subseteq \mathscr{L}$ is a *Boolean subalgebra of $\mathscr{L}$* if it is (a) a sublogic of $\mathscr{L}$ and (b) a Boolean algebra, i.e., if

(i) $0, 1 \in \mathscr{A}$,
(ii) if $a, b \in \mathscr{A}$, then $a \vee b, a \wedge b$, and $a^\perp \in \mathscr{A}$,
(iii) if $a, b, c \in \mathscr{A}$, then
$$a \wedge (b \vee c) = (a \wedge b) \vee (a \wedge c),$$
$$a \vee (b \wedge c) = (a \vee b) \wedge (a \vee c).$$

$\mathscr{A}$ is said to be a *Boolean sub-$\sigma$-algebra of $\mathscr{L}$* if it is a Boolean subalgebra, and if, for any countable sequence $a_1, a_2, \cdots \in \mathscr{A}$, $\bigvee_n a_n \in \mathscr{A}$ and $\bigwedge_n a_n \in \mathscr{A}$.

**Lemma 6.7.** *Let $a, b \in \mathscr{L}$, $\mathscr{L}$ being any logic. Then the following statements are equivalent:*

(a) $a \leftrightarrow b$,
(b) $a - (a \wedge b) \perp b$,
(c) $b - (a \wedge b) \perp a$,
(32)
(d) *there exists an observable $x$ and two Borel sets $A$ and $B$ of the real line such that $x(A) = a$ and $x(B) = b$,*
(e) *there exists a Boolean subalgebra of $\mathscr{L}$ containing $a$ and $b$.*

**Proof.** Suppose $a \leftrightarrow b$. We may then write $a = a_1 \vee c, b = b_1 \vee c$, where $a_1, b_1,$ and $c$ are mutually orthogonal. Clearly $c < a \wedge b$. Hence there is a $d$ such that $c \perp d$ and $c \vee d = a \wedge b$. Since $d \perp c$ and $d < a$, $d < a - c = a_1$ (lemma 6.1). Similarly, $d < b_1$. Hence $d < a_1 \wedge b_1 = 0$. Therefore $c = a \wedge b$. Hence $a_1 = a - (a \wedge b)$. But $a_1 \perp c$ and $a_1 \perp b_1$ so that

$$a_1 = a - (a \wedge b) \perp b_1 \vee c = b.$$

This proves that (a) $\Rightarrow$ (b). By symmetry, (a) $\Rightarrow$ (c). If $a - (a \wedge b) \perp b$, then, on writing $a_1 = a - (a \wedge b)$, $b_1 = b - (a \wedge b)$ and $c = a \wedge b$, we find that $a = a_1 \vee c$ and $b = b_1 \vee c$. Since $a_1 \perp b$, we have $a_1 \perp b_1$ and $a_1 \perp c$, while, by definition, $b_1 \perp c$. Therefore $a \leftrightarrow b$, proving that (b) $\Rightarrow$ (a). (a), (b) and (c) have thus been proved equivalent. We shall complete the proof by showing (a) $\Rightarrow$ (d) $\Rightarrow$ (e) $\Rightarrow$ (a). If $a = a_1 \vee c$, $b = b_1 \vee c$, where $a_1$, $b_1$, and $c$ are mutually orthogonal, we write $d = a_1 \vee b_1 \vee c$ and define $x$ to be the discrete observable such that $x(\{0\}) = a_1$, $x(\{1\}) = b_1$, $x(\{2\}) = c$ and $x(\{3\}) = d^\perp$. Then $x(\{0,2\}) = a$, $x(\{1,2\}) = b$. This proves that (a) $\Rightarrow$ (d). Suppose that (d) is satisfied. Then $x(A - A \cap B) = a - a \wedge b$, $x(B - A \cap B) = b - a \wedge b$. Writing $a_1 = a - a \wedge b$, $a_2 = a \wedge b$, $a_3 = b - a \wedge b$, $a_4 = (a \vee b)^\perp$, we see that the $a_i$ are mutually orthogonal and $a_1 \vee a_2 \vee a_3 \vee a_4 = 1$. If $\mathscr{A}$ is the collection of elements which are the lattice sums

$$a_{i_1} \vee a_{i_2} \vee \cdots \vee a_{i_k} \quad (k \leq 4, 1 \leq i_1 \leq i_2 \leq \cdots \leq i_k \leq 4),$$

then it is easy to verify that $\mathscr{A}$ is a Boolean subalgebra of $\mathscr{L}$. Since $a, b \in \mathscr{A}$, we see that (d) $\Rightarrow$ (e). Finally, let (e) be satisfied, and let $\mathscr{A}$ be a Boolean subalgebra of $\mathscr{L}$ containing $a$ and $b$. Clearly $[a - (a \wedge b)] \wedge b = 0$. But, as $a - (a \wedge b)$, $b$ and $b^\perp$ are in the Boolean algebra $\mathscr{A}$,

$$a - (a \wedge b) = \{(a - (a \wedge b)) \wedge b\} \vee \{(a - (a \wedge b)) \wedge b^\perp\}$$
$$= \{a - (a \wedge b)\} \wedge b^\perp$$
$$< b^\perp,$$

showing that $a - (a \wedge b) \perp b$. This shows that (e) $\Rightarrow$ (b) and hence that (e) $\Rightarrow$ (a).

**Corollary 6.8.** *If $a \leftrightarrow b$, the elements $a_1$, $b_1$, and $c$ of* (31) *are uniquely determined. In fact, $c = a \wedge b$, $a_1 = a - a \wedge b$, and $b_1 = b - a \wedge b$.*

Lemma 6.7 shows that in the presence of simultaneous verifiability of two elements of $\mathscr{L}$, one can operate with the statements corresponding to these elements as if they were classical. We shall now take up the question of generalizing this fact to observables. Our aim is to prove that *simultaneous observability* is essentially a characteristic of classical systems. We shall deduce, as a corollary, that, if $x, y, z, \cdots$ are observables, associated with a logic, they are mutually simultaneously observable if and only if they are all functions of a single observable. This was first proved by von Neumann (cf. [1]) when the logic in question was a standard one. For a general logic, it was proved by Varadarajan [1].

**Theorem 6.9.**† *Let $\mathscr{L}$ be any logic and $\{x_\lambda\}_{\lambda \in D}$ a family of observables. Suppose that $x_\lambda \leftrightarrow x_{\lambda'}$ for all $\lambda, \lambda' \in D$. Then, there exists a space $X$, a*

† The definition of a logic given in Varadarajan [1] does not require it to be a lattice. It was pointed out to us by Dr. S. P. Gudder [1] that theorem 6.9 does not remain valid for these more general classes of partially ordered sets considered in our paper [1].

$\sigma$-algebra $\mathscr{B}$ of subsets of $X$, real valued $\mathscr{B}$-measurable functions $g_\lambda$ on $X(\lambda \in D)$, and a $\sigma$-homomorphism $\tau$ of $\mathscr{B}$ into $\mathscr{L}$ such that

$$(33) \qquad \tau(g_\lambda^{-1}(E)) = x_\lambda(E)$$

for all $\lambda \in D$ and $E \in \mathscr{B}(R^1)$. Suppose further that either $\mathscr{L}$ is separable in the sense that every Boolean sub-$\sigma$-algebra of $\mathscr{L}$ is separable, or that $D$ is countable. Then there exists an observable $x$ and real valued Borel functions $f_\lambda$ of a real variable such that for all $\lambda \in D$,

$$(34) \qquad x_\lambda = f_\lambda \circ x.$$

The proof of this theorem (cf. Varadarajan [1]) depends on a series of lemmas. $\mathscr{L}$ is a fixed logic in these lemmas.

**Lemma 6.10.** *Let* $b, a_1, a_2, \cdots$ *be elements of* $\mathscr{L}$. *If* $b \leftrightarrow a_n$ *for all* $n$, *then*

$$(35) \qquad \begin{aligned} & b \leftrightarrow a_n^\perp, \\ & b \leftrightarrow \bigvee_n a_n, \\ & b \leftrightarrow \bigwedge_n a_n. \end{aligned}$$

*Moreover, we then have the distributivity laws*

$$(36) \qquad \begin{aligned} & b \wedge \left(\bigvee_n a_n\right) = \bigvee_n (b \wedge a_n), \\ & b \vee \left(\bigwedge_n a_n\right) = \bigwedge_n (b \vee a_n). \end{aligned}$$

**Proof.** We use the criteria of (32). It follows from the equivalence of (a) and (d) of (32) that if $c \leftrightarrow d$, then any two of the four elements $c, c^\perp$, $d, d^\perp$ are simultaneously verifiable. This proves the first of the three relations of (35). Now, we come to the proof of the rest of (35). Write $a = \bigvee_m a_m$. Since $b \wedge a_m < b \wedge a$, $b - (b \wedge a) < b - (b \wedge a_m)$ for all $m$. As $b \leftrightarrow a_m$ for all $m$, it follows from (c) of (32) that

$$b - (b \wedge a) < b - (b \wedge a_m) < a_m^\perp.$$

Hence $b - (b \wedge a) < \bigwedge_m a_m^\perp = a^\perp$ which proves that $b \leftrightarrow a$. Changing all the $a_n$ into $a_n^\perp$ we deduce from the relation $b \leftrightarrow \bigvee_n a_n$ that $b \leftrightarrow \bigwedge_n a_n$. Next we come to (36). Once again it is enough to prove only the first of the two relations. Clearly $\bigvee_n (b \wedge a_n) < b \wedge a$, where $a = \bigvee_n a_n$. Let $d < b \wedge a$ be such that $d \perp \bigvee_n (b \wedge a_n)$ and $(\bigvee_n (b \wedge a_n)) \vee d = b \wedge a$. Since $d \perp b \wedge a_n$ and $d < b$, we deduce from the relation $b \leftrightarrow a_n$ that $d < b - (b \wedge a_n)$ (by lemma 6.1) and hence, as $b \leftrightarrow a_n$, we conclude that $d \perp a_n$, from (c) of (32). Since this is true for all $n$, $d \perp a$. As $d < a$, this means $d = 0$, proving the first equation of (36).

Consider the collection $\mathfrak{M}$ of sublogics of $\mathscr{L}$, partially ordered by inclusion. If $\{\mathscr{L}_\alpha\}_{\alpha \in A}$ is any family of sublogics of $\mathscr{L}$, it is obvious that

$\bigcap_\alpha \mathscr{L}_\alpha$ is also a sublogic of $\mathscr{L}$. From this it follows that if $\{\mathscr{L}_\alpha\}_{\alpha \in A}$ is any family of sublogics of $\mathscr{L}$, there exists a smallest sublogic containing all the $\mathscr{L}_\alpha$. We denote it by $\bigvee_\alpha \mathscr{L}_\alpha$. $\mathfrak{M}$ is thus a *complete* lattice. If each $\mathscr{L}_\alpha$ is a Boolean subalgebra of $\mathscr{L}$, it is however not true in general that $\bigvee_\alpha \mathscr{L}_\alpha$ is a Boolean subalgebra. We shall now prove that this is so if and only if the relations $\mathscr{L}_\alpha \leftrightarrow \mathscr{L}_{\alpha'}$ are satisfied for all $\alpha, \alpha' \in A$. We begin by considering the case when there are only two Boolean subalgebras involved.

**Lemma 6.11.** *Let $\mathscr{R}_1$ and $\mathscr{R}_2$ be two Boolean subalgebras of $\mathscr{L}$. Then $\mathscr{R}_1 \leftrightarrow \mathscr{R}_2$ if and only if $\mathscr{R}_1 \vee \mathscr{R}_2$ is a Boolean subalgebra of $\mathscr{L}$.*

**Proof.** Suppose that $\mathscr{R}_1 \vee \mathscr{R}_2$ is a Boolean subalgebra of $\mathscr{L}$. Then $\mathscr{R}_1 \leftrightarrow \mathscr{R}_2$ in view of (e) of (32). We shall now prove the converse. We shall first consider the case when the Boolean subalgebras are finite. Let $\mathscr{F}_i$ ($i = 1, 2$) be *finite* Boolean subalgebras of $\mathscr{L}$ such that $\mathscr{F}_1 \leftrightarrow \mathscr{F}_2$. Then, their Stone spaces (cf. Chapter I) are finite and hence there are elements $a_1, \cdots, a_r \in \mathscr{F}_1$ and $b_1, \cdots, b_s \in \mathscr{F}_2$ such that (i) $a_i \perp a_{i'}$, $i \neq i'$, $b_j \perp b_{j'}$, $j \neq j'$; (ii) $a_1 \vee a_2 \vee \cdots \vee a_r = b_1 \vee b_2 \vee \cdots \vee b_s = 1$; (iii) $\mathscr{F}_1$ is the collection of all lattice sums $a_{i_1} \vee a_{i_2} \vee \cdots \vee a_{i_p}$ ($1 \leq i_1 \leq i_2 \leq \cdots \leq i_p \leq r$) and $\mathscr{F}_2$ is the collection of all lattice sums $b_{j_1} \vee b_{j_2} \vee \cdots \vee b_{j_q}$ ($1 \leq j_1 \leq j_2 \leq \cdots \leq j_q \leq s$). Write

$$(37) \qquad c_{ij} = a_i \wedge b_j \qquad (i = 1, 2, \cdots, r, \quad j = 1, 2, \cdots, s).$$

Obviously $c_{ij} \perp c_{i'j'}$ unless $i = i'$ and $j = j'$. Since $a_i \leftrightarrow b_j$ for all $i$ and $j$, we infer from (36) that

$$(38) \qquad \begin{aligned} \bigvee_{j=1}^s c_{ij} &= a_i, \\ \bigvee_{i=1}^r c_{ij} &= b_j. \end{aligned}$$

Consequently,

$$(39) \qquad \bigvee_{i=1}^r \bigvee_{j=1}^s c_{ij} = 1.$$

If $\mathscr{F}$ denotes the collection of all lattice sums of the $c_{ij}$, then $\mathscr{F}$ is a Boolean subalgebra of $\mathscr{L}$ and (38) implies that $\mathscr{F}_i \subseteq \mathscr{F}$ for $i = 1, 2$. The formulas (37) show that if $\mathscr{F}'$ is any sublogic of $\mathscr{L}$ containing both $\mathscr{F}_1$ and $\mathscr{F}_2$, then $\mathscr{F} \subseteq \mathscr{F}'$. Clearly, therefore, $\mathscr{F} = \mathscr{F}_1 \vee \mathscr{F}_2$. Note that $\mathscr{F}_1 \vee \mathscr{F}_2$ is also finite.

Let $\mathscr{R}_i$ ($i = 1, 2$) be Boolean subalgebras of $\mathscr{L}$ such that $\mathscr{R}_1 \leftrightarrow \mathscr{R}_2$. Let $\mathscr{R}$ be defined by

$$(40) \qquad \mathscr{R} = \bigcup (\mathscr{F}_1 \vee \mathscr{F}_2),$$

where the union is over all pairs $(\mathscr{F}_1, \mathscr{F}_2)$ of finite Boolean subalgebras of $\mathscr{L}$ such that $\mathscr{F}_i \subseteq \mathscr{R}_i$, $i = 1, 2$. We assert that $\mathscr{R}$ is a Boolean subalgebra of $\mathscr{L}$ containing $\mathscr{R}_1$ and $\mathscr{R}_2$. If $a \in \mathscr{R}$, then it is obvious that $a^\perp \in \mathscr{R}$. Clearly, $0, 1 \in \mathscr{R}$. Suppose now that $a, b \in \mathscr{R}$. Then there are finite Boolean subalgebras $\mathscr{F}_1, \mathscr{F}_1', \mathscr{F}_2, \mathscr{F}_2'$ of $\mathscr{L}$ such that $\mathscr{F}_1, \mathscr{F}_1'$ are $\subseteq \mathscr{R}_1, \mathscr{F}_2, \mathscr{F}_2'$ are $\subseteq \mathscr{R}_2$, $a \in \mathscr{F}_1 \vee \mathscr{F}_2$, and $b \in \mathscr{F}_1' \vee \mathscr{F}_2'$. Since $\mathscr{F}_1$ and $\mathscr{F}_1'$ are contained in the Boolean algebra $\mathscr{R}_1$, $\mathscr{F}_1 \leftrightarrow \mathscr{F}_1'$ and hence $\mathscr{F}_1 \vee \mathscr{F}_1' = \mathscr{F}_1''$ is finite and contained in $\mathscr{R}_1$. Similarly, $\mathscr{F}_2 \vee \mathscr{F}_2' = \mathscr{F}_2''$ is finite and contained in $\mathscr{R}_2$. As $\mathscr{R}_1 \leftrightarrow \mathscr{R}_2$, $\mathscr{F}_1'' \leftrightarrow \mathscr{F}_2''$. Therefore $\mathscr{F}_1'' \vee \mathscr{F}_2''$ is a finite Boolean subalgebra of $\mathscr{L}$ contained in $\mathscr{R}$. Let us write $\mathscr{F} = \mathscr{F}_1'' \vee \mathscr{F}_2''$. As $\mathscr{F}_1, \mathscr{F}_1', \mathscr{F}_2$, and $\mathscr{F}_2'$ are contained in $\mathscr{F}$, it follows that $\mathscr{F}_1 \vee \mathscr{F}_2 \subseteq \mathscr{F}$ and $\mathscr{F}_1' \vee \mathscr{F}_2' \subseteq \mathscr{F}$. Thus, $a, b \in \mathscr{F}$. Therefore $a \vee b$ and $a \wedge b$ are in $\mathscr{F}$. This proves that $a \vee b$ and $a \wedge b$ are in $\mathscr{R}$.

We shall next establish the distributivity laws. Let $a_1, a_2, a_3$ be three elements of $\mathscr{R}$ and (for $j = 1, 2, 3$) let $a_j \in \mathscr{F}_j^{(1)} \vee \mathscr{F}_j^{(2)}$, where $\mathscr{F}_j^{(k)}$ is a finite Boolean subalgebra of $\mathscr{L}$ contained in $\mathscr{R}_k$ ($j = 1, 2, 3$, $k = 1, 2$). Since $\mathscr{F}_j^{(k)} \subseteq \mathscr{R}_k$ for all $j$, $\bigvee_{j=1}^3 \mathscr{F}_j^{(k)}$ is a finite Boolean subalgebra of $\mathscr{R}_k$. Let it be denoted by $\mathscr{F}^{(k)}$. Obviously $\mathscr{F}^{(1)} \leftrightarrow \mathscr{F}^{(2)}$, and hence $\mathscr{F} = \mathscr{F}^{(1)} \vee \mathscr{F}^{(2)}$ is a finite Boolean subalgebra of $\mathscr{L}$. Since $\mathscr{F}_j^{(k)} \subseteq \mathscr{F}$ for all $j$ and $k$, $\mathscr{F}_j^{(1)} \vee \mathscr{F}_j^{(2)} \subseteq \mathscr{F}$ for all $j$ so that $a_j \in \mathscr{F}$ for all $j$. As $\mathscr{F}$ is a Boolean subalgebra of $\mathscr{L}$, we have:

$$a_1 \wedge (a_2 \vee a_3) = (a_1 \wedge a_2) \vee (a_1 \wedge a_3),$$

$$a_1 \vee (a_2 \wedge a_3) = (a_1 \vee a_2) \wedge (a_1 \vee a_3).$$

This proves that $\mathscr{R}$ is a Boolean subalgebra of $\mathscr{L}$.

We observe finally that $\mathscr{R}_1$ and $\mathscr{R}_2$ are contained in $\mathscr{R}$. If $a \in \mathscr{R}_1$, we have $a \in \mathscr{F}_1 \vee \mathscr{F}_2$, where $\mathscr{F}_1 = \{0, a, a^\perp, 1\}$ and $\mathscr{F}_2 = \{0, 1\}$. Hence $\mathscr{R}_1 \subseteq \mathscr{R}$. Similarly, $\mathscr{R}_2 \subseteq \mathscr{R}$. $\mathscr{R}_1 \vee \mathscr{R}_2$ is thus a Boolean subalgebra of $\mathscr{L}$. The lemma is completely proved.

**Corollary 6.12.** *If $\mathscr{R}$ is defined by (40), then $\mathscr{R} = \mathscr{R}_1 \vee \mathscr{R}_2$. If $\mathscr{C}$ is any subset of $\mathscr{L}$ such that $\mathscr{C} \leftrightarrow \mathscr{R}_k$, $k = 1, 2$, then $\mathscr{C} \leftrightarrow \mathscr{R}_1 \vee \mathscr{R}_2$.*

**Proof.** If $\mathscr{F}_k$ is a finite Boolean subalgebra of $\mathscr{R}_k$ ($k = 1, 2$) and if $\mathscr{R}'$ is a sublogic of $\mathscr{L}$ which contains both $\mathscr{R}_1$ and $\mathscr{R}_2$, $\mathscr{F}_1 \vee \mathscr{F}_2 \subseteq \mathscr{R}'$. Hence $\mathscr{R} \subseteq \mathscr{R}'$. This shows that $\mathscr{R}_1 \vee \mathscr{R}_2$ coincides with $\mathscr{R}$. To prove the second assertion, let $c \in \mathscr{C}$. Let $\mathscr{F}_k \subseteq \mathscr{R}_k$ be finite Boolean subalgebras of $\mathscr{L}$. From (37) and (35) we may conclude that $c \leftrightarrow \mathscr{F}_1 \vee \mathscr{F}_2$. Equation (40) shows then that $c \leftrightarrow \mathscr{R}$. This proves that $\mathscr{C} \leftrightarrow \mathscr{R}_1 \vee \mathscr{R}_2$.

**Corollary 6.13.** *Let $\mathscr{R}_i$ ($i = 1, 2, \cdots, s$) be Boolean subalgebras of $\mathscr{L}$ such that $\mathscr{R}_i \leftrightarrow \mathscr{R}_j$ for all $i, j = 1, 2, \cdots, s$. Then $\bigvee_{i=1}^s \mathscr{R}_i$ is a Boolean subalgebra of $\mathscr{L}$. If $\mathscr{C}$ is any subset of $\mathscr{L}$ such that $\mathscr{C} \leftrightarrow \mathscr{R}_i$ for all $i = 1, 2, \cdots, s$, then $\mathscr{C} \leftrightarrow \bigvee_{i=1}^s \mathscr{R}_i$.*

**Proof.** The assertions are proved by induction on $s$. For $s = 2$, they follow from lemma 6.11 and corollary 6.12. Assume now that they are valid for all $s \leq s_0$ and let $s = s_0 + 1$. Since $\mathscr{R}_i \leftrightarrow \mathscr{R}_j$ for all $i, j \leq s_0 + 1$, $\mathscr{R} = \bigvee_{i=1}^{s_0} \mathscr{R}_i$ is a Boolean subalgebra of $\mathscr{L}$ and $\mathscr{R}_{s_0+1} \leftrightarrow \mathscr{R}$ by the induction hypothesis. Hence, $\mathscr{R}_{s_0+1} \vee \mathscr{R}$ is a Boolean subalgebra of $\mathscr{L}$. Suppose now that $c$ is an element of $\mathscr{L}$ such that $c \leftrightarrow \mathscr{R}_i$, $i \leq s_0 + 1$. Then, by the induction hypothesis, $c \leftrightarrow \mathscr{R}$. Hence we conclude from corollary 6.12 that $c \leftrightarrow \bigvee_{i=1}^{s_0+1} \mathscr{R}_i$. This completes the induction and the proof of the corollary.

**Lemma 6.14.** *Let* $\{\mathscr{R}_\lambda\}_{\lambda \in D}$ *be a family of Boolean subalgebras of* $\mathscr{L}$ *such that* $\mathscr{R}_\lambda \leftrightarrow \mathscr{R}_{\lambda'}$, *for all* $\lambda, \lambda' \in D$. *Then there exists a Boolean subalgebra* $\mathscr{R}$ *of* $\mathscr{L}$ *such that* $\mathscr{R}_\lambda \subseteq \mathscr{R}$ *for all* $\lambda \in D$.

**Proof.** Let $F$ be a finite subset of $D$. By corollary 6.13, $\bigvee_{\lambda \in F} \mathscr{R}_\lambda$ is a Boolean subalgebra of $\mathscr{L}$. Let us write

$$(41) \qquad \mathscr{R}(F) = \bigvee_{\lambda \in F} \mathscr{R}_\lambda.$$

Obviously, $\mathscr{R}(F) \subseteq \mathscr{R}(F')$ if $F \subseteq F'$. Define $\mathscr{R}$ by

$$(42) \qquad \mathscr{R} = \bigcup_{\substack{F \subseteq D \\ F \text{ finite}}} \mathscr{R}(F).$$

Obviously, $\mathscr{R}_\lambda \subseteq \mathscr{R}$ for all $\lambda \in D$. We shall now complete the proof by showing that $\mathscr{R}$ is a Boolean subalgebra of $\mathscr{L}$. It is enough to prove that any finite subset of $\mathscr{R}$ is contained in a Boolean subalgebra of $\mathscr{L}$ contained in $\mathscr{R}$. If $a_1, a_2, \cdots, a_r$ are elements of $\mathscr{R}$ there are finite subsets $F_1$, $F_2, \cdots, F_r$ of $D$ such that $a_i \in \mathscr{R}(F_i)$. If $F = \bigcup_i F_i$, then $a_i \in \mathscr{R}(F)$ for all $i$. This proves that $\mathscr{R}$ is a Boolean subalgebra of $\mathscr{L}$.

**Corollary 6.15.** *Let* $\{\mathscr{R}_\lambda\}_{\lambda \in D}$ *be a family of Boolean sub-$\sigma$-algebras of* $\mathscr{L}$ *such that* $\mathscr{R}_\lambda \leftrightarrow \mathscr{R}_{\lambda'}$ *for all* $\lambda, \lambda' \in D$. *Then, there exists a Boolean sub-$\sigma$-algebra* $\mathscr{R}$ *of* $\mathscr{L}$ *such that* $\mathscr{R}_\lambda \subseteq \mathscr{R}$ *for all* $\lambda \in D$.

**Proof.** By lemma 6.14 there are Boolean subalgebras $\mathscr{R}'$ such that $\mathscr{R}_\lambda \subseteq \mathscr{R}'$ for all $\lambda$. By Zorn's lemma we can choose a maximal such, say $\mathscr{R}$. We claim that $\mathscr{R}$ is a Boolean $\sigma$-algebra. It is enough to prove that if $a_1, a_2, \cdots$ is a sequence of elements of $\mathscr{R}$, then $a = \bigvee_m a_m$ is also in $\mathscr{R}$. Since $a_m \in \mathscr{R}$, $b \leftrightarrow a_m$ for all $b \in \mathscr{R}$. Hence $a \leftrightarrow \mathscr{R}$ by (35). If $\mathscr{A} = \{0, a, a^\perp, 1\}$ then $\mathscr{A}$ is a Boolean subalgebra of $\mathscr{L}$ and $\mathscr{A} \leftrightarrow \mathscr{R}$. Hence $\mathscr{A} \vee \mathscr{R}$ is a Boolean subalgebra of $\mathscr{L}$ containing $\mathscr{R}$. Since $\mathscr{R}$ is maximal, $\mathscr{A} \vee \mathscr{R} = \mathscr{R}$. Therefore $a \in \mathscr{R}$.

For any observable $x$ associated with $\mathscr{L}$ we write

$$(43) \qquad \mathscr{R}(x) = \{x(E) : E \in \mathscr{B}(R^1)\}.$$

We shall call $\mathscr{R}(x)$ the *range* of $x$.

**Lemma 6.16.** *Let* $\mathscr{R}$ *be a Boolean sub-$\sigma$-algebra of* $\mathscr{L}$. *Then, in order that* $\mathscr{R} = \mathscr{R}(x)$ *for some observable* $x$, *it is necessary and sufficient that* $\mathscr{R}$ *be separable.*

**Proof.** If $\mathscr{R}=\mathscr{R}(x)$ and $\mathscr{D}=\{x(E): E$ an open interval with rational end points$\}$, then $\mathscr{D}$ is a countable subset of $\mathscr{R}$ and $\mathscr{R}$ is the smallest sub-$\sigma$-algebra of itself containing $\mathscr{D}$. $\mathscr{R}$ is thus separable. Conversely, let $\mathscr{R}$ be a separable Boolean sub-$\sigma$-algebra of $\mathscr{L}$. By theorem 1.3, there exists a space $X$, a $\sigma$-algebra $\mathscr{B}$ of subsets of $X$, and a $\sigma$-homomorphism $h$ of $\mathscr{B}$ onto $\mathscr{R}$. Let $\{A_1, A_2, \cdots\}$ be a sequence of subsets of $X$ such that $A_n \in \mathscr{B}$ for all $n$ and $\{h(A_n): n=1, 2, \cdots\}$ generates $\mathscr{R}$. Let $\mathscr{B}_0$ be the sub-$\sigma$-algebra of $\mathscr{B}$ generated by $\{A_n: n=1, 2, \cdots\}$. By theorem 1.6(i), there exists a $\sigma$-homomorphism $u$ of $\mathscr{B}(R^1)$ onto $\mathscr{B}_0$. Define $x$ by

(44) $$x(E) = h(u(E)) \qquad (E \in \mathscr{B}(R^1)).$$

It is obvious that $x$ is an observable and $\mathscr{R}=\mathscr{R}(x)$.

Now to the proof of theorem 6.9. Suppose that $x$ is an observable and $x_\lambda = f_\lambda \circ x$ ($\lambda \in D$), where each $f_\lambda$ is a real Borel function on $R^1$. Then $\mathscr{R}(x_\lambda) \subseteq \mathscr{R}(x)$ and hence $\mathscr{R}(x_\lambda) \leftrightarrow \mathscr{R}(x_{\lambda'})$ for all $\lambda, \lambda' \in D$. This proves that $x_\lambda \leftrightarrow x_{\lambda'}$, for all $\lambda, \lambda' \in D$. Conversely, suppose that $\{x_\lambda\}$ is a family of observables and that $x_\lambda \leftrightarrow x_{\lambda'}$ for all $\lambda, \lambda' \in D$. By corollary 6.15, there exists a Boolean sub-$\sigma$-algebra $\mathscr{R}'$ of $\mathscr{L}$ such that $\mathscr{R}(x_\lambda) \subseteq \mathscr{R}'$ for all $\lambda$. By theorem 1.3, there exists a space $X$, a $\sigma$-algebra $\mathscr{B}$ of subsets of $X$, and a $\sigma$-homomorphism $\tau$ of $\mathscr{B}$ onto $\mathscr{R}'$. It is now clear that for each $\lambda \in D$, there exists, by theorem 1.4, a real valued $\mathscr{B}$-measurable function $g_\lambda$ on $X$ such that, for all $E \in \mathscr{B}(R^1)$,

$$x_\lambda(E) = \tau[g_\lambda^{-1}(E)] \qquad (\lambda \in D).$$

This proves the equation (33). For proving (34) let $\mathscr{R}$ be the smallest sub-$\sigma$-algebra of $\mathscr{R}'$ containing all the $\mathscr{R}(x_\lambda)$. If $\mathscr{L}$ is separable, so is $\mathscr{R}$. On the other hand, if $D$ is countable, and $\mathscr{D}_\lambda$ is a countable set generating $\mathscr{R}(x_\lambda)$, $\bigcup_\lambda \mathscr{D}_\lambda$ is a countable set generating $\mathscr{R}$. Hence $\mathscr{R}$ is separable in either case. By lemma 6.16 there exists an observable $x$ such that $\mathscr{R}(x)=\mathscr{R}$. As $\mathscr{R}(x_\lambda) \subseteq \mathscr{R}(x)$, we conclude from theorem 1.6(ii) that there exists a real Borel function $f_\lambda$ of a real variable such that $x_\lambda = f_\lambda \circ x$. This proves (34) and completes the proof of the entire theorem.

**Remark.** It is obvious that if the $x_\lambda$ satisfy either (33) or (34), $x_\lambda \leftrightarrow x_{\lambda'}$ for all $\lambda, \lambda' \in D$. Theorem 6.9 therefore tells us that the classical logics are precisely those for which any two observables are simultaneously observable. As soon as $\mathscr{L}$ is not a Boolean algebra, it follows that the properties of a physical system which are embodied in the logic $\mathscr{L}$ have too complex a structure to be exhausted by a single set of simultaneously observable quantities. In general, when certain propositions are experimentally verified, certain others cannot be so at the same time.

## 6. FUNCTIONS OF SEVERAL OBSERVABLES

The characterization given in theorem 6.9 of simultaneous observability enables us to construct a calculus of functions of several observables which are mutually simultaneously observable.

**Theorem 6.17.** *Let $\mathscr{L}$ be any logic and $x_1, x_2, \cdots, x_n$ observables such that $x_i \leftrightarrow x_j$ for all $i, j$. Then there exists one and only one $\sigma$-homomorphism $\tau$ of $\mathscr{B}(R^n)$ into $\mathscr{L}$ such that for all $E \in \mathscr{B}(R^1)$ and all $i = 1, 2, \cdots, n$,*

$$（45) \qquad x_i(E) = \tau(\pi_i^{-1}(E)),$$

*where $\pi_i$ is the projection $(t_1, t_2, \cdots, t_n) \to t_i$ of $R^n$ on $R^1$. If $g$ is any real valued Borel function on $R^n$,*

$$(46) \qquad g \circ (x_1, x_2, \cdots, x_n) : E \to \tau(g^{-1}(E))$$

*is an observable. If $g_1, g_2, \cdots, g_k$ are real valued Borel functions on $R^n$ and $y_i = g_i \circ (x_1, \cdots, x_n)$, then $y_1, \cdots, y_k$ are simultaneously observable, and for any real valued Borel function $h$ on $R^k$,*

$$(47) \qquad h \circ (y_1, \cdots, y_k) = (h(g_1, \cdots, g_k)) \circ (x_1, \cdots, x_n),$$

*where $h(g_1, \cdots, g_k)$ is the function*

$$\mathbf{t} = (t_1, \cdots, t_n) \to h(g_1(\mathbf{t}), \cdots, g_k(\mathbf{t})).$$

**Proof.** By theorem 6.9, there exists an observable $x$ and real valued Borel functions $f_1, \cdots, f_n$ of a real variable such that $x_i = f_i \circ x$ for all $i$. Let the Borel map $\mathbf{f}$ of $R^1$ into $R^n$ be defined by

$$\mathbf{f} : t \to (f_1(t), \cdots, f_n(t)).$$

If we define, for $M \in \mathscr{B}(R^n)$,

$$(48) \qquad \tau(M) = x(\mathbf{f}^{-1}(M)),$$

then $\tau$ is a $\sigma$-homomorphism of $\mathscr{B}(R^n)$ into $\mathscr{L}$ which satisfies (45). If $\tau$ and $\tau'$ are two $\sigma$-homomorphisms of $\mathscr{B}(R^n)$ into $\mathscr{L}$ satisfying (45), then

$$\tau(M) = \tau'(M)$$

whenever $M$ is of the form $E_1 \times E_2 \times \cdots \times E_n$, the $E_j$ being Borel subsets of $R^1$. Since the class of such sets generates $\mathscr{B}(R^n)$, it follows that $\tau = \tau'$. The fact that $g \circ (x_1, \cdots, x_n)$ is an observable is trivial. Note that its range is contained in the range $\mathscr{R}$ of $\tau$ which is a Boolean sub-$\sigma$-algebra of $\mathscr{L}$.

Suppose now that $y_i = g_i \circ (x_1, \cdots, x_n)$. Then the range of $y_i$ is contained in $\mathscr{R}$ and hence $y_1, \cdots, y_k$ are simultaneously observable. Let $\mathbf{g}$ be the map $\mathbf{t} \to (g_1(\mathbf{t}), \cdots, g_k(\mathbf{t}))$ of $R^n$ into $R^k$. Then

$$\gamma : M \to \tau(\mathbf{g}^{-1}(M))$$

is a $\sigma$-homomorphism of $\mathscr{B}(R^k)$ into $\mathscr{L}$ such that

$$\gamma(\pi_i^{-1}(E)) = \tau(g_i^{-1}(E)) = y_i(E),$$

$\pi_i$ being the map $(s_1, s_2, \cdots, s_k) \to s_i$ of $R^k$ on $R^1$ $(i = 1, 2, \cdots, k)$. Therefore we conclude from the uniqueness of the map $\tau$ in (45) that, for

$$u = h \circ (y_1, y_2, \cdots, y_k),$$

$$u(E) = \gamma(h^{-1}(E)) \qquad (E \in \mathscr{B}(R^1)).$$

But $\gamma(h^{-1}(E)) = \tau(\mathbf{g}^{-1}(h^{-1}(E)))$, so that we may conclude that

$$h \circ (y_1, \cdots, y_k) = (h(g_1, \cdots, g_k)) \circ (x_1, \cdots, x_n).$$

This proves the theorem.

Theorem 6.17 enables us to define the *joint distributions* of $x_1, \cdots, x_n$. Let $p(a \to p(a))$ be a state of $\mathscr{L}$ and $x_1, \cdots, x_n$ observables such that $x_i \leftrightarrow x_j$ for all $i, j$. We may then clearly define the probability measure $P^p_{x_1, \cdots, x_n}$ on $\mathscr{B}(R^n)$ by

(49)
$$P^p_{x_1, \cdots, x_n}(M) = p(\tau(M)).$$

$P^p_{x_1, \cdots, x_n}$ is called the joint *probability distribution* of $(x_1, \cdots, x_n)$ *in the state p*. It follows easily from (47) that for Borel $M \subseteq R^k$,

(50)
$$P^p_{y_1, \cdots, 1 y_k}(M) = P^p_{x_1, \cdots, x_n}(\mathbf{g}^{-1}(M)),$$

where $\mathbf{g}$ is the map

$$\mathbf{t} = (t_1, \cdots, t_n) \to (g_1(\mathbf{t}), \cdots, g_k(\mathbf{t})).$$

We see from (50) that the rules for the calculation of the joint probability distributions are the standard ones of probability theory.


## 7. THE CENTER OF A LOGIC

We begin by recalling the analysis of Chapter II in which we singled out the geometries among the modular lattices of finite rank by demanding that their centers be trivial. We shall now do the same for logics. The irreducible logics would then have properties very far removed from those of Boolean algebras and would consequently serve as plausible models for the logics of atomic systems.

Let $\mathscr{L}$ be any logic. We define the *center* of $\mathscr{L}$ to be the set $\mathscr{C}$, where

$$(51) \qquad \mathscr{C} = \{a : a \in \mathscr{L}, \quad a \leftrightarrow b, \quad \text{for all } b \in \mathscr{L}\}.$$

$\mathscr{C}$ is nonempty since 0 and 1 are in $\mathscr{C}$. The elements of $\mathscr{C}$ are thus simultaneously verifiable with every element of $\mathscr{L}$. If $x$ is any observable with $\mathscr{R}(x) \subseteq \mathscr{C}$, then for any observable $y$, $x \leftrightarrow y$. Such observables $x$ are called *central*. $\mathscr{L}$ is said to be *irreducible* if $\mathscr{C} = \{0,1\}$. Clearly, $\mathscr{L}$ is irreducible if and only if the only central observables are the constants.

**Theorem 6.18.** *Let $\mathscr{L}$ be any logic and $\mathscr{C}$ its center. Then $\mathscr{C}$ is a Boolean sub-$\sigma$-algebra of $\mathscr{L}$.*

**Proof.** The equations (35) and (36) reveal immediately that $\mathscr{C}$ is a Boolean subalgebra of $\mathscr{L}$. If $a_1, \cdots, a_r, \cdots$ is a sequence of elements in $\mathscr{C}$, then $b \leftrightarrow a_r$ for all $r(b \in \mathscr{L})$ and so $\bigvee_n a_n \leftrightarrow b$ by (35). Hence $\bigvee_n a_n \in \mathscr{C}$ also. This proves that $\mathscr{C}$ is a Boolean sub-$\sigma$-algebra of $\mathscr{L}$.

Since the Boolean $\sigma$-algebras have relatively familiar structure, one may ask whether a decomposition of $\mathscr{L}$ over $\mathscr{C}$ analogous to that of theorem 2.14 can be carried out. There is no difficulty in doing this when $\mathscr{C}$ is *discrete*, i.e., when there exists an at most denumerable set $\{a_n\}_{n \in D}$ of mutually orthogonal elements of $\mathscr{C}$ such that (i) $\bigvee_n a_n = 1$; (ii) $\mathscr{C}$ consists precisely of all the lattice sums $\bigvee_{n \in Z} a_n$, where $Z$ is an arbitrary subset of $D$. The $a_n$ are called the *atoms* of $\mathscr{C}$. If $\mathscr{C}$ is not discrete, then such decompositions seem much more difficult to obtain.

On the other hand, let us define $\mathscr{C}$ to be *continuous* if, given any $c \in \mathscr{C}$ which is nonzero, there exists a nonzero $c_1 \in \mathscr{C}$ such that $c_1 < c$, $c_1 \neq c$. We shall prove that when $\mathscr{C}$ is continuous and separable, $\mathscr{L}$ does not have any pure states.

**Theorem 6.19.** *Let $\mathscr{L}$ be any logic and let $\mathscr{C}$ be its center. Let $\mathscr{P}$ be the set of pure states of $\mathscr{L}$. Suppose that $\mathscr{C}$ is discrete and that $\{a_n : n \in D\}$ is the family of atoms of $\mathscr{C}$. Then for each $n \in D$, $\mathscr{L}[0,a_n] = \mathscr{L}_n$ is an irreducible logic. If $p$ is a pure state of $\mathscr{L}_n$ and we define $p^{\sim}$ on $\mathscr{L}$ by*

$$(52) \qquad p^{\sim}(a) = p(a \wedge a_n) \qquad (a \in \mathscr{L}),$$

*then $p^{\sim}$ is a pure state of $\mathscr{L}$. If*

$$(53) \qquad \mathscr{P}_n = \{p^{\sim} : p \text{ a pure state of } \mathscr{L}_n\},$$

*then the $\{\mathscr{P}_n : n \in D\}$ are disjoint subsets of $\mathscr{P}$ and*

$$(54) \qquad \mathscr{P} = \bigcup_{n \in D} \mathscr{P}_n.$$

*If $\mathscr{C}$ is continuous and separable, $\mathscr{P}$ is empty, i.e., $\mathscr{L}$ has no pure states.*

**Proof.** We have already noted that for any $n$, $\mathscr{L}[0,a_n]=\mathscr{L}_n$ is a logic (corollary 6.3). We prove that $\mathscr{L}_n$ is irreducible. In fact, let $c<a_n$ be such that $c\leftrightarrow\mathscr{L}_n$. Clearly, $c\leftrightarrow a$ for all $a<a_n$. On the other hand, as $a_n\in\mathscr{C}$, $a_n\leftrightarrow b$ for any $b\in\mathscr{L}$, so that $b=(b\wedge a_n)\vee(b\wedge a_n^{\perp})$ (cf. (36)). Now $c\leftrightarrow b\wedge a_n$ as $b\wedge a_n<a_n$ while $c\leftrightarrow b\wedge a_n^{\perp}$ since $c\perp b\wedge a_n^{\perp}$. Therefore (35) enables us to conclude that $c\leftrightarrow b$. This shows that $c\in\mathscr{C}$ and hence that $c=0$ or $c=a_n$. This proves the irreducibility of $\mathscr{L}_n$.

Suppose next that $p$ is a pure state of $\mathscr{L}_n$. Equation (52) defines $p^{\sim}$ as a function on $\mathscr{L}$. From the equations (35) and (36) it follows that $p^{\sim}$ is a state of $\mathscr{L}$. We claim that $p^{\sim}$ is a pure state of $\mathscr{L}$. Suppose that $p^{\sim}=cp_1+(1-c)p_2$, where $0\leq c\leq1$ and $p_1$, $p_2$ are states of $\mathscr{L}$. Since $p^{\sim}(a_n^{\perp})=0$,

$$p_1(a_n^{\perp}) = p_2(a_n^{\perp}) = 0.$$

Hence $p_1(a_n)=p_2(a_n)=1$, and hence the restrictions of $p_1$ and $p_2$ to $\mathscr{L}_n$ are states of $\mathscr{L}_n$. Since $p$ is a pure state of $\mathscr{L}_n$, it follows that

$$p(a) = p_1(a) = p_2(a)$$

for all $a<a_n$. But then for any $b\in\mathscr{L}$, we see that $p^{\sim}(b)=p_1(b)=p_2(b)$ since, by (36), $b=(b\wedge a_n)\vee(b\wedge a_n^{\perp})$ and $p^{\sim}$, $p_1$, $p_2$ vanish for $b\wedge a_n^{\perp}$. $p^{\sim}$ is thus a pure state of $\mathscr{L}$. If $m,n\in D$ and $m\neq n$, $\mathscr{P}_m\cap\mathscr{P}_n=\varnothing$, for, if $q\in\mathscr{P}_m$ and $q'\in\mathscr{P}_n$, $q(a_m)=1$ while $q'(a_m)=0$.

We show now that each element of $\mathscr{P}$ lies in some $\mathscr{P}_n$. Suppose that $p$ is a pure state of $\mathscr{L}$. We claim that $p(a_n)=1$ for some $n\in D$. Otherwise there will be some $m\in D$ such that $0<p(a_m)<1$. Define $q_1$ and $q_2$ on $\mathscr{L}$ by

(55)
$$q_1(a) = (p(a_m))^{-1}p(a\wedge a_m),$$
$$q_2(a) = (1-p(a_m))^{-1}p(a\wedge a_m^{\perp}).$$

Since $a_m\in\mathscr{C}$, it can be easily verified using (35) and (36) that $q_1$ and $q_2$ are states of $\mathscr{L}$. Since $q_1(a_m)=1$, and $q_2(a_m)=0$, $q_1\neq q_2$. As

$$p = p(a_m)\cdot q_1+(1-p(a_m))\cdot q_2,$$

$p$ is not pure, a contradiction. Therefore $p(a_n)=1$ for some $n\in D$. The argument given in the previous paragraph can now be repeated to enable us to conclude that the restriction of $p$ to $\mathscr{L}_n$, say $q$, is a pure state of $\mathscr{L}_n$ and that $p=q^{\sim}$. This proves that $p\in\mathscr{P}_n$ and completes the proof of (54).

We now come to the proof of the last assertion. Assume that $\mathscr{C}$ is continuous and separable. Suppose that $p$ is a state of $\mathscr{L}$. We assert first that for some $c\in\mathscr{C}$, $0<p(c)<1$. If this is not true, then $p(c)=0$ or 1 for each $c\in\mathscr{C}$. Since $\mathscr{C}$ is separable, there exists a countable set

$$\mathscr{D} = \{c_1, c_2, \cdots\}$$

such that $\mathscr{D}$ generates $\mathscr{C}$. Since $p(c_n)=0$ or 1, we may, by replacing $c_n$ by

$c_n^\perp$ if necessary, assume that $p(c_n)=1$ for all $n$. Let $c_0=\bigwedge_n c_n$. Clearly, $p(c_0)=1$. In particular, $c_0\neq 0$. We assert that $c_0$ is an atom of $\mathscr{C}$. In fact, the subset of all elements $c$ in $\mathscr{C}$ such that either $c \perp c_0$ or $c > c_0$, is a sub-$\sigma$-algebra of $\mathscr{C}$ containing all the $c_n$ and so coincides with $\mathscr{C}$; this shows that if $a < c_0$ and $a \in \mathscr{C}$, then $a=0$ or $a=c_0$. This contradicts the assumption that $\mathscr{C}$ is continuous. Consequently, our assumption that $p$ is two-valued on $\mathscr{C}$ is untenable. Let then $d \in \mathscr{C}$ be such that $0 < p(d) < 1$. Define $q_1$ and $q_2$ on $\mathscr{L}$ by

$$q_1(a) = (p(d))^{-1}p(a \wedge d), \qquad q_2(a) = (1-p(d))^{-1}p(a \wedge d^\perp).$$

Then $p=p(d)q_1+(1-p(d))q_2$ and $p$ is not pure. The proof of the theorem is complete.

We shall end this section with a few remarks of a general nature regarding the Heisenberg uncertainty principle. We must point out that a considerable part of its meaning is physical and we do not go into this here (cf. the discussions of von Neumann [1] and Heisenberg [1]). We shall be concerned only with mathematical formulations.

Suppose that $\mathfrak{S}$ is a quantum mechanical system and $\mathscr{L}=\mathscr{L}(\mathfrak{S})$ its logic. For any observable $x$ associated with $\mathscr{L}$ and any state $p$ of $\mathscr{L}$, we write $\sigma_p^2(x)$ for the variance of $x$ in the state $p$ (defined only when $\mathscr{E}(x^2|p) < \infty$):

$$(56) \qquad \sigma_p^2(x) = \mathscr{E}(x^2|p)-(\mathscr{E}(x|p))^2.$$

If $\sigma_p(x)=0$, then the probability distribution of $x$ in the state $p$ is concentrated at the point $\mathscr{E}(x|p)$. $x$ has then a sharply defined value in the state $p$. One might ask the question whether there are states in which *every observable* has, if not a sharply defined value, at least a small variance. The Heisenberg principle of uncertainty asserts that even this is not possible. Roughly speaking, it asserts that in any state, no matter how prepared, there are observables whose distributions have large variances. Notice that this is not possible if the logic is a Boolean $\sigma$-algebra of subsets of a space. In fact, let $\mathscr{L}$ be the $\sigma$-algebra of subsets of a set $X$. Then, for any observable with corresponding function $f$, the observable has a sharply defined value $f(x_0)$ whenever the state $p$ is a measure concentrated in a point $x_0$ of $X$. On the other hand, let us assume that $\mathfrak{S}$ is the physical system of some atomic particle and that $x$ and $y$ are the position and momentum observables along some direction in space. If we assume that the logic $\mathscr{L}$ of $\mathfrak{S}$ is the standard logic associated with the complex number field, then

$$(57) \qquad \sigma_p(x)\sigma_p(y) \geq \tfrac{1}{2}\hbar,$$

where $\hbar$ is Planck's constant divided by $2\pi$ (cf. H. Weyl [1] pp. 77 and 393–394 for a rigorous derivation). From (57) it follows quite simply that in any state in which the distribution of $x$ has small variance (i.e., $x$ is "localized"), the distribution of $y$ has very large variance. It is obvious that this is a property of the structure of the logic $\mathscr{L}$ of $\mathfrak{S}$.

## 8. AUTOMORPHISMS

Let $\mathscr{L}$ be a logic, $\mathcal{O}$ the set of observables of $\mathscr{L}$, and $\mathscr{S}$ the set of all states of $\mathscr{L}$. The set of all automorphisms of $\mathscr{L}$ forms a group in a natural fashion, denoted by $\mathrm{Aut}(\mathscr{L})$. We shall now introduce the notion of an automorphism of $\mathscr{S}$. By a *convex automorphism of* $\mathscr{S}$ we mean a map

(58) $$\xi : p \to p^\xi \qquad (p \in \mathscr{S})$$

such that

(59)
  (i)  $\xi$ is one-one and maps $\mathscr{S}$ onto itself,
  (ii)  if $c_1, c_2, \cdots$ are numbers $\geq 0$ with $\sum_n c_n = 1$, and $p_1, p_2, \cdots \in \mathscr{S}$,

$$\left( \sum_n c_n p_n \right)^\xi = \sum_n c_n p_n{}^\xi.$$

From (ii) of (59) it follows at once that convex automorphisms of $\mathscr{S}$ send pure states of $\mathscr{L}$ into pure states of $\mathscr{L}$ and that the correspondences induced in the set of pure states are one-one and onto.

If

(60) $$\alpha : a \to a^\alpha \qquad (a \in \mathscr{L})$$

is an automorphism of $\mathscr{L}$ and if, for $p \in \mathscr{S}$ we define $p^\alpha$ by

(61) $$p^\alpha(a) = p(a^{(\alpha^{-1})}),$$

then $p \to p^\alpha$ is a convex automorphism of $\mathscr{S}$. We shall call it the automorphism *induced* by $\alpha$. The set of all convex automorphisms of $\mathscr{S}$ also forms a group denoted by $\mathrm{Aut}(\mathscr{S})$.

Let $\mathscr{L}$ be a $\sigma$-algebra of subsets of a space $X$, and let

$$t : x \to t(x) \qquad (x \in X)$$

be any one-one map of $X$ onto itself such that for any set $A \subseteq X$, $A \in \mathscr{L}$ if and only if $t^{-1}(A) \in \mathscr{L}$. When $X$ and $\mathscr{L}$ satisfy some technical regularity conditions, it can be shown that every sufficiently well-behaved automorphism of $\mathscr{S}$ is induced by a mapping $t$ such as the one described above. Suppose $X$ is the phase space of a classical mechanical system with a $C^\infty$ manifold $M$ as its configuration space. $X$ thus appears (cf. Chapter I) as the cotangent bundle of $M$. In this case, the subgroup of those automorphisms of $\mathscr{L}$ induced by (both ways) differentiable homeomorphisms of $X$ onto itself and which preserve the canonical 2-form on $X$, plays undoubtedly a very crucial role (contact transformations).

The axioms satisfied by an arbitrary logic are too weak to allow any reasonable determination of its automorphisms. In the next chapter we shall determine the automorphisms associated with standard logics. In the meantime, we shall briefly illustrate with two (among many) examples the important role played by the group $\text{Aut}(\mathscr{L})$ in physical problems.

As a first example we consider the problem of describing the dynamics of a physical system $\mathfrak{S}$. Let $\mathscr{L}$ be the logic of $\mathfrak{S}$, $\mathscr{S}$ the convex set of all its states. Then, for each real number $t$, there exists a unique one-one map of $\mathscr{S}$ onto itself, say $D(t)$, with the following physical interpretation; if $p \in \mathscr{S}$ is the state of $\mathfrak{S}$ at time $t_0$, then $D(t)p$ is the state of $\mathfrak{S}$ at time $t + t_0$. The dynamical group $\mathscr{D}$ where

$$(62) \qquad \mathscr{D} : t \to D(t)$$

satisfies the conditions (3) of Chapter I. We now postulate that each $D(t)$ is in fact an automorphism of $\mathscr{S}$, i.e., if $p_1, p_2, \cdots$ is a sequence of elements of $\mathscr{S}$ and $c_1, c_2, \cdots$ a sequence of nonnegative numbers such that $c_1 + c_2 + \cdots = 1$, then, for each $t$,

$$(63) \qquad D(t)\Big(\sum_i c_i p_i\Big) = \sum_i c_i D(t)p_i.$$

This postulate may be justified by the following argument. Suppose one does not know the state at time 0 but only that it is one of $p_1, p_2, \cdots$ with probabilities $c_1, c_2, \cdots$, respectively. Then from the fact that the state at time $t$ is $D(t)p_i$ if the state time 0 is $p_i$, it follows that at time $t$ the state of the system $\mathfrak{S}$ is one of $D(t)p_1, D(t)p_2, \cdots$ with the same probabilities $c_1, c_2, \cdots$. But the statement that the state of $\mathscr{L}$ (or $\mathfrak{S}$) is one of $q_1, q_2, \cdots$ with probabilities $c_1, c_2, \cdots$ is physically equivalent to the statement that the state of $\mathscr{L}$ is $c_1 q_1 + c_2 q_2 + \cdots$. This proves the validity of (63). It follows now that each $D(t)$ leaves invariant the subset of pure states of $\mathscr{L}$ and induces a one-one mapping on it. Furthermore, if $a \in \mathscr{L}$, then, for each $p \in \mathscr{S}$,

$$(64) \qquad t \to (D(t)p)(a)$$

is a real valued function of $t$; it is physically reasonable to assume that for any $\mathfrak{S}$, this function is Borel for each $p \in \mathscr{S}$ and $a \in \mathscr{L}$. If this condition is satisfied, we call $\mathscr{D}$ a *Borel one-parameter group. Thus the dynamical group of $\mathfrak{S}$ may be assumed to be a Borel one-parameter group of convex automorphisms of $\mathscr{S}$.*

This leads us to introduce the concept of representations of groups. Let $G$ be a locally compact topological group satisfying the second axiom of countability. The sets of the smallest $\sigma$ algebra of subsets of $G$

containing the open sets are called the *Borel sets* in $G$. By a *representation of $G$ in* $\mathrm{Aut}(\mathscr{S})$ we mean a map

$$(65) \qquad\qquad T : g \to T_g \qquad (g \in G)$$

of $G$ such that

     (i)   each $T_g \in \mathrm{Aut}(\mathscr{S})$,

$(66)$  (ii)  $T_{g_1 g_2} = T_{g_1} T_{g_2} \qquad (g_1, g_2 \in G)$,

     (iii)  for each $a \in \mathscr{L}$ and $p \in \mathscr{S}$, the function $g \to (T_g p)(a)$ is Borel on $G$.

With these definitions we may say that the dynamical group of a system $\mathfrak{S}$ is determined by a representation of the additive group of real numbers into $\mathrm{Aut}(\mathscr{S})$, where $\mathscr{S}$ is the set of states of the logic $\mathscr{L}$ of $\mathfrak{S}$.

As our second example, we consider the problem of describing the quantum mechanical theory of a free particle. The configuration space of the particle in classical mechanics is the three-dimensional space, denoted by $M$. Let $\mathscr{L}$ be the logic of the physical system under consideration and $\mathscr{S}$ the convex set of its states. Suppose now an observer $O$ wants to describe the system. He would then select a point of $M$, an orthogonal frame at $O$, and map $M$ onto $R^3$ by a map

$$(67) \qquad\qquad \gamma_O : M \to R^3.$$

Let $O'$ be another observer and let $\gamma_{O'}$ be the corresponding map. Then there exists a unique Euclidean motion $D_{O,O'}$ of $R^3$ such that for all $m \in M$

$$(68) \qquad\qquad \gamma_{O'}(m) = D_{O,O'}(\gamma_O(m)).$$

Suppose now $O$ describes the state of the system $\mathfrak{S}$ by an element $p_O \in \mathscr{S}$. Then, $O'$, using his orientation, would describe the same physical state by an element $p_{O'}$ of $\mathscr{S}$. It is clear that the map $p_O \to p_{O'}$ is an *automorphism*, say $\alpha_{O,O'}$ of $\mathscr{S}$. In other words, $\alpha_{O,O'}$ has the following physical interpretation: if the physical state of $\mathfrak{S}$ is described by $O$ by the element $g \in \mathscr{S}$, then $\alpha_{O,O'}(g)$ is the element of $\mathscr{S}$ describing the same physical state of $\mathfrak{S}$ from the point of view of $O'$. It is obvious that $\alpha_{O,O'}$ is the identity for $O = O'$, and

$$(69) \qquad\qquad \alpha_{O,O''} = \alpha_{O',O''} \alpha_{O,O'}.$$

We now remark that the basic physical laws of $\mathfrak{S}$ are independent of the choice of observers and their frames. Therefore, we may conclude that $\alpha_{O,O'}$ depends only on the transformation $D_{O,O'}$. Let $G$ be the group of all

Euclidean motions of $R^3$. Then, from (68), (69), and the above remarks on the $\alpha_{O,O'}$, we infer the existence of a homomorphism

$$(70) \qquad\qquad T : g \to T_g$$

of $G$ into $\mathrm{Aut}(\mathscr{S})$ with the property that whenever $O$ and $O'$ are two observers of $\mathfrak{S}$,

$$(71) \qquad\qquad \alpha_{O,O'} = T_{D_{O,O'}}.$$

We may reasonably make the assumption that for each $a \in \mathscr{L}$ and $p \in \mathscr{S}$, $g \to (T_g p)(a)$ is a Borel function on $G$. $T$ is thus a representation of $G$ in $\mathrm{Aut}(\mathscr{S})$.

We see thus that the description of $\mathfrak{S}$ gives rise to a representation of $G$ in $\mathrm{Aut}(\mathscr{S})$. The determination of such representations is therefore the basic problem to be solved in the mathematical description of the physical system of a free particle.

The reader might notice that the arguments given above are very general. In fact, the same type of arguments lead to the remarkable fact that with every *relativistic free particle* there is associated a representation of the *inhomogeneous Lorentz group*. These representations were first completely determined by Wigner under the assumption that the logic of $\mathfrak{S}$ was standard. This led in turn to his celebrated classification of the relativistic wave equations [1].

# CHAPTER VII

# LOGICS ASSOCIATED WITH HILBERT SPACES

## 1. THE LATTICE OF SUBSPACES OF A BANACH SPACE

The general theory that was developed in Chapter VI is concerned mainly with the broad principles of Quantum Theory. Further development of the theory, such as a discussion of simple quantum mechanical systems, leads to problems of a more technical nature. These problems are, however, difficult to answer in the context of abstract logics, and therefore, in dealing with them, it becomes necessary to restrict the class of logics under consideration. In this chapter we shall examine some of these logics and describe, in a somewhat more concrete fashion than in Chapter VI, the observables, states, and symmetries associated with them.

We have seen in Chapter IV that a large class of orthocomplemented geometries are obtained by considering Hilbert space structures on finite dimensional vector spaces. These logics are, however, not of much use in discussing even very simple atomic systems, since every observable associated with them is discrete. Consequently, if one wants to obtain realistic examples, one is forced to deal with *infinite dimensional* vector spaces.

It is known (cf. Baer [1]) that the lattice of *all* linear manifolds of an infinite dimensional vector space does not admit any polarity. Therefore it becomes necessary to consider lattices $\mathscr{L}$ such that the elements of $\mathscr{L}$ are certain linear manifolds of a given vector space $V$ and, wherein, the partial ordering is the inclusion relation. It must be noted that the lattice sum of two elements of such a lattice contains, but in general does not coincide with, the algebraic sum in $V$. A simple and interesting class of such lattices may be obtained in the following way. Let **D** be a topological division ring, say, for example, one of **R**, **C**, or **Q**. Let $V$ be a topological vector space over **D** (cf. Bourbaki [2] for the definitions and elementary properties). Then, the set of all *closed* linear manifolds of $V$ is a lattice—in fact, a complete lattice. One may then construct examples of logics whose underlying lattices are these lattices of closed manifolds. The description of such logics would provide us with a large class of examples of logics which are complex enough to serve as models for the logics of atomic systems.

The main purpose of this section is to prove a theorem of Kakutani and Mackey ([1]), which asserts that if $V$ is a Banach space, the above procedure leads to no new examples of logics other than the standard ones. In particular, if the underlying lattice of a logic is isomorphic to the lattice of all closed linear manifolds of a separable *infinite dimensional* Banach space over one of **R**, **C**, or **Q**, then the logic is standard.

Let **D** be one of **R**, **C**, or **Q** and $V$ any vector space over **D**. We shall say that a topology $\mathcal{T}$ on $V$ is *compatible* with the vector space structure of $V$ if it is Hausdorff, and, if the map, $a, b, x, y \to a \cdot x + b \cdot y$ of $\mathbf{D} \times \mathbf{D} \times V \times V$ into $V$, is continuous. A *topological vector space* over **D** is a pair $(V, \mathcal{T})$, where $V$ is a vector space over **D**, and $\mathcal{T}$, a topology over $V$ compatible with its vector space structure. By the usual abuse of language we shall say that $V$ is a topological vector space. We shall denote by $\mathcal{L}(V, \mathbf{D})$ the lattice of all closed linear manifolds of $V$. This is a complete lattice. If we denote by $\vee$ and $\wedge$ the lattice operations in $\mathcal{L}(V, \mathbf{D})$, then, for any family $\{M_\alpha\}$ of closed linear manifolds of $V$, we have:

$$(1) \qquad \bigwedge_\alpha M_\alpha = \bigcap_\alpha M_\alpha,$$

$$(2) \qquad \bigvee_\alpha M_\alpha = \left( \sum_\alpha M_\alpha \right)^-,$$

where $\sum$ denotes the algebraic sum, and the bar denotes closure. If $N$ is any *finite dimensional* linear manifold of $V$, then $N$ is necessarily closed and for any closed linear manifold $M$, $N \vee M = N + M$. Moreover, if $M$ is a closed linear manifold whose codimension $(= \dim V/M)$ is finite and $N$ any algebraic complement of $M$, i.e., such that $M \cap N = 0$, $M + N = V$, then $N$ is necessarily closed and $V = M \vee N$ (for these facts cf. Bourbaki [2], Ch. 1).

We shall recall the notion of Banach spaces. Let **D** be one of **R**, **C**, or **Q** and $V$ a vector space over **D**. A *norm* over $V$ is a function $x \to \|x\|$ of $V$ into the real numbers such that

$$(3) \qquad \begin{array}{ll} \text{(i)} & \|x\| \geq 0, \ = 0 \quad \text{if and only if} \quad x = 0, \\ \text{(ii)} & \|x + y\| \leq \|x\| + \|y\| \quad \text{for} \quad x, y \in V, \\ \text{(iii)} & \|cx\| = |c| \cdot \|x\| \quad \text{for} \quad c \in \mathbf{D}, x \in V. \end{array}$$

A Banach space over **D** is a pair $(V, \|\cdot\|)$, where $V$ is a vector space over **D** and $\|\cdot\|$ a norm on $V$ such that $V$ is complete under the metric $d$ defined by $d(x,y) = \|x - y\|$. A Banach space over **D** is obviously a topological vector space over **D**.

We are now in a position to formulate the theorem of Kakutani and Mackey. We recall the notion of Hilbert spaces and inner products associated with **D** (cf. Chapter IV, section 3).

**Theorem 7.1.** (*Kakutani-Mackey* [1]). *Let* **D** *be one of the three division rings* **R**, **C**, *or* **Q**, *V an infinite dimensional Banach space over* **D**, *and* $\mathscr{L} = \mathscr{L}(V,\mathbf{D})$ *the lattice of all closed linear manifolds of V. Suppose that* $\perp (M \to M^{\perp})$ *is an orthocomplementation of* $\mathscr{L}$. *Then there exists a* **D**-*valued inner product* $\langle \,.\,,\,.\,\rangle$ *on* $V \times V$ *such that* (i) *V becomes, under* $\langle \,.\,,\,.\,\rangle$, *a Hilbert space over* **D**; (ii) *the topology of V, induced by the norm associated with* $\langle \,.\,,\,.\,\rangle$, *coincides with its original topology; and* (iii) *the map* $M \to M^{\perp}$ *coincides with the orthocomplementation induced by* $\langle \,.\,,\,.\,\rangle$. *In particular, if the underlying lattice of a logic is isomorphic to the lattice of closed linear manifolds of a separable Banach space of infinite dimension over* **D**, *then the logic is standard.*

The proof is rather long and depends on a series of lemmas. With later applications in mind we formulate our first lemma somewhat more generally than is necessary for our immediate purposes.

**Lemma 7.2.** *Let* **K** *be a division ring and W a vector space of infinite dimension over* **K**. *Let* $\mathscr{M}$ *be a lattice of linear manifolds of W such that* (i) $\mathscr{M}$ *contains all finite dimensional linear manifolds of W, and* (ii) *if* $M, N \in \mathscr{M}$ *and at least one of them is finite dimensional, then* $M \vee N = M + N$. *Suppose* $\mathscr{M}(M \to M^{\perp})$ *is an orthocomplementation in* $\mathscr{M}$. *Let* $w_0 \in W$ *be any nonzero vector. Then there exists an involutive anti-automorphism* $\theta$ *of* **K** *and a symmetric* $\theta$-*bilinear form* $\langle \,.\,,\,.\,\rangle$ *on* $W \times W$ *such that* (i) $\langle w_0,w_0 \rangle = 1$ *and* (ii) $\langle x,y \rangle = 0$ *if and only if* $x \in (\mathbf{K} \cdot y)^{\perp} \cdot \theta$ *and* $\langle \,.\,,\,.\,\rangle$ *are uniquely determined. The form* $\langle \,.\,,\,.\,\rangle$ *is definite, i.e.,* $\langle x,x \rangle = 0$ *if and only if* $x = 0$.

**Proof.** Let $F \subseteq W$ be a finite dimensional linear manifold. Then $F \in \mathscr{M}$. For any linear manifold $L \subseteq F$ we have $L \in \mathscr{M}$ also. We now define

$$(4) \qquad\qquad \xi_F(L) = L^{\perp} \cap F.$$

Note that if $M$ is finite dimensional and $N \in \mathscr{M}$, then $M \wedge N = M \cap N$. In fact, $M \wedge N \subseteq M \cap N$ always while the finite dimensionality of $M \cap N$ implies, by (i), that $M \cap N \in \mathscr{M}$, so that $M \cap N \subseteq M \wedge N$.

Let $\mathscr{M}_F$ be the projective geometry of all linear manifolds $L \subseteq F$. $\xi_F$ is a map of $\mathscr{M}_F$ into itself. We shall show first that $\xi_F$ is an orthocomplementation of $\mathscr{M}_F$. Clearly $\xi_F(0) = F$, $\xi_F(F) = F^{\perp} \cap F = F^{\perp} \wedge F = 0$. Since $M \to M^{\perp}$ is order inverting, it is obvious that $\xi_F$ is order inverting. We observe next that for $L \in \mathscr{M}_F$, $L \cap \xi_F(L) \subseteq L \cap L^{\perp} = L \wedge L^{\perp} = 0$. On the other hand, $W = L \vee L^{\perp} = L + L^{\perp}$ so that $F = L + \xi_F(L)$. Thus $L$ and $\xi_F(L)$ are complements of each other in $\mathscr{M}_F$. To complete the proof that $\xi_F$ is an orthocomplementation, it remains to prove that $\xi_F$ is involutive. For $L \in \mathscr{M}_F$, $\xi_F(L) \subseteq L^{\perp}$ so that $L \subseteq \xi_F(L)^{\perp}$. This shows that $L \subseteq \xi_F(L)^{\perp} \cap F = \xi_F(\xi_F(L))$ for all $L \in \mathscr{M}_F$. Let $L' = \xi_F(L)$. Then, by what we proved just now, $\xi_F(L')$ is a complement of $L'$ in $\mathscr{M}_F$. But $L$ is also a complement of $L' = \xi_F(L)$ and we have seen that $L \subseteq \xi_F(L')$. This shows that $L$ must coincide with $\xi_F(L')$. We see thus that $\xi_F$ is an orthocomplementation of $\mathcal{M}_F$.

We shall fix a nonzero vector $w_0 \in W$. Let $\mathcal{F}$ be the class of all finite dimensional linear manifolds $F \subseteq W$ such that (i) $w_0 \in F$, (ii) dim $F \geq 3$. By theorem 4.6 there exists, for any $F \in \mathcal{F}$, an involutive anti-automorphism $\theta_F$ of $\mathbf{K}$ and a nonsingular symmetric $\theta_F$-bilinear form $\langle . , . \rangle_F$ on $F \times F$ such that $\langle . , . \rangle_F$ induces $\xi_F$; i.e., for $L$,

(5) $$\xi_F(L) = \{u : u \in F, \langle x,u \rangle_F = 0 \quad \text{for} \quad \text{all } x \in L\}$$

and

(6) $$\langle w_0,w_0 \rangle = 1.$$

Moreover, (6) determines $\theta_F$ and $\langle . , . \rangle_F$ uniquely. Suppose now that $F_1, F_2 \in \mathcal{F}$ with $F_1 \subseteq F_2$. Then, for any $L \in \mathcal{M}_{F_1}$,

$$\xi_{F_1}(L) = L^\perp \cap F_1 = \{\xi_{F_2}(L)\} \cap F_1.$$

This shows that for any $L \in \mathcal{M}_{F_1}$,

(7) $$\xi_{F_1}(L) = \{u : u \in F_1, \langle x,u \rangle_{F_2} = 0 \quad \text{for all} \quad x \in L\}.$$

In other words, the restriction of $\langle . , . \rangle_{F_2}$ to $F_1 \times F_1$ is a $\theta_{F_2}$-bilinear form which also induces the orthocomplementation $\xi_{F_1}$. In view of the normalizing condition (6), we may conclude at once that

(8) $$\theta_{F_2} = \theta_{F_1},$$
$$\langle x,y \rangle_{F_2} = \langle x,y \rangle_{F_1} \qquad (x, y \in F_1).$$

Since any two elements of $\mathcal{F}$ are contained in a third element of $\mathcal{F}$, we easily deduce from (8) that there exists an involutive anti-automorphism $\theta$ of $\mathbf{K}$, and a symmetric $\theta$-bilinear form $\langle . , . \rangle$ on $W \times W$ such that (i) $\theta = \theta_F$ for all $F \in \mathcal{F}$, and (ii) the restriction of $\langle . , . \rangle$ to $F \times F$ is $\langle . , . \rangle_F$ for all $F \in \mathcal{F}$. Lemma 7.2 follows at once from this.

We now resume our discussion of the lattice $\mathcal{L}$ of all closed linear manifolds of the Banach space $V$ over $\mathbf{D}$. We take $V = W$ in lemma 7.2 and obtain an involutive anti-automorphism $\theta$ of $\mathbf{D}$ and a definite symmetric $\theta$-bilinear form $\langle . , . \rangle$ on $V \times V$ such that $\langle x,y \rangle = 0$ if and only if $x \perp y$. We fix a nonzero vector $v_0 \in V$; then $\theta$ and $\langle . , . \rangle$ are uniquely determined by the condition $\langle v_0,v_0 \rangle = 1$.

Let $V^*$ be the set of all *continuous* linear maps of $V$ into $\mathbf{D}$. Using the definitions of section 1 of Chapter IV, it is easy to see that $V^*$ is a vector space over $\mathbf{D}^0$, the division ring dual to $\mathbf{D}$. For any $u \in V$, let $\beta_u$ be the linear map of $V$ into $\mathbf{D}$ defined by

(9) $$\beta_u(x) = \langle x,u \rangle \qquad (x \in V).$$

We shall also use the conjugate norm on $V^*$; this is defined by

$$(10) \qquad \|\lambda\| = \sup_{\|u\| \le 1} |\lambda(u)| \qquad (\lambda \in V^*).$$

It is well known that $V^*$, under this norm, is a Banach space over the division ring $\mathbf{D}^0$.

**Lemma 7.3.** $\beta_u \in V^*$ *for any* $u \in V$. *Moreover,* $u \to \beta_u$ *is an additive isomorphism of the abelian group* $V$ *onto the abelian group* $V^*$.

**Proof.** It is a well known fact (cf. Bourbaki [2]) that a linear map $\lambda$ of $V$ into $\mathbf{D}$ is continuous if and only if the linear manifold

$$(11) \qquad Z_\lambda = \{x : x \in V, \quad \lambda(x) = 0\}$$

is closed in $V$. Let now $\lambda = \beta_u$, and write $Z_u$ for $Z_\lambda$, $u \in V$. If $y \in V$, $y \in Z_u$ if and only if $\langle y, u \rangle = 0$, i.e., if and only if $y \perp u$. Hence

$$(12) \qquad Z_u = (\mathbf{D} \cdot u)^\perp.$$

But $(\mathbf{D} \cdot u)^\perp \in \mathscr{L}$ and is therefore closed by assumption. This proves that $\beta_u \in V^*$. The map $u \to \beta_u$ is clearly additive. If, for $u \in V$, $\beta_u = 0$, then $\langle u, u \rangle = \beta_u(u) = 0$; this implies that $u = 0$. In order to complete the proof of the lemma it remains to prove only that $u \to \beta_u$ maps $V$ onto $V^*$. Suppose $\lambda \in V^*$ and $\neq 0$. Let $Z_\lambda$ be defined by (11). Then $Z_\lambda \in \mathscr{L}$ and $Z_\lambda \neq V$. Therefore $Z_\lambda^\perp \neq 0$. Let $u$ be a nonzero vector in $Z_\lambda^\perp$. Since $\langle x, u \rangle = 0$ for all $x \in Z_\lambda$, $\beta_u$ vanishes over $Z_\lambda$; and since $u \neq 0$, $\beta_u \neq 0$. Since $Z_\lambda$ and $Z_u$ are both of codimension 1 and $Z_\lambda \subseteq Z_u$, we infer that $Z_\lambda = Z_u$. Let $x_0 \in V$ be such that $\lambda(x_0) = 1$. Since $x_0 \notin Z_\lambda$, $x_0 \notin Z_u$ and hence

$$\beta_u(x_0) = \langle x_0, u \rangle \neq 0.$$

Let $c = \langle x_0, u \rangle^{-1}$ and let us write $u_0 = c^\theta u$. Then for $x \in V$,

$$\langle x, u_0 \rangle = \langle x, u \rangle c.$$

This shows that $\beta_{u_0}(x_0) = 1 = \lambda(x_0)$ and implies that $\beta_{u_0} = \lambda$.

The main question at this stage is whether $\theta$ is continuous. The nontrivial case is when $\mathbf{D} = \mathbf{C}$ and we handle it first. It is at this point that essential use is made of the infinite dimensionality of $V$.

**Lemma 7.4.** *Let* $W$ *be a complex Banach space of infinite dimension. Then one can find a sequence of vectors* $x_1, x_2, \cdots \in W$ *with the property that, for any bounded infinite sequence* $\{c_n\}$ *of complex numbers, there exists a continuous linear functional* $\lambda$ *on* $W$ *such that*

$$(13) \qquad \lambda(x_n) = c_n \qquad (n = 1, 2, \cdots).$$

**Proof.** Let $\|\cdot\|$ be the norm on $W$. Let $W^*$ be the space of all complex valued continuous linear functionals on $W$. We define $x_1 \in W$ to be an arbitrary vector of norm 1 and choose $x_1^* \in W^*$ such that

$$\|x_1^*\| = 1,$$
$$x_1^*(x_1) = 1.$$

The celebrated Hahn-Banach theorem ensures that such an $x_1^* \in W^*$ exists. We shall now define by induction two sequences $\{x_n\}$ and $\{x_n^*\}$ in $W$ and $W^*$, respectively. Suppose $x_1, x_2, \cdots, x_n \in W$ and $x_1^*, \cdots, x_n^* \in W^*$ have been already constructed so that

(14)
$$x_i^*(x_j) = \delta_{ij} \text{ (Kronecker delta)} \qquad (i, j = 1, 2, \cdots, n),$$
$$\|x_i^*\| = 2^{-(i-1)} \qquad (i = 1, 2, \cdots, n).$$

Since $W$ is infinite dimensional, there is a nonzero vector $x_{n+1}$ in $W$ linearly independent of $x_1, \cdots, x_n$ such that

$$x_i^*(x_{n+1}) = 0 \qquad (i = 1, 2, \cdots, n).$$

Using the Hahn-Banach theorem once again, we can find $x_{n+1}^* \in W^*$ such that $x_{n+1}^*(x_{n+1}) \neq 0$, $x_{n+1}^*(x_i) = 0$, $i \leq n$. Replacing $x_{n+1}$ and $x_{n+1}^*$ by suitable multiples, we may assume that $\|x_{n+1}^*\| = 2^{-n}$, $x_{n+1}^*(x_{n+1}) = 1$. The sequences $x_1, x_2, \cdots, x_{n+1}$ and $x_1^*, \cdots, x_{n+1}^*$ then satisfy (14) with $n$ replaced by $n+1$. By induction it follows that there exist infinite sequences $\{x_n\}$ and $\{x_n^*\}$ such that $x_n \in W$ for all $n$, $x_n^* \in W^*$ for all $n$, and

(15)
$$x_i^*(x_j) = \delta_{ij} \qquad (i, j = 1, 2, \cdots),$$
$$\|x_i^*\| = 2^{-(i-1)} \qquad (i = 1, 2, \cdots).$$

We claim that the sequence $\{x_n\}$ has the properties asserted in the lemma. In fact, let $\{c_n\}$ be any bounded sequence of complex numbers. For $x \in W$, let $\lambda(x)$ be defined by

(16)
$$\lambda(x) = \sum_{n=1}^{\infty} c_n x_n^*(x).$$

The inequality $|x_n^*(x)| \leq \|x_n^*\| \cdot \|x\| = 2^{-(n-1)}\|x\|$ shows that $\lambda$ is well defined and that $x \to \lambda(x)$ is a continuous linear functional on $W$, i.e., $\lambda \in W^*$. Clearly, $\lambda(x_n) = c_n$ for all $n$.

We now resume our discussion of $V$ and $\theta$.

**Lemma 7.5.** *If* $\mathbf{D} = \mathbf{R}$, $\theta$ *is the identity; if* $\mathbf{D} = \mathbf{C}$, $\theta$ *is the conjugation; and if* $\mathbf{D} = \mathbf{Q}$, $\theta$ *is the canonical conjugation.*

**Proof.** Let $F$ be any linear manifold of finite dimension $\geq 3$ containing $v_0$. The map $L \to L^\perp \cap F$ is, as we saw in the proof of lemma 7.2, an orthocomplementation in the geometry of subspaces of $F$ and is, moreover, induced by $\langle \,.\,,\,.\,\rangle_F$ (the restriction of $\langle \,.\,,\,.\,\rangle$ to $F \times F$). From theorem 4.7 we deduce that $\theta$ is the identity if $\mathbf{D} = \mathbf{R}$ and is the canonical conjugation if $\mathbf{D} = \mathbf{Q}$. Suppose now that $\mathbf{D} = \mathbf{C}$. Clearly, as $\langle x,x \rangle_F = 0$ for an $x \in F$ implies that $x = 0$, $\theta$ is not the identity. $\theta$ will therefore have to be the conjugation in this case, provided we show that it is continuous. Since $\theta$ is additive, this reduces to showing that if $c_n \to 0$ in $\mathbf{D}$, $\{c_n{}^\theta\}$ is a bounded sequence. Suppose then that $\mathbf{D} = \mathbf{C}$ and that $\theta$ is not the conjugation. Then there exists a sequence $\{c_n\}$ in $\mathbf{D}$ such that

$$c_n \to 0,$$
(17)
$$|c_n{}^\theta| \to \infty.$$

Since dim $V = \infty$, we can select a sequence $\{x_n\}$ in $V$ such that it has the property described in lemma 7.4. Let $\beta_n$ be the element $x \to \langle x,x_n \rangle$ of $V^*$ (cf. lemma 7.3). Since $|c_n{}^\theta| \to \infty$, we may, by passing to a subsequence if necessary, assume in addition that for all $n$,

(18)
$$|c_n{}^\theta| > n \cdot \|\beta_n\|.$$

By lemma 7.4 we can find a $\lambda \in V^*$ such that $\lambda(x_n) = c_n$ for all $n$. Evidently, $\lambda \neq 0$. Moreover, it follows from lemma 7.3 that there is a $u \neq 0$ in $V$ such that $\lambda = \beta_u$. Then $\langle u,u \rangle \neq 0$ and $\langle x_n,u \rangle = c_n$ for all $n$. If

(19)
$$z_n = \langle u,u \rangle^{-1} u - c_n{}^{-1} x_n,$$

then

$$\lambda(z_n) = \langle z_n,u \rangle = 0$$

for all $n$. But then, as $\langle \,.\,,\,.\,\rangle$ is symmetric,

$$\langle u,z_n \rangle = 0$$

for all $n$, i.e.,

(20)
$$(\langle u,u \rangle^\theta)^{-1} \langle u,u \rangle - (c_n{}^\theta)^{-1} \langle u,x_n \rangle = 0.$$

Since $|(c_n{}^\theta)^{-1} \langle u,x_n \rangle| \leq |c_n{}^\theta|^{-1} \|\beta_n\| \|u\|$, (18) implies that

$$(c_n{}^\theta)^{-1} \langle u,x_n \rangle \to 0 \qquad (n \to \infty)$$

and hence we infer from (20) that $\langle u,u \rangle (\langle u,u \rangle^\theta)^{-1} = 0$, which is impossible as $u \neq 0$. This contradiction proves that $\theta$ must be the conjugation and completes the proof of lemma 7.5.

**Lemma 7.6.** $\beta(u \to \beta_u)$ *is a continuous map of $V$ onto $V^*$.*

**Proof.** Since we may obviously consider $\mathbf{R}$ as a subfield of $\mathbf{D}$ as well as $\mathbf{D}^0$, $V$ and $V^*$ may both be regarded as Banach spaces over $\mathbf{R}$, denoted by $V_{\mathbf{R}}$ and $V_{\mathbf{R}}^*$, respectively. From lemma 7.5 we conclude that $\beta(u \to \beta_u)$ is an $\mathbf{R}$-linear map. As $\beta$ is defined on the whole of $V_{\mathbf{R}}$, we may use the closed graph theorem to reduce the proof of the continuity of $\beta$ to the proof that $\beta$ is a *closed* map. Let $\{x_n\}$ be a sequence in $V_{\mathbf{R}}$ such that

$x_n \to x$ and $\beta_{x_n} \to \lambda$. We must prove that $\lambda = \beta_x$. Since $\beta$ is onto, we may assume that $\lambda = \beta_u$ for some $u \in V$. From the formula (10) for the norm in $V^*$, it follows that $\beta_{x_n}(v) \to \beta_u(v)$ for all $v \in V$. Since, by lemma 7.5, $\theta$ is continuous, we have, for $v \in V$,

$$\begin{aligned}
\langle x,v \rangle &= \lim_n \langle x_n,v \rangle \\
&= \lim_n (\langle v,x_n \rangle^\theta) \\
&= \langle v,u \rangle^\theta \\
&= \langle u,v \rangle.
\end{aligned}$$

This proves that $x = u$ or $\beta_x = \lambda$. We have thus proved lemma 7.6.

Lemma 7.5 shows that $\langle \,.\,,\,.\, \rangle$ is an inner product on $V \times V$. Thus, on defining $\|z\|_0^2 = \langle z,z \rangle$, we obtain a norm on $V$. $V$ is a pre-Hilbert space with respect to $\langle \,.\,,\,.\, \rangle$.

**Lemma 7.7.** *$V$ is a Hilbert space under* $\langle \,.\,,\,.\, \rangle$.

**Proof.** We must prove that $V$ is complete under $\|\cdot\|_0$. Let $\{x_n\}$ be a sequence in $V$ such that $\|x_n - x_m\|_0^2 \to 0$, $n, m \to \infty$. Then $\langle y,x_n - x_m \rangle \to 0$ as $n, m \to \infty$ for each $y \in V$. Let $\lambda(y) = \lim_n \langle y,x_n \rangle$. Then $\lambda$ is a linear map of $V$ into $\mathbf{D}$. Since $\beta_{x_n} \in V_\mathbf{R}^*$ for all $n$, we may apply the well known uniform boundedness principle to $V_\mathbf{R}$, a Banach space over $\mathbf{R}$, to conclude that $\lambda \in V^*$. By lemma 7.3 there exists a $z \in V$ such that $\lambda = \beta_z$. We claim that $\|x_n - z\|_0 \to 0$. Let $\varepsilon > 0$ be arbitrary and $N$ be such that

$$\|x_n - x_m\|_0 \le \varepsilon$$

for $n, m \ge N$. Then, for $y \in V$,

$$|\langle y, x_n - x_m \rangle| \le \varepsilon \|y\|_0 \qquad (n, m \ge N)$$

and hence

$$|\langle y, x_n - z \rangle| \le \varepsilon \|y\|_0 \qquad (n \ge N),$$

which shows that $\|x_n - z\|_0 \le \varepsilon$ for $n \ge N$.

**Lemma 7.8.** *The topologies induced on $V$ by $\|\cdot\|$ (the original norm) and $\|\cdot\|_0$ coincide.*

**Proof.** Let $y, x_1, x_2, \cdots$ be elements in $V$. We must show that as $n \to \infty$, $\|x_n - y\|_0 \to 0$ if and only if $\|x_n - y\| \to 0$. Since $V$ is a Banach space over $\mathbf{R}$ under both $\|\cdot\|$ and $\|\cdot\|_0$, it is sufficient, in view of the open mapping theorem, to show the implication in one direction only. Let then $\|x_n - y\| \to 0$. Since the map $\beta$ from $V$ to $V^*$ is continuous, $\beta_{x_n} - \beta_y \to 0$ in $V^*$ so that

$$(21) \qquad \sup_{\|z\| \le 1} |\langle z, x_n - y \rangle| \to 0 \qquad (n \to \infty).$$

Now, $\|x_n - y\| \leq 1$ for all sufficiently large $n$ and hence we infer from (21) that

$$\|x_n - y\|_0{}^2 = \langle x_n - y, \, x_n - y \rangle \to 0,$$

which is the relation required.

We can now complete the proof of theorem 7.1. $V$ is a Hilbert space under $\langle \, . \, , . \, \rangle$ and the topology induced by the corresponding norm has been shown to coincide with the original topology for $V$. Consequently, the same linear manifolds are closed in both topologies. Let $\xi(M \to \xi(M))$ be the orthocomplementation of the Hilbert space $V$. Now, $\langle y,x \rangle = 0$ if and only if $x \perp y$, and hence for any $M \in \mathscr{L}$, $y \in M^\perp$ if and only if $y \in \xi(M)$. This proves that $\perp$ and $\xi$ coincide. The proof of theorem 7.1 is complete.

Theorem 7.1 shows that a logic may be asserted to be standard as soon as it is identified as a member of an apparently more general class of lattices. It seems to be an interesting open question to formulate and prove extensions of theorem 7.1 when, for instance, $V$ is a Frechet space. We have proved theorem 7.1 to emphasize our point of view that the important role played by standard logics is not due to accident but stems from deeper mathematical reasons, and that theorems such as the present one lead to a clarification of some of these reasons. This said, the stage is set for the detailed analysis of the standard logics and we proceed to do it now.

## 2. THE STANDARD LOGICS:
## OBSERVABLES AND STATES

We now proceed to describe the structure of the set of observables and the set of states associated with a standard logic and examine the manner in which the general concepts of Chapter VI specialize. Throughout this section we write $\mathbf{D}$ to denote one of $\mathbf{R}$, $\mathbf{C}$, or $\mathbf{Q}$. Let $\mathscr{H}$ be a separable infinite dimensional Hilbert space over $\mathbf{D}$. We write $\mathscr{L}$ for the logic $\mathscr{L}(\mathscr{H}, \mathbf{D})$ of all closed linear manifolds of $\mathscr{H}$ (with its canonical orthocomplementation).

For any closed linear manifold $M$ of $\mathscr{H}$, let us write $P^M$ for the orthogonal projection on $M$. If $f(E \to f(E))$ is any observable associated with the logic $\mathscr{L}$, then the map $E \to P^{f(E)}$ is a *projection valued measure*† based on $\mathscr{B}(R^1)$. Conversely, it is obvious that to any projection valued measure

---

† The concept of a projection valued measure is nothing new; it is a standard tool of spectral theory. For complex Hilbert spaces we refer the reader to sections 35–38 of Halmos [2]. For the real case very few changes have to be made. For the quaternionic case and for projection valued measures defined *on the real line*, the theory is essentially the same, since the real field is the center of $\mathbf{Q}$. We shall assume the basic facts concerning projection valued measures as known.

$P(E \to P_E)$ based on $\mathscr{B}(R^1)$ there exists a unique observable $f(E \to f(E))$ such that $P_E = P^{f(E)}$ for all real Borel sets $E$.

**Lemma 7.9.** *Let* $M_1, M_2 \in \mathscr{L}$. *Then* $M_1 \leftrightarrow M_2$ *if and only if the projections* $P^{M_1}$ *and* $P^{M_2}$ *commute.*

**Proof.** Let $M_1, M_2 \in \mathscr{L}$. Assume first that $M_1 \leftrightarrow M_2$. Then there exists mutually orthogonal elements $N_1, N_2, N$ of $\mathscr{L}$ such that $M_i = N_i + N$ $(i = 1, 2)$. Clearly, $P^{M_i} = P^{N_i} + P^N$, and one is led immediately to the equation $P^{M_1}P^{M_2} = P^{M_2}P^{M_1}$. Conversely, let $P^{M_1}$ and $P^{M_2}$ commute and let $P = P^{M_1}P^{M_2}$. Then $P$ is a projection. If we write $Q_i = P^{M_i} - P$, then it is easily verified that $Q_i$ is a projection $(i = 1, 2)$ and $PQ_i = Q_iP = 0$, $Q_1Q_2 = Q_2Q_1 = 0$. If $N_1, N_2$, and $N$ are the closed linear manifolds which are the ranges of $Q_1, Q_2$, and $P$, respectively, then it follows easily that $N_1, N_2$, and $N$ are mutually orthogonal and $M_i = N_i \vee N$ $(i = 1, 2)$. This proves that $M_1 \leftrightarrow M_2$.

**Lemma 7.10.** *Let* $X$ *be a set and* $\mathscr{B}$ *a* $\sigma$-*algebra of subsets of* $X$. *Let* $P(E \to P_E)$ *be a projection valued measure in* $\mathscr{H}$ *based on* $\mathscr{B}$ *and* $\mathscr{F}$ *the algebra (over* **R***) of all real valued bounded measurable functions on* $X$. *For* $g \in \mathscr{F}$ *let* $\|g\| = \sup\{|g(x)| : x \in X\}$. *Then, for any* $g \in \mathscr{F}$, *there exists a unique, bounded, self-adjoint operator* $B_g$ *on* $\mathscr{H}$ *such that*

$$
(22) \qquad \langle B_g u, v \rangle = \int_X g(x) d\nu_{u,v}(x) \qquad (u, v \in \mathscr{H}),
$$

$$
\left( B_g = \int_X g dP, \qquad in\ symbols \right)
$$

*where* $\nu_{u,v}$ *is the* **D**-*valued measure on* $\mathscr{B}$ *defined by*

$$
\nu_{u,v}(E) = \langle P_E u, v \rangle.
$$

*The spectral measure of* $B_g$ *is the projection valued measure* $E \to P_{g^{-1}(E)}$. *One has:*

$$
(23) \qquad\qquad \|B_g\| \leq \|g\| \qquad (g \in \mathscr{F}).
$$

*The correspondence* $g \to B_g$ *is a homomorphism from the algebra* $\mathscr{F}$ *into the algebra (over* **R***) of all bounded operators on* $\mathscr{H}$. *In particular,* $B_{g_1}$ *and* $B_{g_2}$ *commute for all* $g_1, g_2 \in \mathscr{F}$.

**Proof.** The proofs are similar to the ones in section 37 of Halmos [2] and we omit them. In the quaternionic case we have to use the fact that the real field is the center of **Q**.

**Theorem 7.11.** *Let* **D** *be one of* **R**, **C**, *or* **Q** *and* $\mathscr{L}$ *the logic of all closed linear manifolds of* $\mathscr{H}$. *For any observable* $f(E \to f(E))$ *associated with*

*$\mathscr{L}$, let $A_f$ be the self-adjoint (not necessarily bounded) linear operator with spectral measure $E \rightarrow P^{f(E)}$. Then*

(24)                                    $$f \rightarrow A_f$$

*is a one-one correspondence between the set of all observables associated with $\mathscr{L}$ and the set of all self-adjoint operators on $\mathscr{H}$. The observable $f$ is bounded if and only if the operator $A_f$ is bounded. Two bounded observables $f_1$ and $f_2$ are simultaneously observable if and only if the (bounded) operators $A_{f_1}$ and $A_{f_2}$ commute. If $f$ is any bounded observable and $p$ is a polynomial with real coefficients (in one variable), then the operator corresponding under (24) to $p \circ f$ is $p(A_f)$. More generally, if $f_1, \cdots, f_r$ are bounded observables, any two of which are simultaneously observable, and if $p$ is a real polynomial of $r$ real variables, then the observable $p \circ (f_1, \cdots, f_r)$ (cf. theorem 6.17) has the corresponding operator $p(A_{f_1}, \cdots, A_{f_r})$.*

**Proof.** The first assertion concerning the correspondence $f \rightarrow A_f$ is an immediate consequence of the spectral theorem. Next, an observable $f$ is bounded if and only if for some compact set $K \subseteq R^1$, $f(K) = \mathscr{H}$. This is possible if and only if $P^{f(K)} = I$, which in turn is well known to be equivalent to the requirement that $A_f$ be bounded. Let now $f_1$ and $f_2$ be bounded observables. Then $f_1$ and $f_2$ are simultaneously observable if and only if $f_1(E_1) \leftrightarrow f_2(E_2)$ for all pairs of Borel sets $E_1$ and $E_2$. From lemma 7.9 and standard spectral theory, it now follows that $f_1 \leftrightarrow f_2$ if and only if $A_{f_1}$ and $A_{f_2}$ commute. We now come to the last pair of assertions. Since the first of these is a special case of the second for $r = 1$, we shall confine ourselves to the proof of the second. Let $f_1, \cdots, f_r$ be bounded observables such that $f_i \leftrightarrow f_j$ for all $i, j = 1, 2, \cdots, r$. By theorem 6.17 there exists a $\sigma$-homomorphism $F \rightarrow f(F)$ of $\mathscr{B}(R^r)$ into $\mathscr{L}$ such that for any $i$ ($1 \leq i \leq r$) and any $E \in \mathscr{B}(R^1)$,

$$f_i(E) = f(\pi_i^{-1}(E)),$$

$\pi_i$ being the projection $(t_1, \cdots, t_r) \rightarrow t_i$ of $R^r$ onto $R^1$. Let $P_F = P^{f(F)}$. Then $F \rightarrow P_F$ is a projection valued measure on $\mathscr{B}(R^r)$. Since the $f_i$ are bounded observables, there exists a compact set $K \subseteq R^1$ such that $f_i(K) = \mathscr{H}$ for $i = 1, 2, \cdots, r$. We now apply lemma 7.10 by taking $X = K^r$, $\mathscr{B} = \mathscr{B}(K^r)$. For any $E \in \mathscr{B}(K)$, $P_{\pi_i^{-1}(E)} = P^{f_i(E)}$, and so, writing

$$\nu_{u,v}(F) = \langle P_F u, v \rangle, \qquad \nu_{u,v}^i(E) = \langle P^{f_i(E)} u, v \rangle,$$

we get

$$\langle B_{\pi_i} u, v \rangle = \int_{K^r} \pi_i(t_1, t_2, \cdots, t_r) d\nu_{u,v}(t_1, \cdots, t_r)$$

$$= \int_K t \, d\nu_{u,v}^i(t)$$

$$= \langle A_{f_i} u, v \rangle.$$

Thus, $B_{\pi_i} = A_{f_i}$, $i = 1, 2, \cdots, r$. Since $g \to B_g$ is a homomorphism, we have, for any real polynomial $p$ of $t_1, \cdots, t_r$,

$$B_p = p(B_{\pi_1}, \cdots, B_{\pi_r}) = p(A_{f_1}, \cdots, A_{f_r}).$$

But the self-adjoint operator $B_p$ has the spectral measure $E \to P_{p^{-1}(E)}$ by lemma 7.10. $B_p$ therefore coincides with the operator corresponding to the observable $E \to f(p^{-1}(E))$ which is precisely $p \circ (f_1, \cdots, f_r)$. This proves the theorem completely.

**Remark.** That $f_1 \leftrightarrow f_2$ is equivalent to the equation $A_{f_1} A_{f_2} = A_{f_2} A_{f_1}$ is a celebrated result of von Neumann. The fact that $p \circ (f_1, \cdots, f_r)$ corresponds to the operator $p(A_{f_1}, \cdots, A_{f_r})$ is remarkable since it links the *algebra of functions* of $f_1, \cdots, f_r$ with the *algebra of operators* on $\mathscr{H}$.

We now take up the problem of determining the states of the logic $\mathscr{L}$. Our basic result is the theorem of Gleason [1] which asserts that every state of $\mathscr{L}$ can be described in a canonical way by what is usually known as a *density matrix*. We shall now proceed to a detailed discussion of this theorem.

To any vector $u \in \mathscr{H}$ with $\|u\| = 1$, we associate the mapping $p_u$ of $\mathscr{L}$ into the set of nonnegative real numbers by defining

(25) $$p_u(M) = \langle P^M u, u \rangle = \|P^M u\|^2 \qquad (M \in \mathscr{L}).$$

If $M = \mathscr{H}$, $p_u(M) = \|u\|^2 = 1$, while $p_u(0) = 0$. If $M_1, M_2, \cdots$ is a sequence of elements of $\mathscr{L}$ such that $M_i \perp M_j$ $(i \neq j)$ then, writing $M = \bigvee_i M_i$, we have:

$$p_u(M) = \|P^M u\|^2$$
$$= \sum_i \|P^{M_i} u\|^2$$
$$= \sum_i p_u(M_i).$$

In other words, $p_u$ is a state of $\mathscr{L}$. It is clear that if $c \in \mathbf{D}$ and $|c| = 1$, $p_{cu} = p_u$.

The general description of states depends on the concept of an operator of trace class. On complex Hilbert spaces they are defined and treated in many books on Hilbert space theory (cf. Dunford and Schwartz [2], for example). The treatment in the real and quaternionic cases is similar. A bounded operator $A$ of $\mathscr{H}$ is of *trace class* if, for any orthonormal basis $\{e_i\}$, the series

$$\sum_i |\langle Ae_i, e_i \rangle| < \infty;$$

then the sum

$$\mathrm{tr}(A) = \sum_i \langle Ae_i, e_i \rangle$$

exists for any orthonormal basis $\{e_i\}$ and is independent of the basis used; it is called the trace of $A$. If $A$ is of trace class and $B$ is *any* bounded operator, $AB$ and $BA$ are of trace class; and moreover,

$$\mathrm{tr}(AB) = \mathrm{tr}(BA).$$

If $A$ and $B$ are of trace class, so are $\alpha A + \beta B$ where $\alpha$, $\beta$ are in the center of the division ring over which $\mathscr{H}$ is defined. We shall assume the reader to be familiar with the basic properties of these operators.

The states of the form $p_u (u \in \mathscr{H}, \|u\|=1)$ can also be described in another way. Let $U$ be the projection on the one-dimensional linear manifold $\mathbf{D} \cdot u$. Then, for any bounded operator $A$, $AU$ is a bounded operator, which is of trace class, since $U$ is (trivially) of trace class. Let $\{e_n\}$ be an orthonormal basis for $\mathscr{H}$ with $u=e_1$. Then

$$\mathrm{tr}(AU) = \mathrm{tr}(UA)$$
(26)
$$= \sum_i \langle AUe_i,e_i \rangle$$
$$= \langle Au,u \rangle.$$

In particular,

(27)
$$p_u(M) = \mathrm{tr}(P^M U).$$

Suppose that $u_1, u_2, \cdots$ is any sequence of vectors in $\mathscr{H}$ with $\|u_i\|=1$ for all $i$. Let $a_1, a_2, \cdots$ be a sequence of nonnegative numbers with $a_1+a_2+\cdots=1$. Let $U_i$ be the projection on the one-dimensional manifold $\mathbf{D} \cdot u_i$. Then

(28)
$$U = \sum_i a_i U_i$$

is a well-defined, bounded, nonnegative, self-adjoint operator of trace class and

(29)
$$\mathrm{tr}(U) = 1.$$

If $M \in \mathscr{L}$, we have

$$\mathrm{tr}(P^M U) = \sum_i a_i \, \mathrm{tr}(P^M U_i)$$
$$= \sum_i a_i p_{u_i}(M).$$

Thus the function $p_U$ defined by

(30)
$$p_U(M) = \mathrm{tr}(P^M U)$$

is a state of $\mathscr{L}$ and in fact is the state $\sum_i c_i p_{u_i}$. Conversely, let $U$ be a bounded, self-adjoint operator such that (i) $U$ is nonnegative, i.e., $\langle Ux,x \rangle \geq 0$ for all $x \in \mathscr{H}$, and (ii) $U$ is of trace class and $\mathrm{tr}(U)=1$. Then, the function $p_U$ defined by (30) is a state of $\mathscr{L}$. We call the operators $U$ which are bounded, self-adjoint, nonnegative, and of trace class, *von Neumann operators*.

The question naturally arises whether every state of $\mathscr{L}$ is of the form $p_U$ for a suitable von Neumann operator $U$ of trace 1. It was Gleason [1] who first proved that this is indeed so. His result, which is a cornerstone of the mathematical foundations of quantum mechanics, is undoubtedly one of the most profound theorems in this subject.

Gleason's theorem is quite complicated to prove and we need to develop a number of technical lemmas. We begin with the concept of a frame function. Let $\mathscr{E}$ be the unit sphere of $\mathscr{H}$, i.e.,

$$(31) \qquad \mathscr{E} = \{x : x \in \mathscr{H}, \|x\| = 1\}.$$

A real valued function $f(x \to f(x))$ defined on $\mathscr{E}$ is a *frame function* if

$$(32) \quad \begin{array}{l} \text{(i)} \quad f(cx) = f(x) \quad \text{for} \quad x \in \mathscr{E} \quad \text{and} \quad c \in \mathbf{D} \quad \text{with } |c| = 1, \\ \text{(ii)} \quad \text{there exists a constant } W \text{ such that } \sum_n f(e_n) = W \text{ for any ortho-} \\ \qquad \text{normal basis } \{e_n\} \text{ of } \mathscr{H} \text{ (recall that } \mathscr{H} \text{ is separable).} \end{array}$$

The constant $W$ is called the *weight* of $f$.

Suppose that $U$ is a bounded, self-adjoint operator of trace class. Let us define the function $f_U$ by

$$(33) \qquad f_U(x) = \langle Ux, x \rangle \qquad (x \in \mathscr{E}).$$

Then $f_U$ is obviously a frame function whose weight is tr $U$. A frame function $f$ is called *regular* if there exists a bounded, self-adjoint operator $U$ such that

$$(34) \qquad f = f_U.$$

Clearly, if $f$ is regular, there exists only one bounded, self-adjoint operator $U$ such that (34) holds; for, if $U$ and $V$ satisfy (34), $\langle (U - V)x, x \rangle = 0$ for all $x \in \mathscr{H}$ and hence $U - V = 0$.

Suppose that $\mu$ is a state of $\mathscr{L}$. For any vector $x \in \mathscr{E}$ let us define

$$(35) \qquad f_\mu(x) = \mu(\mathbf{D} \cdot x).$$

Then $f_\mu$ is a *nonnegative* frame function of weight 1. If $U$ is a von Neumann operator of trace 1 and $\mu = p_U$ the state defined by (30), a simple calculation shows

$$(36) \qquad f_\mu = f_U,$$

i.e., $f_\mu$ is regular. Conversely, if $\mu$ is a state of $\mathscr{L}$ and if we assume that

$f_\mu = f_U$ for a bounded, self-adjoint operator, then it can be shown that $U$ is a von Neumann operator of trace 1, and $\mu = p_U$. In fact, as

$$\langle Ux, x \rangle = f_\mu(x) \geq 0,$$

$U$ is nonnegative; then, if $\{e_n\}$ is any orthonormal basis of $\mathscr{H}$,

$$\sum_n \langle Ue_n, e_n \rangle = \sum_n f_\mu(e_n) = 1$$

so that $U$ is of trace class and has unit trace. This shows that the states $\mu$ and $p_U$ coincide for all one-dimensional subspaces of $\mathscr{H}$ and hence coincide for all elements of $\mathscr{L}$. In other words, Gleason's theorem is entirely equivalent to proving that every nonnegative frame function is regular.

We shall first examine the special case when $\mathbf{D} = \mathbf{R}$ and when $\mathscr{H}$ is finite dimensional. If $\mathscr{H}$ is the real line, then the only frame functions are constants. If $\mathscr{H}$ is the plane $R^2$, then it is obvious that a frame function can be arbitrarily defined on any quadrant of the unit circle and hence need have no special properties.

**Lemma 7.12.** *Let $\mathscr{H} = R^2$, the plane ($\mathbf{D} =$ the real field) and let $\mathscr{E}$ be described as*

(37) $$\mathscr{E} = \{(\cos\theta, \sin\theta) : 0 \leq \theta < 2\pi\}.$$

*Then the function $f : (\cos\theta, \sin\theta) \to \cos n\theta$, $n$ being an integer, is a frame function if and only if either $n = 0$ or $n \equiv 2 \pmod 4$.*

**Proof.** In order that $f$ be a frame function we must have, for some constant $W$,

(38) $$\cos n\theta + \cos\left(n\left(\theta + \frac{\pi}{2}\right)\right) = W$$

for all $\theta$. Differentiating with respect to $\theta$, we have:

$$n\left\{\sin n\theta + \sin n\left(\theta + \frac{\pi}{2}\right)\right\} = 0$$

for all $\theta$, i.e.,

$$n\left\{(\sin n\theta)\left(1 + \cos\frac{n\pi}{2}\right) + \sin\frac{n\pi}{2}\cos n\theta\right\} = 0.$$

This is possible if and only if either $n = 0$ or $\cos(n\pi/2) = -1$, i.e., if and only if $n = 0$ or $n \equiv 2$ modulo 4.

**Lemma 7.13.** *Let $\mathscr{H} = R^3$ be the three dimensional real Euclidean space. Then every continuous frame function on the unit sphere $\mathscr{E}$ is regular.*

**Proof.** The proof makes use of harmonic analysis on $\mathscr{E}$ (cf. Weyl [1], pp. 60–63, 142–146). Let $\mathscr{C}$ be the set of all real valued continuous functions on $\mathscr{E}$ and $G$ the group of all orthogonal transformations of $R^3$ which have determinant $+1$. For any element $h$ of $\mathscr{C}$ and any $a \in G$, we define $h^a$ by

$$(39) \qquad h^a(x) = h(a^{-1}x) \qquad (x \in \mathscr{E}).$$

A linear manifold $\mathscr{M} \subseteq \mathscr{C}$ is said to be *invariant* if $h^a \in \mathscr{M}$ for all $a \in G$ whenever $h \in \mathscr{M}$. Then, according to classical spherical harmonic analysis, one has the following description of $\mathscr{C}$: (1) for each integer $n = 0, 1, \cdots$ there is a $2n+1$ dimensional subspace $\mathscr{F}_n$ of $\mathscr{C}$ which is invariant and no proper linear submanifold of which is invariant, i.e., $\mathscr{F}_n$ is irreducible under the action (39) of the group $G$; (2) an element $h \in \mathscr{C}$ belongs to $\mathscr{F}_n$ if and only if it is the restriction to $\mathscr{E}$ of a polynomial $p$ of $x$, $y$, $z$ (the coordinates on $R^3$) with the properties

$$(40) \quad \begin{array}{ll} \text{(i)} & p \text{ is homogeneous in } x, y, z \text{ of degree } n, \\ \text{(ii)} & \left(\dfrac{\partial^2}{\partial x^2} + \dfrac{\partial^2}{\partial y^2} + \dfrac{\partial^2}{\partial z^2}\right)p = 0; \end{array}$$

(3) every continuous function on $\mathscr{E}$ is the uniform limit of a sequence of functions each of which is a finite linear combination of elements of the $\mathscr{F}_n$; and finally (4) if $\mathscr{F}$ is any invariant linear manifold, closed under the uniform convergence topology of $\mathscr{C}$, and $n_1, n_2, \cdots$ $(0 \leq n_1 < n_2 < \cdots)$ are all the integers such that $\mathscr{F}_{n_j} \subseteq \mathscr{F}$, $j = 1, 2, \cdots$, then

$$(41) \qquad \mathscr{F} = \left(\sum_j \mathscr{F}_{n_j}\right)^-,$$

where $\sum$ denotes the algebraic sum, and the bar denotes the closure.

Let now $\mathscr{F}$ be the set of all continuous frame functions on $\mathscr{E}$. Evidently $G$-transforms (cf. (39)) and uniform limits of continuous frame functions are continuous frame functions. Thus the set $\mathscr{F}$ is a closed linear manifold in $\mathscr{C}$ which is invariant. Therefore, there exist integers $n_1, n_2, \cdots$ with the properties described in (41). We now claim that if $n$ is any integer other than 0 and 2, then, $\mathscr{F}_n \not\subseteq \mathscr{F}$. In fact, let $n$ be any integer. We use cylindrical coordinates $\rho$, $\theta$, $z$ on $\mathscr{E}$ defined by

$$x = \rho \cos \theta, \quad y = \rho \sin \theta, \quad z = z.$$

Then it is well known that

$$\frac{\partial^2}{\partial x^2} + \frac{\partial^2}{\partial y^2} + \frac{\partial^2}{\partial z^2} = \frac{\partial^2}{\partial \rho^2} + \frac{1}{\rho^2}\frac{\partial^2}{\partial \theta^2} + \frac{1}{\rho}\frac{\partial}{\partial \rho} + \frac{\partial^2}{\partial z^2}.$$

One can easily check that the functions

$$\rho^n \cos n\theta, \ [\rho^n - 2(n-1)z^2\rho^{n-2}] \cos (n-2)\theta$$

are homogeneous polynomials of degree $n$ which satisfy the equation

$$\left(\frac{\partial^2}{\partial x^2} + \frac{\partial^2}{\partial y^2} + \frac{\partial^2}{\partial z^2}\right)p = 0.$$

Thus if $\mathscr{F}_n \subseteq \mathscr{F}$, then $\rho^n \cos n\theta$ and $[\rho^n - 2(n-1)z^2\rho^{n-2}] \cdot \cos(n-2) \ \theta$ are frame functions. For any $\theta$, $(\cos \theta, \sin \theta, 0)$, $(-\sin \theta, \cos \theta, 0)$ and $(0,0,1)$ form a frame of $R^3$ so that the functions obtained by putting $z=0$ are frame functions on the unit circle of the $x$, $y$ plane. Thus $\cos n\theta$ and $\cos(n-2)\theta$ are both frame functions. By lemma 7.12 this is not possible unless $n=0$ or 2. Thus we must have $\mathscr{F} \subseteq (\mathscr{F}_0 + \mathscr{F}_2)^-$ i.e., $\mathscr{F} \subseteq \mathscr{F}_0 + \mathscr{F}_2$, since $\mathscr{F}_0$ and $\mathscr{F}_2$ are finite dimensional. We now claim that $\mathscr{F} = \mathscr{F}_0 + \mathscr{F}_2$ and that every element of $\mathscr{F}_0 + \mathscr{F}_2$ is a regular frame function. In fact, $\mathscr{F}_0$ consists of the constants which are regular. On the other hand, $\mathscr{F}_2$ consists of the quadratic forms $q(x,y,z)$ which satisfy

$$\left(\frac{\partial^2}{\partial x^2} + \frac{\partial^2}{\partial y^2} + \frac{\partial^2}{\partial z^2}\right)q = 0,$$

i.e.,

$$q(x,y,z) = ax^2 + by^2 + cz^2 + 2fyz + 2gzx + 2hxy$$

with

$$a+b+c = 0.$$

Thus a function of $\mathscr{C}$ lies in $\mathscr{F}_0 + \mathscr{F}_2$ if and only if it is of the form

$$x \to \langle Ax, x \rangle$$

($x$ is a vector in $\mathscr{E}$), where $A$ is a symmetric matrix of order 3. In other words, every element of $\mathscr{F}_0 + \mathscr{F}_2$ is a regular frame function. Thus $\mathscr{F} = \mathscr{F}_0 + \mathscr{F}_2$. This completes the proof that every continuous frame function is regular.

We now take up the proof of the deep lemma that every nonnegative frame function on the unit sphere in real three-dimensional space is actually continuous. Gleason's proof of this result is an intricate one based on spherical geometry. We shall first introduce some terminology. We utilize the usual latitude-longitude coordinates on a sphere. For any point $p$ of the unit sphere $\mathscr{E}$ of $R^3$, we define the *northern hemisphere relative to $p$* to be all the points whose latitude $\theta$ relative to $p$ as north pole satisfies $0 < \theta < \pi/2$. We shall denote this by $N_p$. Given $p$, let $q$ be some point of $N_p$. Clearly, $q \neq p$. Among the great circles which pass through this point $q$ there is one whose plane cuts the equator relative to $p$ at points which are orthogonal to $q$. If the latitude of $q$ is $\theta$, it can be shown that this great circle passes through only those points whose latitudes $\varphi$ satisfy $-\theta \leq \varphi \leq \theta$. It is therefore appropriate to call this the *EW great circle* through $q$.

The essence of our argument is contained in the next lemma. To motivate this lemma, let us consider in the usual coordinates $x$, $y$, $z$ the function

$$(x, y, z) \rightarrow x^2 + y^2.$$

This is a frame function which is nonnegative and vanishes at the north pole $p = (0,0,1)$. It is constant on points with the same latitude. For any point $q$ of the northern hemisphere, the points of $N_p$ other than $q$ on the EW great circle through $q$, have latitudes strictly less than the latitude of $q$, and consequently this frame function reaches its minimum on the EW great circle through $q$, at $q$. The next lemma asserts that every frame function which is nonnegative has this property *approximately*.

**Lemma 7.14.** *Let $p \in \mathscr{E}$ and $g$ be a nonnegative frame function which is constant on the equator opposite to $p$. Then for any $q$ in $N_p$ we have:*

$$(42) \qquad g(q) \leq g(x) + g(p)$$

*for every point $x$ on $C$, the EW great circle through $q$.*

**Proof.** We first assert that if $r$ is any point of $N_p$, then

$$(43) \qquad g(r) \leq k + g(p),$$

where $k$ is the constant value which $g$ takes on the equator. To see this, consider the EW great circle through $r$. If $r'$ is one of the points at which this meets the equator, then $r \perp r'$ and hence $r, r'$ are two points of a possible frame. The frame function $g$ being nonnegative, one has:

$$g(r) + g(r') \leq W,$$

where $W$ is the weight of $g$. But if we take any two points $a$, $a'$ on the equator which are orthogonal, $a, a', p$ is a frame and, consequently,

$$2k + g(p) = W.$$

Thus

$$g(r) \leq W - g(r') \leq 2k + g(p) - k \leq k + g(p).$$

Suppose now $q$ is an arbitrary point in the northern hemisphere. The inequality just now established proves the lemma if $x$ lies on the equator. For $x$ below the equator, $-x$ lies above the equator, and, since $g(u) = g(-u)$ for all $u$, it is enough to prove the inequality (42) when $x$ lies on the EW great circle $C$ through $q$ and is also situated in the northern hemisphere.

Let $y$ be a point on $C$, orthogonal to $x$, and lying in the northern hemisphere. We then have, if $q'$ is a point where $C$ meets the equator,

$$g(x)+g(y) = g(q)+g(q') = g(q)+k$$

and, since $g(y) \le k+g(p)$ by (43), one has:

$$g(x) = g(q)+k-g(y)$$
$$\ge g(q)-g(p),$$

which establishes the lemma.

**Lemma 7.15.** *With $p$ and $g$ as in lemma 7.14, let $z$ be a fixed point in $N_p$. Let $M_z$ be the set of points $x$ on $N_p$ which have the property that for some point $y$ of $N_p$ the EW great circle through $x$ contains $y$ and the EW great circle through $y$ contains $z$. Then the interior of $M_z$ is nonempty. Moreover, for any $x$ of $M_z$, one has:*

$$(44) \qquad\qquad g(x) \le g(z)+2g(p).$$

**Proof.** Since $g(x) \le g(y)+g(p)$ and $g(y) \le g(z)+g(p)$, the required inequality follows for all the points $x$ in question. It now remains to establish that $M_z$ contains a nonempty open subset of $N_p$. We use Cartesian coordinates. We can arrange matters so that the coordinates of $p$ are $(0,0,1)$, while the coordinates of $z$ are $(\cos \alpha, 0, \sin \alpha)$. We have $0 < \alpha < \pi$, $\alpha \ne \pi/2$. One can easily see that for any point $y$ whose coordinates are $(\xi,\eta,\zeta)$ $(0 < \zeta < 1)$ the EW great circle through $y$ contains $z$ if and only if

$$(\xi^2+\eta^2) \sin \alpha - \xi\zeta \cos \alpha = 0.$$

Consider now the function $\psi$, where

$$\psi(\xi,\eta,\zeta) = (\xi^2+\eta^2) \sin \alpha - \xi\zeta \cos \alpha.$$

This is greater than 0 on the equator. On the other hand, there are points of $N_p$ for which it is $< 0$. Therefore, if we define $A$ to be the set of points

$$A = \{(\xi,\eta,\zeta) : 0 < \zeta < 1, \quad \psi(\xi,\eta,\zeta) < 0\},$$

then $A$ is a nonempty open subset of $N_p$. Suppose $x$ lies in $A$. Then $\psi(x) < 0$ while the EW great circle through $x$ meets the equator at a point at which $\psi$ is positive. Since $\psi$ is continuous, there must be a point $y$ on the EW great circle through $x$ at which $\psi$ vanishes; thus $x \in M_z$. In other words, $A \subseteq M_z$. This proves the lemma.

**Lemma 7.16.** *With $p$ and $g$ as in lemma 7.14, let $\eta > 0$ be a positive number such that $g(p) < \eta$. Then there exists a point $q$ of $N_p$ and an open set $M$ around $q$ such that*

$$(45) \qquad\qquad 0 \le \sup_{u \in M} g(u) - \inf_{u \in M} g(u) \le 3\eta.$$

**Proof.** Define $b = \inf_{u \in N_p} g(u)$. Then $b \geq 0$. Choose $z \in N_p$ such that $b \leq g(z) \leq b + \eta$. Consider the set $M_z$. By lemma 7.15, $M_z$ has a nonempty interior and for every point $x$ of $M_z$ one has:

$$g(x) \leq g(z) + 2\eta,$$

that is,

$$b \leq g(x) \leq b + 3\eta.$$

Let $q$ be any point in the interior $M$ of $M_z$. Then $M$ is an open neighborhood of $q$ and

$$0 \leq \sup_{u \in M} g(u) - \inf_{u \in M} g(u) \leq 3\eta.$$

This proves the lemma.

**Lemma 7.17.** *Let $f$ be any nonnegative frame function and $r$ any point such that for some open neighborhood $M$ of $r$ we have:*

(46) $$0 \leq \sup_{u \in M} f(u) - \inf_{u \in M} f(u) \leq \alpha.$$

*Then for every point $s$ of $\mathscr{E}$ there is an open neighborhood $M_s$ of $s$ such that*

(47) $$0 \leq \sup_{u \in M_s} f(u) - \inf_{u \in M_s} f(u) \leq 4\alpha.$$

**Proof.** Use coordinates so that $r$ appears as the north pole. Let $t$ be any point on the equator opposite $r$. Since $M$ is an open neighborhood of $r$, we can assume that every point whose latitude is $\geq (\pi/2) - \theta_0$ belongs to $M$, $\theta_0$ being a suitable angle in $]0, \pi/2[$. Consider now a point $u$ due south of $t$ and latitude $-\frac{1}{2}\theta_0$. Then by continuity it is clear that there exists an open set $M_t$ around $t$ with the following property: if $k$ is any point of $M_t$, then, on the great circle through $u$ and $k$, there are points orthogonal to $u$ and $k$, respectively, which are situated in $M$. Let $k$, $k'$ be two points of $M_t$, and $C$, $C'$ the respective great circles through $u$, $k$ and $u$, $k'$. Let $x$, $y$ and $x'$, $y'$ be pairs of points, respectively, on these two great circles such that

$$x, y, x', y' \in M,$$

$$x \perp u, \quad y \perp k, \quad x' \perp u, \quad y' \perp k'.$$

We then have:

$$f(x) + f(u) = f(k) + f(y),$$
$$f(x') + f(u) = f(k') + f(y').$$

Subtracting and rearranging, we have:

$$|f(k) - f(k')| \leq |f(x) - f(x')| + |f(y) - f(y')|$$
$$\leq 2\alpha,$$

so that

$$0 \leq \sup_{u \in M_t} f(u) - \inf_{u \in M_t} f(u) \leq 2\alpha.$$

If $s$ is any point of $\mathscr{E}$, there exists a point $t$ of $\mathscr{E}$ such that $t$ is on the equator opposite $r$ and $s$ is on the equator opposite $t$. Applying the preceding argument twice, we see that there is an open set $M_s$ around $s$ such that

$$0 \le \sup_{u \in M_s} f(u) - \inf_{u \in M_s} f(u) \le 4\alpha.$$

This proves the lemma.

**Lemma 7.18.** *Let $f$ be a nonnegative frame function on $\mathscr{E}$. Then $f$ is continuous.*

**Proof.** Let $\varepsilon > 0$ be a given positive number. We shall prove that every point of $\mathscr{E}$ has a neighborhood in which the oscillation of $f$ is at most $\varepsilon$. Since a constant is a continuous frame function, we can, by subtracting the infimum of $f$ (over $\mathscr{E}$) from $f$, assume without any loss of generality that

$$\inf_{u \in \mathscr{E}} f(u) = 0.$$

Let $\eta > 0$ and $p$ a point such that $f(p) < \eta/2$. Let $\sigma$ be the rotation around the $z$-axis with $p$ as north pole through an angle $\pi/2$. Let the frame function $g$ be defined by

$$g(x) = f(x) + f(\sigma x).$$

$g$ is nonnegative, and at $p$ we have:

$$g(p) < \eta;$$

moreover, $g$ is constant on the equator. By lemma 7.16 there exists a point $q$ of the northern hemisphere and some neighborhood $M_q$ of $q$ such that

$$0 \le \sup_{u \in M_q} g(u) - \inf_{u \in M_q} g(u) \le 3\eta.$$

By lemma 7.17 there exists an open set $M_p$ around $p$ such that

$$0 \le \sup_{u \in M_p} g(u) - \inf_{u \in M_p} g(u) \le 12\eta.$$

Since $g(p) < \eta$, we have:

$$0 \le \sup_{u \in M_p} g(u) \le 13\eta.$$

Since $0 \le f(u) \le g(u)$ for all $u$, we have:

$$0 \le \sup_{u \in M_p} f(u) \le 13\eta$$

and hence we have:

$$0 \le \sup_{u \in M_p} f(u) - \inf_{u \in M_p} f(u) \le 13\eta.$$

Applying lemma 7.17 again, we see that every point of $\mathscr{E}$ has a neighborhood over which the oscillation of $f$ is at most $52\eta$. If we choose $\eta = \varepsilon/52$, we are through.

**Lemma 7.19.** *Let $\mathscr{H}$ be a real separable Hilbert space of dimension at least 3. Then every nonnegative frame function $f$ on the unit sphere $\mathscr{E}$ of $\mathscr{H}$ is regular.*

**Proof.** Since every two-dimensional subspace $L$ of $\mathscr{H}$ can be imbedded in a three-dimensional subspace, it follows from lemma 7.18 that the restriction of $f$ to the unit sphere $\mathscr{E}(L)$ of $L$ is regular, and consequently there is a *unique symmetric* bilinear form on $L \times L$, say $B_L$, such that

$$(48) \qquad B_L(u,u) = f(u)$$

for all $u \in \mathscr{E}(L)$. We shall now define a real valued function $B$ on $\mathscr{H} \times \mathscr{H}$ as follows. Let $x$ and $y$ be two vectors of $\mathscr{H}$ and $L$ a two-dimensional subspace containing $x$ and $y$. We define

$$(49) \qquad B(x,y) = B_L(x,y).$$

Clearly, $B(x,y)$ is well defined if $x$ and $y$ are linearly independent, since in this case $L$ is unique; or if one or both of them is zero, since we then have $B_L(x,y)=0$ for any such $L$. If $x$ and $y$ were dependent and neither is zero, then they span a one-dimensional subspace. If $L_1$ and $L_2$ are two two-dimensional subspaces containing $x$ and $y$, then both $L_1$ and $L_2$ are contained in a three-dimensional subspace, say $M$. Let $C$ be a symmetric bilinear form on $M \times M$ such that

$$C(a,a) = f(a)$$

for all vectors $a$ in $\mathscr{E}(M)$. The restrictions of $C$ to $L_1 \times L_1$ and $L_2 \times L_2$ are symmetric bilinear forms whose quadratic forms coincide with $f$ on the unit spheres of $L_1$ and $L_2$, respectively. Since $B_{L_1}$ and $B_{L_2}$ also have this property, we conclude that

$$B_{L_1}(x,y) = C(x,y),$$
$$B_{L_2}(x,y) = C(x,y),$$

which proves that $B(x,y)$ is well defined. Moreover, we have

$$(50) \qquad B(x,x) = f(x)$$

for all unit vectors $x$ in $\mathscr{H}$. We now claim that $B$ is bilinear. The homogeneity of $B$ as well as its symmetry involves only two vectors and so follows from the homogeneity and symmetry of $B_L$. To complete the proof of the bilinearity (in view of the symmetry of $B$), it is enough to show that

$$B(x, y+z) = B(x,y) + B(x,z)$$

for any three vectors $x$, $y$, $z$. Let $M$ be a three-dimensional subspace containing $x$, $y$ and $z$. Let $L_1$, $L_2$, $L_3$ be two-dimensional subspaces of $M$ containing, respectively, $x$, $y$; $x$, $z$; and $x$, $y+z$. Let $C$ be a symmetric bilinear form on $M \times M$ such that $C(u,u)=f(u)$ for all unit vectors $u$ in $M$. Then we see at once that

$$C(x,y) = B_{L_1}(x,y), \qquad C(x,z) = B_{L_2}(x,y)$$

and

$$C(x, y+z) = B_{L_3}(x, y+z).$$

Since $C$ is bilinear, we have:

$$
\begin{aligned}
B(x, y+z) &= B_{L_3}(x, y+z) \\
&= C(x, y+z) \\
&= C(x,y) + C(x,z) \\
&= B_{L_1}(x,y) + B_{L_2}(x,z) \\
&= B(x,y) + B(x,z),
\end{aligned}
$$

which proves the bilinearity of $B$.

Since

$$0 \le B(x,x) \le 1$$

for all $x$ with $\|x\| = 1$, $x$, $y \to B(x,y)$ is a *bounded* bilinear form. Thus there exists a bounded, self-adjoint operator $U$ such that for all $x$, $y$ in $\mathscr{H}$

$$B(x,y) = \langle Ux,y \rangle,$$
$$f(x) = \langle Ux,x \rangle.$$

Thus we have proved that $f$ is regular.

We now proceed to the case of Hilbert spaces over $\mathbf{D}$, where $\mathbf{D}$ may either be the complex number field or the quaternion division ring. Let $\mathscr{H}$ be a Hilbert space over $\mathbf{D}$. A closed $\mathbf{R}$-linear manifold $S$ of $\mathscr{H}$ is called *completely real* if the inner product $\langle \,.\, , \,.\, \rangle$ in $\mathscr{H} \times \mathscr{H}$ takes real values on $S \times S$; equivalently, if and only if there is an orthonormal set $\{e_j\}$ such that $S$ is the closure of the real linear combinations of the $e_j$.

**Lemma 7.20.** *Let $\mathscr{R}$ be a real separable Hilbert space, and $f_0$ a regular nonnegative frame function of weight $W$. Then for all $a, b \in \mathscr{R}$ with $\|a\| = \|b\| = 1$,*

(51)
$$|f_0(a) - f_0(b)| \le 2W\|a-b\|.$$

**Proof.** There is an operator $T$, of trace class and self-adjoint such that $\langle Tc,c \rangle = f_0(c)$ for all unit vectors $c$. Then

$$
\begin{aligned}
|f_0(a) - f_0(b)| &= |\langle Ta,a \rangle - \langle Tb,b \rangle| \\
&= |\langle T(a-b), (a+b) \rangle| \\
&\le 2\|T\| \cdot \|a-b\|.
\end{aligned}
$$

But $0 \leq \langle Tc,c \rangle \leq W$ for all unit vectors $c$ so that $\|T\| \leq W$. Thus

$$|f_0(a) - f_0(b)| \leq 2W\|a-b\|.$$

**Lemma 7.21** *Let $\mathscr{H}$ be a Hilbert space over $\mathbf{D}$ of finite dimension n. If f is a nonnegative frame function which is regular on each completely real subspace, then f is regular.*

**Proof.** We prove this by induction on $n$. For $n=1$, the lemma is trivial. Let $n>1$. Let $d = \sup_{\|u\|=1} f(u)$ and $\{x_n\}$ a sequence of points on $\mathscr{E}$, the unit sphere of $\mathscr{H}$, such that $f(x_n) \to d$. We may assume, in view of the compactness of the unit sphere, that $x_n \to y$, $\|y\| = 1$. We first show that $f(y) = d$. Let $\lambda_n = |\langle y, x_n \rangle|^{-1} \langle y, x_n \rangle$. Since $x_n \to y$, $\lambda_n \to 1$. The inner product $\langle \lambda_n x_n, y \rangle$ is real and consequently $\lambda_n x_n$ and $y$ span, over $\mathbf{R}$, a completely real subspace. We now have, if $W$ is the weight of $f$,

$$\begin{aligned} |f(y) - d| &\leq |f(y) - f(\lambda_n x_n)| + |f(\lambda_n x_n) - d| \\ &\leq 2W\|y - \lambda_n x_n\| + |f(x_n) - d|, \end{aligned}$$

since $f$, by hypothesis, is regular when restricted to the completely real subspace spanned by $\lambda_n x_n$, $y$, and $f(x_n) = f(\lambda_n x_n)$ ($|\lambda_n| = 1$). This shows that $f(y) = d$.

Let us now extend the function $f$ to a function $F$ defined on all of $\mathscr{H}$ by setting

(52) $$F(v) = \begin{cases} 0 & v = 0. \\ \|v\|^2 f(\|v\|^{-1}v), & v \neq 0 \end{cases}$$

Clearly for $c \in \mathbf{D}$,

(53) $$F(cv) = |c|^2 F(v).$$

We now assert that if $u$ is any vector of $\mathscr{H}$ orthogonal to $y$, then

(54) $$F(cy + u) = |c|^2 d + F(u)$$

for all $c \in \mathbf{D}$. Let $L$ be the two-dimensional real linear manifold spanned by $y$ and $u$. This is completely real. $f$ is regular on its unit sphere so that $f$ is the restriction to $L$ of a nonnegative definite quadratic form $Q$. But $y$ is the point at which the maximum of the quadratic form is reached and $u$ is orthogonal to $y$ in $L$. Thus the matrix of the quadratic form $Q$ is diagonal with respect to the basis $\{y, u\}$ of $L$, and consequently we have, whenever $r$ and $r'$ are two *real* numbers,

$$F(ry + r'u) = |r|^2 d + |r'|^2 F(u).$$

It is to be noted that $u$ here is an arbitrary vector orthogonal to $y$.

Suppose now that $v$ is any vector orthogonal to $y$ and $c \neq 0$ an element from **D**, not necessarily real. We have:

$$F(cy + v) = F(c(y + c^{-1}v))$$
$$= |c|^2 F(y + c^{-1}v)$$
$$= |c|^2 F(y + |c|^{-1}|c|c^{-1}v),$$

but $u = |c|c^{-1}v$ is a vector orthogonal to $y$. Thus

$$F(y + c^{-1}v) = d + |c|^{-2} F(|c|c^{-1}v)$$
$$= d + |c|^{-2} F(v),$$

proving that

$$F(cy + v) = |c|^2 d + F(v).$$

The restriction of $f$ to the orthogonal complement $\mathcal{K}$ of $y$ is a frame function, which, on $\mathcal{K}$, has the same properties as $f$. Suppose we assume the present lemma to be true for all Hilbert spaces of dimension $k < n$. Then $F$ restricted to $\mathcal{K}$ is regular by the induction hypothesis and hence there is an orthonormal basis $\{e_1, \cdots, e_{n-1}\}$ for $\mathcal{K}$ and real numbers $d_1, \cdots, d_{n-1} \geq 0$ such that

$$F(c_1 e_1 + \cdots + c_{n-1} e_{n-1}) = |c_1|^2 d_1 + \cdots + |c_{n-1}|^2 d_{n-1}$$

for all $c_1, \cdots, c_{n-1} \in$ **D**. By the proof given in the previous paragraph, this means that

$$F(cy + c_1 e_1 + \cdots + c_{n-1} e_{n-1}) = |c|^2 d + |c_1|^2 d_1 + \cdots + |c_{n-1}|^2 d_{n-1},$$

which shows that $f$ is the restriction to the unit sphere of the regular frame function $f_U$, where $U$ is the operator defined by $Uy = dy$, $Ue_j = d_j e_j$, $j = 1, 2, \cdots, n-1$. This proves the lemma.

**Lemma 7.22.** *Let $\mathcal{H}$ be a separable Hilbert space over* **D** *which is one of* **R**, **C**, *or* **Q** *of dimension at least 3 and $f$ a nonnegative frame function on the unit sphere $\mathcal{E}$ of $\mathcal{H}$. Then $f$ is regular.*

**Proof.** Since the dimension of $\mathcal{H}$ is at least 3, it follows that the restriction of $f$ to any completely real subspace is regular. Only the case dim $\mathcal{H} = \infty$ remains. Lemma 7.21 is applicable to any finite dimensional subspace of $\mathcal{H}$. Thus for any finite dimensional subspace $S$ of $\mathcal{H}$ there is an operator $U_S$ which is an endomorphism of $S$, bounded, self-adjoint, and $\geq 0$ such that

$$f(x) = \langle U_S x, x \rangle \qquad (x \in S, \quad \|x\| = 1).$$

The uniqueness of $U_S$ implies that if $S_1 \subseteq S_2$, $\langle U_{S_1} x, y \rangle = \langle U_{S_2} x, y \rangle$ if $x, y \in S_1$. This implies in the usual way that there exists a symmetric semi-bilinear form on $\mathcal{H} \times \mathcal{H}$, say, $B$ such that

$$B(x, x) = f(x)$$

for all $x$ with $\|x\|=1$. Since $0 \le B(x,x) \le 1$, there exists a bounded, non-negative, self-adjoint operator $U$ such that

$$\langle Ux,x \rangle = B(x,x) = f(x).$$

This proves the lemma.

**Theorem 7.23.** (*Gleason* [1]). *Let $\mathscr{W}$ be the convex set of all von Neumann operators of unit trace on a separable Hilbert space $\mathscr{H}$ of dimension at least 3 (possibly infinite) over* **D.** *Then the map*

(55) $$U \to p_U \qquad (U \in \mathscr{W})$$

(*where $p_U$ is defined by* (30)) *is a convex† isomorphism of $\mathscr{W}$ onto the convex set $\mathscr{S}$ of all states of the logic $\mathscr{L}$. A state $p \in \mathscr{S}$ is pure if and only if $p = p_u$ for a unit vector $u$ of $\mathscr{H}$, $p_u$ being defined as in* (25). $p_u = p_v$ *if and only if for some $c \in$* **D** *with $|c|=1$, $v=cu$. In particular, the pure states of $\mathscr{L}$ are in natural one-one correspondence with the rays of $\mathscr{H}$.*

**Proof.** That $U \to p_U$ is an isomorphism of $\mathscr{W}$ onto $\mathscr{S}$ is immediate from lemma 7.22. Next we shall obtain a description of the pure states of $\mathscr{L}$. For any vector $u \in \mathscr{H}$ with $\|u\|=1$, let $p_u$ be the state of $\mathscr{L}$ defined by

$$p_u(M) = \|P^M u\|^2 \qquad (M \in \mathscr{L}).$$

We assert that $p_u$ is a pure state. Let $U_0$ be the projection on the one-dimensional space **D** $\cdot u$. Clearly $p_u(M) = \mathrm{tr}(P^M U_0)$ so that

$$p_u = p_{U_0}.$$

To prove that $p_u$ is pure, let $p_1$, $p_2$ be states of $\mathscr{L}$ such that

(56) $$p_u = ap_1 + (1-a)p_2,$$

where $0 < a < 1$. Since $U \to P_U$ is a one-one convex map of $\mathscr{W}$ onto the set of all states, there are (unique) elements $U_1$, $U_2 \in \mathscr{W}$ such that $p_j = p_{U_j}$ $(j=1,2)$ and hence

(57) $$U_0 = aU_1 + (1-a)U_2.$$

Since $\langle U_j x,x \rangle \ge 0$ for all $x \in \mathscr{H}$, $j = 0$, 1, 2, and since $\langle U_0 x,x \rangle = 0$ if $x$ is orthogonal to $u$, we conclude from (57) that for $x \perp u$, $\langle U_j x,x \rangle = 0$ $(j=1, 2)$. Now $U_j$ is $\ge 0$ and hence there is a bounded self-adjoint $V_j$ such that $V_j^2 = U_j$ and we have $\langle U_j x,x \rangle = \|V_j x\|^2$. This implies that $V_j x = 0$ for all $x$ orthogonal to $u$ and, consequently, that $U_j x = 0$ for all $x$ orthogonal to $u$. Since $U_j$ is self-adjoint, this implies that $U_j = c_j U_0$ for some constant

† If $A$ and $B$ are convex subsets of two vector spaces over the real number field and if $u$ is a map of $A$ into $B$, we say that $u$ is convex if $u(ax+by) = au(x) + bu(y)$ for $x, y \in A$, $0 \le a, b \le 1$ and $a+b=1$.

$c_j (j=1, 2)$, and $c_j = 1$ as $\text{tr}(U_j) = 1$. Therefore $U_1 = U_2 = U_0$, which proves that $p_u$ is a pure state. Conversely let $U_0 \in \mathscr{W}$ be such that $p_{U_0}$ is a pure state. If $a_1, \cdots, a_n, \cdots$ ($\geq 0$, $a_1 + a_2 + \cdots = 1$) are the eigenvalues of $U_0$, and $u_1, u_2, \cdots, u_n, \cdots$ corresponding eigenvectors of norm 1, then

$$(58) \qquad\qquad p_{U_0} = \sum_n a_n p_{u_n}.$$

As $p_{U_0}$ is pure, (58) implies that all but one of the $a_n$ must be 1, the rest being 0. This shows that $p_{U_0} = p_{u_j}$ for some $j$.

**Remark.** From theorem 7.23 we can obtain at once an important characterization of the principle of superposition of pure states. Let $\{u_\alpha\}$ be a family of unit vectors of $\mathscr{H}$ and let us write $p_\alpha$ for $p_{u_\alpha}$. Let $p = p_u$ be a pure state and let $M$ be the smallest closed linear manifold containing all the $u_\alpha$. If $p$ is a superposition of the collection $\{p_\alpha\}$, then $p(M^\perp) = 0$ as $p_\alpha(M^\perp) = 0$ for all $\alpha$. Hence $u \in M$. On the other hand, if $u \in M$, then for any $N \in \mathscr{L}$ having the property that $p_\alpha(N) = 0$ for all $\alpha$, $p(N) = 0$, since any such $N$ is contained in $M^\perp$. In other words, $p_u$ is a superposition of the family $\{p_{u_\alpha}\}$ if and only if $u$ lies in the smallest closed linear manifold of $\mathscr{H}$ containing all the $u_\alpha$. Thus, if we make the assumption that the logic of the physical system $\mathfrak{S}$ is standard, *the pure states can be identified with the points of an infinite dimensional projective geometry with the principle of superposition translating into the usual concept of linear dependence of points.*

Our next object is to discuss the nature of the statistics of one or more observables associated with the standard logic $\mathscr{L}$. We begin with the following theorem:

**Theorem 7.24.** *Let $x(E \rightarrow x(E))$ be an observable associated with $\mathscr{L}$, $U$ a von Neumann operator on $\mathscr{H}$ of trace 1 and $p_U$, the state $M \rightarrow \text{tr}(P^M U)$ of $\mathscr{L}$. Let $A_x$ be the self-adjoint operator on $\mathscr{H}$ which corresponds to $x$. If $f$ is any real Borel function bounded on the spectrum of $x$, $f \circ x$ is a bounded observable and*

$$(59) \qquad\qquad \mathscr{E}(f \circ x \,|\, p_U) = \text{tr}(f(A_x)U).$$

*If $x$ is nonnegative, so is $A_x$ and then $\mathscr{E}(x \,|\, p_U)$ exists if and only if $B = A_x^{1/2} U^{1/2}$ is an everywhere defined, bounded operator of Hilbert-Schmidt class; in this case*

$$(60) \qquad\qquad \mathscr{E}(x \,|\, p_U) = \text{tr}(B^*B).$$

*If $x$ is arbitrary, then $x$ has finite variance in the state $p_U$ if and only if $A_x U^{1/2}$ is an everywhere defined, bounded operator of Hilbert-Schmidt class. In this case, (60) reduces to*

$$(61) \qquad\qquad \mathscr{E}(x \,|\, p_U) = \text{tr}(U^{1/2} A_x U^{1/2}).$$

*In particular, if $u$ is a unit vector in $\mathscr{H}$ and $p_u$ is the state $M \to \|P^M u\|^2$ of $\mathscr{L}$, $x$ has a variance in the state $p_u$ if and only if $u \in \mathscr{D}(A_x)$;† in this case,*

$$(62) \qquad\qquad \mathscr{E}(x \,|\, p_u) = \langle A_x u, u \rangle.$$

**Proof.** If $S$ is the spectrum of $x$ and $K = (f[S])^-$, the closure of $f[S]$, then $(f \circ x)(K) = \mathscr{H}$; and as $K$ is compact, this proves that $y = f \circ x$ is bounded. The spectral measure of the operator $A_y$ is the measure $E \to Q_{f^{-1}(E)}$ where $Q$ is the spectral measure of $A_x$. Thus $A_y = f(A_x)$ in the usual sense of the functional calculus of self-adjoint operator on $\mathscr{H}$. This proves (59) at once.

We next take up the more delicate questions involving possibly unbounded $x$. Let $x$ be any nonnegative observable i.e., $x([0,\infty[) = \mathscr{H}$, associated with $\mathscr{L}$. Then $A_x$ is a nonnegative, self-adjoint operator. We denote by $A_x^{1/2}$ the unique, nonnegative, self-adjoint operator $C$ such that $C^2 = A_x$. Let $U$ be any von Neumann operator of unit trace on $\mathscr{H}$ such that $\mathscr{E}(x \,|\, p_U) < \infty$. Let $Q(E \to Q_E)$ be the spectral measure of $A_x$ and $k(E) = \operatorname{tr}(Q_E U)$. Clearly $k([0,\infty[) = 1$ and

$$\mathscr{E}(x \,|\, p_U) = \int_0^\infty t \, dk(t).$$

If $\varphi \in \mathscr{H}$ is any unit vector, $\langle Q_E U^{1/2}\varphi, U^{1/2}\varphi \rangle \le \operatorname{tr}(U^{1/2} Q_E U^{1/2}) = k(E)$; hence, on writing $\psi = U^{1/2}\varphi$,

$$\int_0^\infty (t^{1/2})^2 \, dk_\psi(t) < \infty,$$

where $k_\psi$ is the measure $E \to \langle Q_E \psi, \psi \rangle$. This implies that $\psi$ lies in the domain of $A_x^{1/2}$. In other words, $A_x^{1/2} U^{1/2}$ is everywhere defined. Since $A_x^{1/2}$ is closed and $U^{1/2}$ is bounded, it is easily seen that $A_x^{1/2} U^{1/2}$ is closed. Consequently, $B = A_x^{1/2} U^{1/2}$ is a bounded operator. To prove that $B$ is of Hilbert-Schmidt class it is enough to prove that $\sum_n \|B\varphi_n\|^2 < \infty$ for some orthonormal basis of $\mathscr{H}$. Let $\{\varphi_n\}$ be an orthonormal basis of $\mathscr{H}$ such that $U\varphi_n = a_n \varphi_n$ for all $n$; then $a_n \ge 0$, $\sum_n a_n = 1$. Let $k_n(E) = \langle Q_E \varphi_n, \varphi_n \rangle$. Then each $k_n$ is a probability measure and $k = \sum_n a_n k_n$. But

$$\sum_n \|B\varphi_n\|^2 = \sum_n a_n \|A_x^{1/2} \varphi_n\|^2$$

$$= \sum_n a_n \int_0^\infty (t^{1/2})^2 \, dk_n(t)$$

$$= \sum_n a_n \int_0^\infty t \, dk_n(t)$$

$$= \int_0^\infty t \, dk(t)$$

$$< \infty.$$

† $\mathscr{D}(L)$ is the domain of the linear transformation $L$.

For the converse, if $B = A_x^{1/2} U^{1/2}$ is defined everywhere and is a bounded Hilbert-Schmidt operator, we have, using the above notation,

$$\mathrm{tr}(B^*B) = \sum_n \| B\varphi_n \|^2 = \sum_n a_n \int_0^\infty t\,dk_n(t) < \infty.$$

But then, by Fatou's lemma,

$$\int_0^\infty t\,dk(t) = \mathscr{E}(x|p_U) < \infty.$$

At the same time, the above argument proves that

$$\mathscr{E}(x|p_U) = \mathrm{tr}(B^*B).$$

Next we consider the case of finite variance. We use the same notation. $x$ has a finite variance in the state $p_U$ if and only if $\int_{-\infty}^\infty t^2\,dk(t) < \infty$. Proceeding exactly as before, we conclude that if this condition is satisfied, $D = A_x U^{1/2}$ is an everywhere defined operator of Hilbert-Schmidt class. Note that, if $a_n > 0$, $\varphi_n = a_n^{-1/2} U^{1/2}\varphi_n$ so that $\varphi_n \in \mathscr{D}(A_x)$. In this case, $\langle A_x\varphi_n, \varphi_n \rangle = \int_{-\infty}^\infty t\,dk_n(t)$ by standard spectral theory. Now, $U^{1/2}D$ is a bounded operator and, being symmetric, is self-adjoint. As $U^{1/2}$ is also Hilbert-Schmidt, $U^{1/2}D$ is of trace class. We then obtain

$$\begin{aligned}
\mathrm{tr}(U^{1/2}D) &= \sum_n \langle A_x U^{1/2}\varphi_n, U^{1/2}\varphi_n \rangle \\
&= \sum_{n:a_n>0} a_n \langle A_x\varphi_n, \varphi_n \rangle \\
&= \sum_n a_n \int_{-\infty}^\infty t\,dk_n(t) \\
&= \int_{-\infty}^\infty t\,dk(t).
\end{aligned}$$

This proves (61). For proving the converse, let $A_x U^{1/2} = D$ be everywhere defined and of Hilbert-Schmidt class. We want to prove that

$$\int_{-\infty}^\infty t^2\,dk(t) < \infty.$$

Write, for any Borel set $E \subseteq R^1$,

$$k_n(E) = \langle Q_E U^{1/2}\varphi_n, U^{1/2}\varphi_n \rangle.$$

Then

$$\begin{aligned}
k(E) &= \mathrm{tr}(U^{1/2}Q_E U^{1/2}) \\
&= \sum_n k_n(E)
\end{aligned}$$

and

$$\sum_n \int_{-\infty}^\infty t^2\,dk_n(t) = \sum_n \| A_x U^{1/2}\varphi_n \|^2 \\
< \infty.$$

It follows once again by Fatou's lemma that $\int_{-\infty}^\infty t^2\,dk(t) < \infty$.

For the last part, let $U$ be the projection on the one-dimensional space spanned by $\varphi$. Then $U^{1/2} = U$ and $A_x U^{1/2}$ is defined everywhere if and only if $\varphi \in \mathscr{D}(A_x)$; in this case, it is easily seen that $A_x U^{1/2}$ has at most one-dimensional range and $\mathrm{tr}(U^{1/2} A_x U^{1/2}) = \langle A_x \varphi, \varphi \rangle$ as $\|\varphi\| = 1$. Theorem 7.24 is completely proved.

We next come to the analysis of the joint statistics of several observables. For simplicity we deal only with *bounded* observables. Let $x_j$ $(1 \le j \le k)$ be bounded observables associated with $\mathscr{L}$. Let $A_j$ be the bounded self-adjoint operator which corresponds to $x_j$. If $c_1, c_2, \cdots, c_k \in \mathbf{D}$ are *real* numbers, and $\mathbf{c} = (c_1, \cdots, c_k)$, $A(\mathbf{c}) = c_1 A_1 + \cdots + c_k A_k$ is also a bounded self-adjoint operator. Let $E \to Q(\mathbf{c}; E)$ be the spectral measure of $A(\mathbf{c})$. If $\varphi \in \mathscr{H}$ is a unit vector, and if we define $q_\varphi(\mathbf{c}; E)$ by

$$(63) \qquad q_\varphi(\mathbf{c}; E) = \|Q(\mathbf{c}; E)\varphi\|^2,$$

$q_\varphi(\mathbf{c}; \cdot)$ is a probability measure on $\mathscr{B}(R^1)$. We say that the observables $\{x_1, \cdots, x_k\}$ have *joint statistical distributions* if for each unit vector $\varphi \in \mathscr{H}$, there exists a probability measure $q_\varphi$ on $\mathscr{B}(R^k)$ such that for all vectors $\mathbf{c} = (c_1, \cdots, c_k)$ of $R^k$ and all $E \in \mathscr{B}(R^1)$,

$$(64) \qquad q_\varphi(E(\mathbf{c})) = q_\varphi(\mathbf{c}; E),$$

where

$$(65) \qquad E(\mathbf{c}) = \{(t_1, \cdots, t_k) : c_1 t_1 + \cdots + c_k t_k \in E\}.$$

The sets $E(\mathbf{c})$ are the "half-spaces" in $R^k$. Since any **D**-valued measure on $\mathscr{B}(R^k)$ is uniquely determined by its values on the sets of the form $E(\mathbf{c})$, it follows that $q_\varphi$, if it exists at all, is unique. Obviously, the above sense is a quite conservative one in which we may speak of the statistics of the observables $\{x_1, \cdots, x_k\}$; the probability measure $q_\varphi$ will then be the joint distribution of $\{x_1, \cdots, x_k\}$ under the state of $\mathscr{L}$ determined by $\varphi$. We shall now prove the following theorem (Varadarajan [1]).

**Theorem 7.25.** *With the notations described above, $\{x_1, \cdots, x_k\}$ have joint statistical distributions if and only if the operators $A_j (1 \le j \le k)$ commute with one another.*

**Proof.** If the $A_j$ commute with one another, the observables $x_j$ are simultaneously observable and hence there exists, by theorem 6.17, a $\sigma$-homomorphism $\beta$ of $\mathscr{B}(R^k)$ into $\mathscr{L}$ such that

$$(66) \qquad \beta(\pi_j{}^{-1}(E)) = x_j(E)$$

for all $E \in \mathscr{B}(R^1)$ and $j = 1, 2, \cdots, k$, $\pi_j$ being the projection $(t_1, \cdots, t_k) \to t_j$ of $R^k$ into $R^1$. If we define for a unit vector $\varphi \in \mathscr{H}$, and $E \in \mathscr{B}(R^k)$,

$$(67) \qquad q_\varphi(E) = \|P^{\beta(E)}\varphi\|^2,$$

then (63) and (64) are satisfied. Thus $\{x_1, \cdots, x_k\}$ possess joint distributions.

We now proceed to prove the converse. If $\{x_1, \cdots, x_k\}$ possess joint distributions, it is obvious that for $i, j \le k$, $i \ne j$, $\{x_i, x_j\}$ have joint distributions. We may (and do) therefore assume that $k = 2$ and prove that $A_1 A_2 = A_2 A_1$. For any $\varphi \in \mathscr{H}$ which is nonzero, we write $\psi = (\|\varphi\|)^{-1} \varphi$ and define $q_\varphi = \|\varphi\|^2 q_\psi \cdot q_\varphi$ is a nonnegative measure on $\mathscr{B}(R^2)$ and $q_\varphi(R^2) = \|\varphi\|^2$. Set $q_0 = 0$. We now define the $\mathbf{D}$-valued measure $q_{\varphi, \varphi'}$, for an arbitrary pair of vectors $\varphi$, $\varphi'$, as follows:

$$
\begin{aligned}
& q_{\varphi, \varphi'} = \tfrac{1}{4}(q_{\varphi + \varphi'} - q_{\varphi - \varphi'}) && (\mathbf{D} = \mathbf{R}), \\
(68) \quad & q_{\varphi, \varphi'} = \tfrac{1}{4}(q_{\varphi + \varphi'} - q_{\varphi - \varphi'} + i q_{-i\varphi + \varphi'} - i q_{-i\varphi - \varphi'}) && (\mathbf{D} = \mathbf{C}), \\
& q_{\varphi, \varphi'} = \tfrac{1}{4}\left( q_{\varphi + \varphi'} - q_{\varphi - \varphi'} + \sum_{r=1}^{3} (q_{-\mathbf{j}_r \varphi + \varphi'} - q_{-\mathbf{j}_r \varphi - \varphi'})\mathbf{j}_r \right) && (\mathbf{D} = \mathbf{Q}).
\end{aligned}
$$

We assert that for each $M \in \mathscr{B}(R^2)$, the map $\varphi, \varphi' \to q_{\varphi, \varphi'}(M)$ is bounded and $*$-bilinear on $\mathscr{H} \times \mathscr{H}$. To verify this, let $\varphi_1$, $\varphi_2$, $\varphi' \in \mathscr{H}$ and let us write

$$
\nu(M) = q_{\varphi_1 + \varphi_2, \varphi'}(M) - q_{\varphi_1, \varphi'}(M) - q_{\varphi_2, \varphi'}(M);
$$

then $\nu$ is a $\mathbf{D}$-valued measure on $\mathscr{B}(R^2)$. However, if $M = E(\mathbf{c})$, where $E \in \mathscr{B}(R^1)$, then $q_\varphi(M) = \langle Q(\mathbf{c}; E)\varphi, \varphi \rangle$ and hence from (68) we infer that

$$
q_{\varphi, \varphi'}(E(\mathbf{c})) = \langle Q(\mathbf{c}; E)\varphi, \varphi' \rangle.
$$

Consequently, $\nu(M) = 0$ whenever $M = E(\mathbf{c})$. Hence $\nu = 0$. Similar arguments complete the proof that $\varphi, \varphi' \to q_{\varphi, \varphi'}(M)$ is $*$-bilinear. Since

$$
0 \le q_{\varphi, \varphi}(M) \le \|\varphi\|^2,
$$

it is clear that $\varphi, \varphi' \to q_{\varphi, \varphi'}(M)$ is a bounded form. We can now use a well known theorem to construct a unique bounded self-adjoint operator $P_M$ such that

$$
q_{\varphi, \varphi'}(M) = \langle P_M \varphi, \varphi' \rangle.
$$

Clearly, $0 \le P_M \le I$ for all $M$, $P_\phi = 0$, and $P_{R^2} = I$. Moreover, as $M \to q_{\varphi, \varphi'}(M)$ is a measure, $P_M$ is additive over disjoint sets $M$, i.e., if $M_1$, $M_2$, $\cdots$ are pairwise disjoint Borel sets of $R^2$ and $M = \bigcup_n M_n$,

$$
\langle P_M \varphi, \varphi' \rangle = \sum_{n=1}^{\infty} \langle P_{M_n} \varphi, \varphi' \rangle.
$$

We note also, as $q_{\varphi, \varphi}(M) \ge 0$, that for $M_1 \subseteq M_2$, $P_{M_1} \le P_{M_2}$. Finally, if $M = E(\mathbf{c})$, $P_M = Q(\mathbf{c}; E)$. To complete the proof we need another lemma.

**Lemma 7.26.** *Let $B$ be a nonnegative self-adjoint operator and $S$, $T$ two projections such that $B \le S$ and $B \le T$. Then $B \le S \wedge T$.*

**Proof.** Let $X$ and $Y$ be the ranges of $S$ and $T$, respectively, and let $C = B^{1/2}$. Since $\|Cx\|^2 \le \|Sx\|^2$, $C$, and hence $B$, vanishes on $X^\perp$. Similarly,

$B$ vanishes on $Y^\perp$ and hence $B=0$ on $(X \cap Y)^\perp \cdot B$, being self-adjoint, therefore leaves $X \cap Y$ invariant and for $x \in X \cap Y$, $\langle Bx,x \rangle \leq \|x\|^2$. Thus $B \leq P^{X \cap Y} = S \wedge T$.

We are now in a position to complete the argument. We must show that for any two sets $E_1$, $E_2$ in $\mathscr{B}(R^1)$, $Q((1,0); E_1)$ and $Q((0,1); E_2)$ commute. Write $Q_1 = Q((1,0); E_1)$ and $Q_2 = Q((0,1); E_2)$. Since $E_1 \times E_2 \subseteq E_1 \times R^1$, we have

$$P_{E_1 \times E_2} \leq P_{E_1 \times R^1} = Q_1.$$

Similarly,

$$P_{E_1 \times E_2} \leq Q_2.$$

From lemma 7.26 we may conclude that

$$P_{E_1 \times E_2} \leq Q_1 \wedge Q_2.$$

Replacing $E_2$ by $R^1 - E_2$ we obtain

$$P_{E_1 \times R^1 - E_2} \leq Q_1 \wedge (I - Q_2).$$

The last two relations yield, on addition,

(69)     $$Q_1 \leq Q_1 \wedge Q_2 + Q_1 \wedge (I - Q_2).$$

However, $Q_1 \wedge Q_2$ and $Q_1 \wedge (I - Q_2)$ are orthogonal projections which are both $\leq Q_1$. Hence we infer from (69) that

$$Q_1 = Q_1 \wedge Q_2 + Q_1 \wedge (I - Q_2).$$

This last equation leads quite simply to the conclusion that $Q_1$ and $Q_2$ commute (cf. lemma 6.7).

This theorem, taken together with theorem 6.9 may be regarded as giving a complete description of the circumstances under which the statistics of several observables may be regarded as arising from observables with joint distributions.

We end these remarks with a mention of the concept of the quasi-probability distributions, introduced by Wigner [2] and studied extensively by Moyal [1]. Let $x_1, x_2, \cdots, x_k$ be bounded observables with $A_1, \cdots, A_k$ as their corresponding operators. We use the same notation as in theorem 7.25. For fixed $\varphi$ in $\mathscr{H}$, and for a given $\mathbf{c}$, $E \to Q(\mathbf{c}; E) = q_\varphi(\mathbf{c}; E)$ is a non-negative measure on $\mathscr{B}(R^1)$. We define

(70)
$$\Phi(c_1, c_2, \cdots, c_k; \varphi) = \frac{1}{(2\pi)^{k/2}} \int_{R^k} \exp\{(-1)^{1/2}(c_1 t_1 + \cdots + c_k t_k)\} dq_\varphi(\mathbf{c}; \cdot).$$

It is easy to prove that $\Phi(\cdot; \varphi)$ is a continuous function of $c_1, \cdots, c_k$ for each $\varphi \in \mathscr{H}$ and

$$|\Phi(c_1, \cdots, c_k; \varphi)| \leq 1.$$

We may therefore introduce its Fourier transform, in the sense of distributions of Schwartz, say $\hat{\Phi}(\cdot\,;\varphi)$. It is known as the *Wigner-Moyal quasi-probability distribution* of the observables $x_1, \cdots, x_k$ in the state determined by $\varphi$.

## 3. THE STANDARD LOGICS: SYMMETRIES

At the focal point of the axiomatic development of modern physics lies the concept of automorphism or symmetry. We have already pointed out that the momentum observables of a physical system are intimately related to one-parameter groups of automorphisms of the configuration manifold of the system. Moreover, we had described in Chapter VI how the dynamical group of a physical system can be described by a one-parameter group of convex automorphisms of the set of states. It is therefore extremely important to examine the concept of an automorphism when the logic in question is a standard one. The main purpose of this section is to obtain a complete description of the automorphisms associated with a standard logic.

We shall introduce, for this purpose, the notion of a symmetry of a Hilbert space $\mathscr{H}$. As always, $\mathscr{H}$ is separable and the field of scalars $\mathbf{D}$ is one of $\mathbf{R}$, $\mathbf{C}$, or $\mathbf{Q}$. A mapping $T(x \to Tx)$ of $\mathscr{H}$ into itself is said to be a *symmetry* (of $\mathscr{H}$) if (i) $T$ is additive, one-one, and maps $\mathscr{H}$ onto itself, and (ii) there exists a continuous automorphism $\theta$ of $\mathbf{D}$ such that $T$ is $\theta$-linear and, for all $x, y \in \mathscr{H}$,

$$(71) \qquad\qquad \langle Tx, Ty \rangle = \langle x,y \rangle^\theta.$$

If $\mathbf{D} = \mathbf{R}$, then $\theta$ is the identity and the symmetries are none other than the unitary operators of $\mathscr{H}$. If $\mathbf{D} = \mathbf{C}$, then $\theta$ is either the identity or the conjugation; in the former case, $T$ is unitary, whereas in the latter case $T$ is anti-unitary. If $\mathbf{D} = \mathbf{Q}$, then there exists a $c \in \mathbf{D}$ such that $|c| = 1$ and $d^\theta = cdc^{-1}$ for all $d \in \mathbf{D}$; in this case,

$$T(dx) = (cdc^{-1})Tx$$

and

$$\langle Tx, Ty \rangle = c \langle x,y \rangle c^{-1}.$$

Equation (71) implies that

$$\begin{aligned} \|Tx\| &= \|x\| \\ |\langle Tx, Ty \rangle| &= |\langle x,y \rangle| \end{aligned} \qquad (x, y \in \mathscr{H}).$$

In the general case of (71) we shall call $T$ $\theta$-*unitary*. The symmetries of $\mathscr{H}$ form a group; if $T_j$ is $\theta_j$-unitary $(j=1,2)$, $T_1 T_2$ is $\theta_1 \theta_2$-unitary and $T_j^{-1}$ is $\theta_j^{-1}$-unitary. The unitary (linear) operators of $\mathscr{H}$ form a normal subgroup

$\mathscr{U}(\mathscr{H})$ of the group of all symmetries. We shall write $S(\mathscr{H})$ for the group of symmetries. The map which associates with any $\theta$-unitary $T$, the automorphism $\theta$ of **D**, is a homomorphism of $S(\mathscr{H})$ onto the group Aut(**D**) of all continuous automorphisms of **D**. Since the kernel of this map is $\mathscr{U}(\mathscr{H})$, we have:

(72) $$S(\mathscr{H})/\mathscr{U}(\mathscr{H}) \simeq \text{Aut}(\mathbf{D}).$$

Note finally that if $T$ is a symmetry and $c \in \mathbf{D}$ is such that $|c|=1$, $cT$ is a symmetry.

**Theorem 7.27.** *Let $\mathscr{H}$ be a separable infinite dimensional Hilbert space over* **D**. *Let $\alpha(M \to M^\alpha)$ be an automorphism of the logic $\mathscr{L}$. Then, there exists a symmetry $T$ of $\mathscr{H}$ such that*

(73) $$M^\alpha = T[M] \qquad (M \in \mathscr{L}).$$

*If $T'$ is a symmetry such that (73) is satisfied for all $M$, then there exists a $c \in D$ with $|c|=1$ such that $T'=cT$. Finally if $T$ is any symmetry of $\mathscr{H}$, $M \to T[M]$ is an automorphism of the logic $\mathscr{L}$.*

**Proof.** It is quite trivial to check that if $T$ is a symmetry of $\mathscr{H}$, $M \to T[M]$ is an automorphism of the logic $\mathscr{L}$.

Suppose now that $\alpha(M \to M^\alpha)$ is an automorphism of the logic $\mathscr{L}$. Let $F$ be a linear manifold, chosen once for all, such that dim $F=3$. By theorem 3.1 there exists an automorphism $\theta$ of **D** and a $\theta$-linear isomorphism $L_0$, of $F$ onto $F^\alpha$, such that for any linear manifold $M \subseteq F$,

$$M^\alpha = L_0[M].$$

Let us define $\mathscr{F}$ to be the collection of all finite dimensional linear manifolds $G$ which contain $F$. We claim that for each $G \in \mathscr{F}$ there exists a unique $\theta$-linear isomorphism $L_G$ of $G$ onto $G^\alpha$ such that

(74) $$L_G u = L_0 u \qquad (u \in F)$$

and

(75) $$M^\alpha = L_G[M] \qquad (M \subseteq G).$$

In fact, by theorem 3.1 there exists an automorphism $\theta'$ of **D** and a $\theta'$-linear isomorphism $L'$ of $G$ onto $G^\alpha$ such that $M^\alpha = L'[M]$ for all linear manifolds $M \subseteq G$. Since $M^\alpha = L'[M] = L_0[M]$ for all linear manifolds $M \subseteq F$, we conclude from the same theorem that there exists a nonzero $c \in \mathbf{D}$ such that (i) $L'u = cL_0u$ for all $u \in F$, and (ii) $a^{\theta'} = ca^\theta c^{-1}$ for all $a \in \mathbf{D}$. If we write $L_G = c^{-1}L'$, then $L_G$ is a $\theta$-linear isomorphism of $G$ onto $G^\alpha$ satisfying (74) and (75). The uniqueness of $L_G$ follows from (74) and (75).

Since $L_G$ is uniquely determined by (74) and (75), it follows quite easily that there exists a $\theta$-linear map $L$ of $\mathscr{H}$ into itself such that

$$(76) \qquad Lu = L_G u \qquad (u \in G, \quad G \in \mathscr{F}).$$

We claim that $L$ is one-one and maps $\mathscr{H}$ onto itself.

To prove that $L$ is one-one, let $x \in \mathscr{H}$ and $Lx=0$. Evidently, $x \in G$ for some $G \in \mathscr{F}$ and $Lx=L_G x=0$. Therefore $x=0$ as $L_G$ is an isomorphism. If $y \in \mathscr{H}$ there is a $G \in \mathscr{F}$ such that $y \in G^\alpha$ and once again, as $L_G$ maps $G$ onto $G^\alpha$, there will exist an $x \in G$ such that $Lx=y$. Since any $M \in \mathscr{L}$ with finite dimension is contained in some element of $\mathscr{F}$, we see that $L$ is a $\theta$-linear isomorphism of $\mathscr{H}$ onto itself such that

$$(77) \qquad M^\alpha = L[M] \qquad (\dim M < \infty).$$

Let now $G \in \mathscr{F}$. Since $\alpha$ preserves orthogonal complementation, it follows that for $x, y \in G$, $\langle x,y \rangle =0$ if and only if $\langle Lx,Ly \rangle =0$. Thus, the semi-bilinear forms $x, y \to \langle x, y \rangle$ and $x, y \to \langle Lx,Ly \rangle^{(\theta-1)}$ of $G \times G$ induce the same polarity of the geometry of subspaces of $G$, and hence there exists, by virtue of theorem 4.1, a unique $d_G \neq 0$ in $\mathbf{D}$ such that

$$\langle Lx,Ly \rangle = \langle x,y \rangle^\theta d_G \qquad (x, y \in G).$$

Since $G \in \mathscr{F}$ is arbitrary and since $d_G$ is uniquely determined for each $G$, it follows that $d_G$ is independent of $G$ and that

$$(78) \qquad \langle Lx,Ly \rangle = \langle x,y \rangle^\theta d \qquad (x, y \in \mathscr{H})$$

for a nonzero $d \in \mathbf{D}$.

We now show that $\theta$ is continuous. This is obvious for $\mathbf{D} = \mathbf{R}$ or $\mathbf{Q}$, since $\theta$ is the identity in the former case and is an inner automorphism in the latter. Consider now the case $\mathbf{D} = \mathbf{C}$. If $\theta$ is not continuous, there exists a sequence $\{c_n\}$ in $\mathbf{D}$ such that $c_n \to 0$, but $|c_n^\theta| \to \infty$. Choose an orthonormal *infinite* sequence $\{e_n : n=1, 2, \cdots\}$ in $\mathscr{H}$ and let $x_n=ne_n$. By replacing $c_n$ by a subsequence if necessary, we may assume that

$$(79) \qquad \|Lx_n\|/|c_n^\theta| \to 0 \qquad (n \to \infty).$$

Write

$$z = \sum_n \frac{c_n{}^*}{n} e_n.$$

Since $c_n{}^* \to 0$, $z$ is well defined in $\mathscr{H}$. Clearly, $z \neq 0$. Then, $\langle x_n,z \rangle =c_n$ and hence, for all $n$, $u_n=\langle z,z \rangle^{-1}z-c_n^{-1}x_n$ is orthogonal to $z$. Consequently, from (78) we obtain, for all $n$,

$$\langle Lu_n,Lz \rangle = 0.$$

This implies, on simplification, that

(80) $$(\langle z,z\rangle^\theta)^{-1}\langle Lz,Lz\rangle = (c_n{}^\theta)^{-1}\langle Lx_n,Lz\rangle$$

for all $n$. But

$$|(c_n{}^\theta)^{-1}||\langle Lx_n,Lz\rangle| \le |c_n{}^\theta|^{-1}\|Lx_n\|\|Lz\|,$$

which tends to zero by virtue of our assumption (79). Hence (80) implies that $\langle Lz,Lz\rangle=0$ or $z=0$. This contradiction shows that $\theta$ is continuous.

We are now ready to complete the proof of theorem 7.27. Since $\theta$ is continuous, it follows that for any real number $r$, $r^\theta=r$. Hence we see, by putting $x=y$ in (78), that $d$ is a positive real number. Write $T=d^{-1/2}L$. Then $T$ is a $\theta$-linear isomorphism of $\mathscr{H}$ onto itself such that

(81) $$\langle Tx,Ty\rangle = \langle x,y\rangle^\theta$$

and

$$M^\alpha = T[M] \qquad (M \in \mathscr{L}, \dim M < \infty).$$

Since $\|Tx\|=\|x\|$, $T$ is an isometry and is hence continuous. It follows therefore that

$$M^\alpha = T[M] \qquad (M \in \mathscr{L}).$$

The remaining statements are easy consequences of theorem 4.1. Therefore, we omit their easy verifications. The proof of theorem 7.27 is complete.

We shall say that $T$ *induces* $\alpha$ if (71) is satisfied.

**Corollary 7.28.** *If* $\mathbf{D}=\mathbf{R}$ *or* $\mathbf{Q}$, *then any automorphism* $\alpha$ *of* $\mathscr{L}$ *is induced by a unitary operator of* $\mathscr{H}$. *If* $\mathbf{D}=\mathbf{C}$, *then* $\alpha^2$ *is induced by a unitary operator.*

**Proof.** For $\mathbf{D}=\mathbf{R}$ there is nothing to prove. If $\mathbf{D}=\mathbf{Q}$ and $T_1$ is a $\theta$-unitary operator inducing $\alpha$ where $\theta$ is the automorphism

$$d \to cdc^{-1}(|c| = 1),$$

$T=c^{-1}T_1$ is a unitary operator inducing $\alpha$. If $\mathbf{D}=\mathbf{C}$ and $\alpha$ is induced by a $*$-unitary $T_1$, $T_1{}^2$ is unitary and induces $\alpha^2$.

In the physical literature it is customary to prove the above theorem in a somewhat different formulation (cf. Wigner [3]). To motivate Wigner's formulation we must introduce the notion of *transition probabilities*. Let $\mathbf{r}$, $\mathbf{r}'$ be rays in $\mathscr{H}$ and $\varphi$, $\varphi'$ unit vectors in $\mathbf{r}$ and $\mathbf{r}'$, respectively. Then $|\langle\varphi,\varphi'\rangle|^2$ evidently depends only on $\mathbf{r}$ and $\mathbf{r}'$ and not on $\varphi$ and $\varphi'$. We denote it by $[\mathbf{r},\mathbf{r}']$. It is called the *transition probability* between the *states* $p$ and $p'$ which correspond (cf. theorem 7.23) to the rays $\mathbf{r}$ and $\mathbf{r}'$. If a physical system $\mathfrak{S}$ is in the state $p$, $[\mathbf{r},\mathbf{r}']$ is the probability that it will be actually found in the state $p'$ when an experiment is performed to decide whether it is in the state $p'$ or not. We shall define a *physical symmetry associated with the logic* $\mathscr{L}$ to be any one-one map $\alpha(\mathbf{r} \to \mathbf{r}^\alpha)$ of the set of all rays of $\mathscr{H}$ onto itself with the property that

$$(82) \qquad\qquad [\mathbf{r}^\alpha, \mathbf{r}'^\alpha] = [\mathbf{r}, \mathbf{r}']$$

for all rays $\mathbf{r}$, $\mathbf{r}'$. The following theorem describes the natural connection between physical symmetries and symmetries of $\mathscr{H}$.

**Theorem 7.29.** (*Wigner* [3]). *Let $\mathscr{H}$ be a separable infinite dimensional Hilbert space over* $\mathbf{D}$ *and* $T$ *a symmetry of* $\mathscr{H}$. *Then* $\mathbf{r} \to T[\mathbf{r}]$ *is a physical symmetry associated with* $\mathscr{L}$. *Conversely, let* $\alpha(\mathbf{r} \to \mathbf{r}^\alpha)$ *be any one-one map of the set* $\mathscr{R}$ *of all the rays of* $\mathscr{H}$ *onto itself with the property that* $\mathbf{r} \perp \mathbf{r}'$ *if and only if* $\mathbf{r}^\alpha \perp \mathbf{r}'^\alpha$. *Then,* $\alpha$ *is a physical symmetry associated with* $\mathscr{L}$, *and there exists a symmetry* $T$ *of* $\mathscr{H}$ *such that* $\mathbf{r}^\alpha = T[\mathbf{r}]$ *for all* $\mathbf{r} \in \mathscr{R}$. *T is determined by* $\alpha$ *up to multiplication by a number* $c \in \mathbf{D}$ *with* $|c| = 1$.

**Proof.** If $T$ is a symmetry of $\mathscr{H}$, $|\langle Tx, Ty \rangle| = |\langle x, y \rangle|$ for all $x$, $y \in \mathscr{H}$. From this we conclude easily that $\mathbf{r} \to T[\mathbf{r}]$ is a physical symmetry associated with $\mathscr{L}$. We now examine the converse. Let $\alpha(\mathbf{r} \to \mathbf{r}^\alpha)$ be any one-one map of $\mathscr{R}$ onto itself which preserves orthogonality. For any *subset* $A$ of $\mathscr{R}$ let

$$(83) \qquad\qquad A^\alpha = \{\mathbf{r}^\alpha : \mathbf{r} \in A\},$$

$$(84) \qquad\qquad [A] = \{x : x \in \mathscr{H}, x \in \mathbf{r} \quad \text{for some } \mathbf{r} \text{ in } A\},$$

and

$$(85) \qquad\qquad A^\perp = \{\mathbf{r} : \mathbf{r} \perp \mathbf{r}' \quad \text{for all} \quad \mathbf{r}' \in A\}.$$

We shall first prove that if $A \subseteq \mathscr{R}$ is such that $M = [A]$ is a closed linear manifold of $\mathscr{H}$, i.e., if $A$ is the set of all rays of a closed linear manifold $M$ of $\mathscr{H}$, then $[A^\alpha]$ is also a closed linear manifold. To prove this, we note that as $M = [A]$ is a closed linear manifold, a ray $\mathbf{r}$ belongs to $A$ if and only if $\mathbf{r} \in (A^\perp)^\perp$. But as $\alpha$ preserves orthogonality, this means that a ray $\mathbf{r}' \in A^\alpha$ if and only if $\mathbf{r}' \in (A^{\perp\alpha})^\perp$, i.e., $A^\alpha = (A^{\perp\alpha})^\perp$. But for any *subset* $S \subseteq \mathscr{R}$, the set $[S^\perp]$ is a closed linear manifold. Consequently $[A^\alpha]$ is a closed linear manifold.

We now set up a correspondence, also denoted by $\alpha$, between elements of $\mathscr{L}$. For any $M \in \mathscr{L}$, let $A$ be the set of all rays $\mathbf{r}$ such that $\mathbf{r} \subseteq M$; we set:

$$(86) \qquad\qquad M^\alpha = [A^\alpha].$$

The argument of the preceding paragraph has shown that $M^\alpha \in \mathscr{L}$. By very definition it is clear that $\alpha(M \to M^\alpha)$ is an order-preserving map of $\mathscr{L}$. Since $\mathbf{r} \subseteq M^\perp$ if and only if $\mathbf{r}$ is orthogonal to all rays contained in $M$, it follows that $(M^\perp)^\alpha = (M^\alpha)^\perp$. Thus $\alpha$ preserves orthogonality. These results applied to the map $\alpha^{-1}$ of $\mathscr{R}$ show that the map $M \to M^{(\alpha^{-1})}$ defined by (86) is the inverse of the map $M \to M^{\alpha}$ of $\mathscr{L}$. Consequently, we may conclude that $M \to M^{\alpha}$ is a lattice automorphism of $\mathscr{L}$ which preserves orthogonality.

By theorem 7.27 there exists a symmetry $T$ of $\mathscr{H}$ such that $M^{\alpha} = T[M]$ for all $M \in \mathscr{L}$. But then $\mathbf{r}^{\alpha} = T[\mathbf{r}]$ for all rays $\mathbf{r}$ showing that $\mathbf{r} \to \mathbf{r}^{\alpha}$ is a physical symmetry associated with $\mathscr{L}$. Since any automorphism of $\mathscr{L}$ is determined by its restriction to the set of all one-dimensional subspaces of $\mathscr{H}$, it is clear that $T$ is determined by the map $\alpha$ of $\mathscr{R}$ up to multiplication by a number $c \in \mathbf{D}$ with $|c| = 1$. This completes the proof of the theorem.

In Chapter VI we introduced the concept of a convex automorphism of the set of all states. We shall describe all such automorphisms of the set of states of a standard logic.

Let $T$ be a symmetry of the Hilbert space $\mathscr{H}$, and $\mathscr{W}$ the convex set of all bounded, nonnegative, self-adjoint operators $U$ of trace class with $\mathrm{tr}(U) = 1$. For any $U \in \mathscr{W}$ let $\alpha_T(U)$ be defined by

$$(87) \qquad \alpha_T(U) = TUT^{-1}.$$

**Lemma 7.30.** *Let $U \in \mathscr{W}$ and let $T$ be a symmetry of $\mathscr{H}$. Then $\alpha_T(U) \in \mathscr{W}$ and $U \to \alpha_T(U)$ is a convex automorphism of $\mathscr{W}$. Moreover, $T \to \alpha_T$ is a homomorphism of the group of symmetries of $\mathscr{H}$ into the group of convex automorphisms of $\mathscr{W}$.*

The proof is a routine verification. We leave it to the reader.

If $T$ is a symmetry of $\mathscr{H}$ and if we set, for $U \in \mathscr{W}$,

$$(88) \qquad \alpha_T(p_U) = p_{\alpha_T(U)},$$

where $p_U$ is the state $M \to \mathrm{tr}(P^M U)$ of $\mathscr{L}$, then the map $p_U \to \alpha_T(p_U)$ is a convex automorphism of $\mathscr{S}$. We shall prove that any convex automorphism of $\mathscr{S}$ is of this form. Let $\mathscr{W}_+$ denote the set of all von Neumann operators on $\mathscr{H}$. Clearly, $\mathscr{W} \subseteq \mathscr{W}_+$. If $T_1, T_2 \in \mathscr{W}_+$, we write $T_1 \leq T_2$ to mean $T_2 - T_1 \geq 0$.

**Lemma 7.31.** *Let $\alpha$ be a convex automorphism of $\mathscr{W}$. Then there exists a unique one-one map $\alpha^{\sim}$ of $\mathscr{W}_+$ onto itself such that*

$$(89) \quad \begin{array}{ll} \text{(i)} & \alpha(U) = \alpha^{\sim}(U) \qquad (U \in \mathscr{W}), \\ \text{(ii)} & \alpha^{\sim}(c_1 A_1 + c_2 A_2) = c_1 \alpha^{\sim}(A_1) + c_2 \alpha^{\sim}(A_2) \\ & \qquad\qquad (A_1, A_2 \in \mathscr{W}_+, c_1, c_2 \text{ real numbers } \geq 0); \end{array}$$

$\alpha^{\sim}$ *has then the property*:

$$(89) \quad \begin{array}{ll} \text{(iii)} & \mathrm{tr}(\alpha^{\sim}(A)) = \mathrm{tr}(A) \qquad (A \in \mathscr{W}_+), \\ \text{(iv)} & T_1 \leq T_2 \text{ if and only if } \alpha^{\sim}(T_1) \leq \alpha^{\sim}(T_2). \end{array}$$

**Proof.** Define $\alpha^{\sim}(0)=0$. If $T \in \mathscr{W}_+$ and $T \neq 0$, $t=\mathrm{tr}(T)>0$, and $t^{-1}T \in \mathscr{W}$; we then put

$$(90) \qquad\qquad \alpha^{\sim}(T) = t\alpha(t^{-1}T).$$

It is trivial to check that $\alpha^{\sim}$ has the properties described in the lemma. The uniqueness of $\alpha^{\sim}$ follows from the fact that the property (ii) of $\alpha^{\sim}$ implies (90). Equation (90) implies that $\mathrm{tr}(\alpha^{\sim}(T))=\mathrm{tr}(T)$, proving (iii). Finally, let $T_1 \leq T_2$. Then

$$\alpha^{\sim}(T_2) = \alpha^{\sim}(T_1)+\alpha^{\sim}(T_2-T_1) \geq \alpha^{\sim}(T_1)$$

as $\alpha^{\sim}(T_2-T_1) \in \mathscr{W}_+$ and is hence $\geq 0$. Conversely, let $\alpha^{\sim}(T_1) \leq \alpha^{\sim}(T_2)$. Since $\alpha^{\sim}$ maps $\mathscr{W}_+$ onto itself, $\alpha^{\sim}(T_2)=\alpha^{\sim}(T_1)+\alpha^{\sim}(T)$ for some $T \in \mathscr{W}_+$. Evidently, $T_2 = T_1 + T$, and hence $T_2 \geq T_1$.

**Lemma 7.32.** *Let $\varphi_j \in \mathscr{H}$ $(j=1, 2)$ be two unit vectors and let $P_j$ be the orthogonal projection on the one-dimensional subspace $\mathbf{D} \cdot \varphi_j$. Then the two following statements are equivalent.*

$$(91) \qquad \begin{array}{ll} \text{(i)} & \varphi_1 \perp \varphi_2. \\ \text{(ii)} & \textit{For any } A \in \mathscr{W}_+, \textit{ the relations } P_1 \leq A \textit{ and } P_2 \leq A \textit{ imply that} \\ & \textit{tr } A \geq 2. \end{array}$$

**Proof.** Suppose that $\varphi_1 \perp \varphi_2$ and suppose that $A \in \mathscr{W}_+$ satisfies the relations $P_1 \leq A$ and $P_2 \leq A$. Let $\varphi_3, \varphi_4, \cdots$ be vectors in $\mathscr{H}$ such that $\{\varphi_1, \varphi_2, \cdots\}$ is an orthonormal basis for $\mathscr{H}$. Then, as $A \geq 0$,

$$\begin{aligned} \mathrm{tr}(A) &= \sum_{n=1}^{\infty} \langle A\varphi_n, \varphi_n \rangle \\ &\geq \langle A\varphi_1, \varphi_1 \rangle + \langle A\varphi_2, \varphi_2 \rangle \\ &\geq \langle P_1\varphi_1, \varphi_1 \rangle + \langle P_2\varphi_2, \varphi_2 \rangle. \end{aligned}$$

Consequently,

$$\mathrm{tr}(A) \geq 2.$$

This shows that (i) implies (ii).

Conversely, let (ii) be satisfied. Let us assume that $\varphi_1$ is not orthogonal to $\varphi_2$. We shall construct an $A \in \mathscr{W}_+$ such that $P_1 \leq A$ and $P_2 \leq A$ but $\mathrm{tr}(A)<2$. Two cases arise.

*Case (a)*: $\varphi_1$ and $\varphi_2$ are linearly dependent. In this case $P_1 = P_2 \, (=P$ say), and if $A = P$, then $\mathrm{tr}(A)=1$.

*Case (b)*: $\varphi_1$ and $\varphi_2$ span a two-dimensional subspace $S$ of $\mathscr{H}$. It is obviously enough to consider the case when $S=\mathscr{H}$. Let $\varphi_2'$ be a unit vector of $S$ orthogonal to $\varphi_1$. Then for some $a, b \in \mathbf{D}$, $\varphi_2=a\varphi_1+b\varphi_2'$. Neither $a$ nor $b$ is zero and $|a|^2 + |b|^2=1$. Write $\psi=|a|a^{-1}\varphi_2$ and

$$\psi_2 = |a|a^{-1}|b|^{-1}b \cdot \varphi_2'.$$

Then $\{\varphi_1, \psi_2\}$ is an orthonormal basis for $S$ and $\psi = |a|\varphi_1 + |b|\psi_2$. Clearly $P_2$ is the projection on the subspace $\mathbf{D} \cdot \psi$. With respect to the orthonormal basis $\{\varphi_1, \psi_2\}$, $P_1$ and $P_2$ have the matrices given by

$$P_1 \sim \begin{pmatrix} 1 & 0 \\ 0 & 0 \end{pmatrix}, \qquad P_2 \sim \begin{pmatrix} |a|^2 & |a||b| \\ |a||b| & |b|^2 \end{pmatrix}.$$

Since $|a|^2 + |b|^2 = 1$, the eigenvalues of the matrix of $P_2 - P_1$ are $\pm |b|$, and hence there exists a unitary operator $V$ such that the operator $V(P_2 - P_1)V^{-1}$ has the matrix given by

$$V(P_2 - P_1)V^{-1} \sim \begin{pmatrix} |b| & 0 \\ 0 & -|b| \end{pmatrix}.$$

Let $M$ be the unique operator such that $VMV^{-1}$ has the matrix given by

$$VMV^{-1} \sim \begin{pmatrix} |b| & 0 \\ 0 & 0 \end{pmatrix}.$$

Obviously $M$ is self-adjoint, $\geq 0$ and $\operatorname{tr}(M) = |b| < 1$. Further,

$$VMV^{-1} - V(P_2 - P_1)V^{-1} \geq 0$$

and hence $M \geq P_2 - P_1$. Let $A = P_1 + M$. Then $P_1 \leq A$, $P_2 \leq A$ but $\operatorname{tr}(A) = 1 + |b| < 2$. This proves the lemma.

**Theorem 7.33.** *Let $\mathscr{H}$ be a separable infinite dimensional Hilbert space over $\mathbf{D}$ and $T$ a symmetry of $\mathscr{H}$. For any $U \in \mathscr{W}$ let $p_U$ be the state $M \to \operatorname{tr}(P^M U)$ of $\mathscr{L}$ and $U_T = TUT^{-1}$. If*

$$(92) \qquad\qquad \alpha_T(p_U) = p_{U_T},$$

*then $\alpha_T(p_U \to p_{U_T})$ is a convex automorphism of $\mathscr{S}$. Conversely, let $\alpha$ be a convex automorphism of $\mathscr{S}$. Then there exists a symmetry $T$ of $\mathscr{H}$ such that*

$$(93) \qquad\qquad \alpha = \alpha_T.$$

*$T$ is determined up to multiplication by a number $c \in \mathbf{D}$ with $|c| = 1$.*

**Proof.** The first part of the theorem is essentially the content of lemma 7.30. To prove the converse, let $\alpha$ be a convex automorphism of $\mathscr{S}$. By theorem 7.23, $\alpha$ induces a convex automorphism of $\mathscr{W}$, denoted once again by $\alpha$. Let $\alpha^\sim$ be the map of $\mathscr{W}_+$, determined by $\alpha$ (cf. lemma 7.31). Since the extreme points of $\mathscr{W}$ are the orthogonal projections on the one-dimensional subspaces of $\mathscr{H}$ and since $\alpha$ is convex, $\alpha$ induces a one-one correspondence of the set $\mathscr{R}$, of all rays of $\mathscr{H}$, onto itself. Let $\alpha(\mathbf{r} \to \mathbf{r}^\alpha)$ be this correspondence. Since $\alpha^\sim$ preserves the trace and the partial ordering $\leq$ of $\mathscr{W}_+$ (by (iv) of lemma 7.31), and since the orthogonality of two rays has been completely characterized in terms of the trace function and the partial ordering $\leq$ in lemma 7.32, it follows at once that $\mathbf{r} \to \mathbf{r}^\alpha$ is orthogonality-preserving. By theorem 7.29 there exists a symmetry $T$ such that $\mathbf{r}^\alpha = T[\mathbf{r}]$ for all rays $\mathbf{r}$. If $\alpha_T$ is the convex automorphism of $\mathscr{S}$ associated with $T$, this means that $\alpha_T$ and $\alpha$ coincide on the set of extreme points of $\mathscr{W}$. From this it follows that $\alpha = \alpha_T$. The fact that $T$ is determined up to multiplication by an element $c \in \mathbf{D}$ with $|c| = 1$ now follows from theorem 7.29. The theorem is completely proved.

## 4. LOGICS ASSOCIATED WITH VON NEUMANN ALGEBRAS

If the logic $\mathscr{L}$ of a quantum mechanical system is not isomorphic to a standard one, then the question of describing its observables, states, and symmetries becomes a more difficult one. There are no general results in this connection. It is our aim to give a few examples which illustrate the wide possibilities as well as the difficulties involved in the construction of any general theory.

A large class of logics which are sublogics of standard logics may be constructed using the theory of von Neumann algebras. We confine ourselves to the case of *complex scalars*. Let $\mathbf{D} = \mathbf{C}$ be the complex number field and $\mathscr{H}$ a separable infinite dimensional Hilbert space over $\mathbf{C}$. We write $\mathfrak{A}(\mathscr{H})$ for the algebra of all operators on $\mathscr{H}$. For $u, v \in \mathscr{H}$, let

$$\lambda_{u,v} : A \to \langle Au, v \rangle \qquad (A \in \mathfrak{A}(\mathscr{H})).$$

Then the $\lambda_{u,v}$ are linear functionals on $\mathfrak{A}(\mathscr{H})$. The *weak topology* on $\mathfrak{A}(\mathscr{H})$ is the smallest one with respect to which all the $\lambda_{u,v}$ are continuous. A *von Neumann algebra* $\mathfrak{A}$ is a subalgebra (containing $I$) of $\mathfrak{A}(\mathscr{H})$ such that (i) if $A \in \mathfrak{A}$, then $A^* \in \mathfrak{A}$, and (ii) $\mathfrak{A}$ is a closed subset of $\mathfrak{A}(\mathscr{H})$ in the weak topology. If $\mathfrak{A}'$ is the set of all elements of $\mathfrak{A}(\mathscr{H})$ commuting with all the elements of $\mathfrak{A}$, $\mathfrak{A}'$ is also a von Neumann algebra and $(\mathfrak{A}')' = \mathfrak{A}$ (cf. Dixmier [1] for the general theory of von Neumann algebras).

Let $\mathfrak{A}$ be a von Neumann algebra. We define

(94) $$\mathscr{L}_{\mathfrak{A}} = \{M : M \in \mathscr{L}(\mathscr{H}), P^M \in \mathfrak{A}\}.$$

It is then easy to verify that $\mathscr{L}_{\mathfrak{A}}$ is a logic. We shall call it the logic associated with $\mathfrak{A}$. A closed linear manifold $M$ lies in $\mathscr{L}_{\mathfrak{A}}$ if and only if every element of $\mathfrak{A}'$ leaves $M$ invariant. Thus the logic $\mathscr{L}_{\mathfrak{A}}$ may also be introduced as the logic of closed invariant linear manifolds of some von Neumann algebra.

The one-one correspondence $x \to A_x$ between observables of $\mathscr{L}_{\mathfrak{A}}$ and self-adjoint operators on $\mathscr{H}$, which was discussed in section 2 of this chapter, clearly persists even in this case. However, not every self-adjoint operator is the operator of an observable associated with $\mathscr{L}_{\mathfrak{A}}$.

Let $A$ be a self-adjoint operator, not necessarily bounded. Then $A = A_x$ for an observable $x$ of $\mathscr{L}_\mathfrak{A}$ if and only if the spectral projections of $A$ lie in $\mathfrak{A}$. If $A$ is bounded, the condition will then be that $A \in \mathfrak{A}$. If $A$ is unbounded, the condition will have to be stated more carefully. In this case, $A = A_x$ for an $\mathscr{L}_\mathfrak{A}$-observable if and only if $UAU^{-1} = A$ for all unitary operators $U \in \mathfrak{A}'$ (cf. Dixmier [1]; such $A$'s are said to be *affiliated* to $\mathfrak{A}$). $\mathscr{C} = \mathfrak{A} \cap \mathfrak{A}'$ is the center of the algebra $\mathfrak{A}$. If we write $\mathscr{L}_\mathscr{C} = \mathscr{C} \cap \mathscr{L}_\mathfrak{A}$, then, $\mathscr{L}_\mathscr{C}$ is the center of the logic $\mathscr{L}_\mathfrak{A}$. $\mathscr{L}_\mathfrak{A}$ is irreducible if and only if $\mathscr{L}_\mathscr{C} = \{0, I\}$, or, equivalently, if $\mathscr{C}$ consists only of multiples of the identity, i.e., in the standard terminology of von Neumann algebras, if and only if $\mathfrak{A}$ is a factor.

It was Murray and von Neumann [1] who pioneered the entire study of factors. They classified factors into three types, I, II, and III. A factor $\mathfrak{A}$ is of type I if and only if $\mathfrak{A}$ is isomorphic to the algebra $\mathfrak{A}(\mathscr{K})$ of some Hilbert space $\mathscr{K}$. From our point of view, $\mathfrak{A}$ is a factor of type I if and only if $\mathscr{L}_\mathfrak{A}$ is isomorphic to the standard logic $\mathscr{L}(\mathscr{K})$ for some $\mathscr{K}$. The results of sections 7.2 and 7.3 therefore give a complete description of the sets of observables and states when $\mathscr{L} = \mathscr{L}_\mathfrak{A}$ for some factor $\mathfrak{A}$ of type I. When $\mathfrak{A}$ is a factor but not of type I, no similar theory exists. As an example, we may mention that the problem of determining all the states of $\mathscr{L}_\mathfrak{A}$, when $\mathfrak{A}$ is a factor of type II or III, is still open.

We have remarked previously that if $\mathfrak{A}$ is not a factor, the center $\mathscr{L}_\mathscr{C}$ of $\mathscr{L}_\mathfrak{A}$ is nontrivial. We have also seen in Chapter VI that there is an intimate connection between $\mathscr{L}_\mathscr{C}$ and the pure states of $\mathscr{L}_\mathfrak{A}$. It is clear from theorem 6.19 that if any contact is to be made with conventional quantum theory, $\mathscr{L}_\mathscr{C}$ cannot be continuous. At the other extreme lies the situation in which $\mathscr{L}_\mathscr{C}$ is *discrete*, i.e., when there exist mutually orthogonal elements $M_1, M_2, \cdots$ in $\mathscr{L}_\mathscr{C}$ such that (i) $\bigvee_n M_n = \mathscr{H}$, and (ii) $M \in \mathscr{L}_\mathscr{C}$ if and only if for some $n_1 < n_2 < \cdots, M = \bigvee_k M_{n_k}$. The $M_i$'s are then the minimal elements of $\mathscr{L}_\mathscr{C}$. A case when $\mathscr{L}_\mathscr{C}$ is discrete is obtained when we choose $M_n$ as above, and define $\mathfrak{A}$ to be the set of all operators which leave each $M_n$ invariant. Then, for a closed linear manifold $M$ of $\mathscr{H}$, $M \in \mathscr{L}_\mathfrak{A}$ if and only if $M = \bigvee_n (M \wedge M_n)$. If we assume that $\dim M_n \geq 3$ for all $n$, we can describe all the pure states of $\mathscr{L}_\mathfrak{A}$. In fact, from theorem 6.19 and Gleason's theorem we conclude immediately that $p$ is pure if and only if there exists an $n$ and a unit vector $\varphi$ in $M_n$ such that

$$(95) \qquad p(M) = \| P^M \varphi \|^2 \qquad (M \in \mathscr{L}_\mathfrak{A}).$$

In other words, the pure states of $\mathscr{L}_\mathfrak{A}$ are still in one-one correspondence with the rays of $\mathscr{H}$; however, not every ray can be used. *Only the rays which belong to some $M_n$ correspond to pure states.* Physicists describe this situation by saying that no ray of $\mathscr{H}$, which is a nontrivial superposition of rays in *distinct* $M_n$, can describe a (pure) state of $\mathscr{L}_\mathfrak{A}$. Each $M_n$ is

called a *coherent* subspace of (pure) states. The conditions which demand
that the rays describing the pure states should lie in $M_n$ for some $n$
are usually referred to as *superselection* rules. (cf. Wick, Wightman, and
Wigner [1]).

## 5. ISOMORPHISM AND IMBEDDING THEOREMS

It is very important in the foundations of quantum mechanics to examine the extent of generality of the concept of an abstract logic. In
particular, the question arises whether every logic can be regarded as a
sublogic of a standard logic. Definitive answers to such questions are
not known. We shall prove in this section some theorems which analyze
the structure of a somewhat restricted class of logics. The main theorem
of this section was proved by Piron [1]. A related but somewhat weaker
result was obtained by Zierler [1].

The main tool of our analysis is the coordinatization theorem of Chapter
V. In order to be able to apply that theorem we must impose a sharp
restriction on the class of logics to be analyzed. We introduce accordingly
the following definition. A logic $\mathscr{L}$ is said to be *projective* if the following
conditions are satisfied:

(96)
- (i)  given $a \neq 0$ in $\mathscr{L}$, there is a point $x < a$;
- (ii)  if $a \neq 0$ in $\mathscr{L}$ is the (lattice) sum of a finite set of points, then $\mathscr{L}[0,a]$ is a geometry of finite rank; we shall say that $a$ is a *finite* element of $\mathscr{L}$ and write $\dim(a)$ for the dimension of $\mathscr{L}[0,a]$;
- (iii)  if $x, a \in \mathscr{L}$, $a \neq 0$, $\neq 1$ and $x$ is a point, then there are points $y, z \in \mathscr{L}$ such that $y < a$, $z < a^\perp$ and $x < y \vee z$;
- (iv)  there exists at least one $a \in \mathscr{L}$ such that $4 \leq \dim(a) < \infty$.

For any $a \in \mathscr{L}$, let

(97) $$\mathfrak{P}(a) = \{x : x \text{ a point, } x < a\}.$$

Note that if $\mathscr{L}$ is projective and its lattice is complete, then every element
$a$ of $\mathscr{L}$ is the lattice sum of the points it contains. In fact, if $b$ is the sum
of these points and $b \neq a$, $c = b^\perp \wedge a \neq 0$ and there would exist a point $x < c$
by (i) of (96) which contradicts the definition of $b$.

**Lemma 7.34.**  *Let $\mathscr{L}$ be a projective logic whose underlying lattice is
complete. If $a$ and $b_j$ ($j \in J$) are elements of $\mathscr{L}$ and if $a \perp b_j$ for all $j$, $a \perp \bigvee_j b_j$.
We have the usual identities:*

$$\left(\bigvee_j b_j\right)^\perp = \bigwedge_j b_j^\perp,$$
$$\left(\bigwedge_j b_j\right)^\perp = \bigvee_j b_j^\perp.$$

*If* $a, b \in \mathscr{L}$, *then* $a < b$ *if and only if* $\mathfrak{P}(a) \subseteq \mathfrak{P}(b)$; $a \perp b$ *if and only if* $\mathfrak{P}(a) \perp \mathfrak{P}(b)$.

**Proof.** The first two assertions are proved exactly like the corresponding assertions in lemma 6.1. We therefore come to the proof of the last assertion. If $a < b$, $\mathfrak{P}(a) \subseteq \mathfrak{P}(b)$ obviously. On the other hand, let $a \not< b$. Then $a \wedge b \neq a$ and hence, by (96) (i), there exists a point $x \perp a \wedge b$ such that $x \in \mathfrak{P}(a)$. Clearly $x \notin \mathfrak{P}(b)$. If $a \perp b$, $\mathfrak{P}(a) \perp \mathfrak{P}(b)$ obviously. Suppose now that $\mathfrak{P}(a) \perp \mathfrak{P}(b)$. Then for any $x \in \mathfrak{P}(a)$, $x \perp \bigvee_{y \in \mathfrak{P}(b)} y = b$. Therefore $b \perp \bigvee_{x \in \mathfrak{P}(a)} x = a$.

Let **D** be a division ring and $V$ a vector space, not necessarily finite dimensional, over **D** with dimension at least 4. Let $\theta$ be an involutive anti-automorphism of **D** and let $\langle . , . \rangle$ be a $\theta$-bilinear symmetric form on $V \times V$. Let us assume that $\langle . , . \rangle$ is *definite*; i.e., $\langle x, x \rangle = 0$ if and only if $x = 0$. For any set $M$ of vectors we write

(98)
$$M^{\perp} = \{u : \langle x, u \rangle = 0 \quad \text{for all} \quad x \in M\}.$$

Obviously, $M^{\perp}$ is a linear manifold in $V$, $M \cap M^{\perp} = 0$, and $M \subseteq M^{\perp\perp}$. If $M$ is a linear manifold and $M = M^{\perp\perp}$, we shall say that $M$ is $\langle . , . \rangle$-closed. *Note that no topology is involved in this definition.* The pair $(V, \langle . , . \rangle)$ is said to be *Hilbertian* if for any closed linear manifold $M$, one has:

(99)
$$V = M + M^{\perp}$$

*algebraically.* For any set $M \subseteq V$ we write

(100)
$$M^{-} = M^{\perp\perp}$$

If $A, B \subseteq V$ we write $A \perp B$ whenever $\langle a, b \rangle = 0$ for all $a \in A$ and $b \in B$. Clearly $0^{-} = 0$, $V^{-} = V$, and $0^{\perp} = V$, $V^{\perp} = 0$. If $M$ and $N$ are linear manifolds and $M \subseteq N$, then $N^{\perp} \subseteq M^{\perp}$. If $\{M_j\}$ is a collection of linear manifolds, $M$ their algebraic sum, and $N \perp M_j$ for all $j$, then $N \perp M$. All this is trivial.

**Lemma 7.35.** *The following statements on a set* $M \subseteq V$ *are equivalent.*

(i) $M$ *is a* $\langle . , . \rangle$-*closed linear manifold.*
(ii) $M = M^{-}$.
(iii) $M = N^{\perp}$ *for some set* $N \subseteq V$.

*Moreover, for any set* $M \subseteq V$,

(101)
$$M^{\perp\perp\perp} = M^{\perp},$$

(102)
$$(M^{-})^{\perp} = M^{\perp},$$

*and*

(103)
$$(M^{-})^{-} = M^{-}.$$

*Finally, if $\{M_j\}$ is a collection of $\langle\,.\,,\,.\,\rangle$-closed linear manifolds, $\bigcap_j M_j$ is also a $\langle\,.\,,\,.\,\rangle$-closed linear manifold.*

**Proof.** Clearly for any set $M \subseteq V$, $M \subseteq M^{\perp\perp}$. Thus $M^\perp \subseteq (M^\perp)^{\perp\perp}$. On the other hand, as $M \subseteq M^{\perp\perp}$, $(M^{\perp\perp})^\perp \subseteq M^\perp$. Therefore $M^\perp = M^{\perp\perp\perp}$, which is (101). Since $M^- = M^{\perp\perp}$, (102) follows from (101). Further,

$$(M^-)^- = (M^{\perp\perp})^{\perp\perp} = (M^{\perp\perp\perp})^\perp = M^{\perp\perp}$$

by (101), so that $(M^-)^- = M^-$. This proves (103). We now come to the proof of the equivalence of (i) through (iii). Suppose $M$ is a $\langle\,.\,,\,.\,\rangle$-closed linear manifold. Then $M = M^{\perp\perp}$, so that $M = M^-$. Thus (i) $\Rightarrow$ (ii). If $M = M^-$, then $M = M^{\perp\perp} = (M^\perp)^\perp$, proving that (ii) $\Rightarrow$ (iii). Suppose now that $M = N^\perp$. Then, by (98), $M^{\perp\perp} = N^{\perp\perp\perp} = N^\perp = M$, proving (iii) $\Rightarrow$ (i). Finally, let $M = \bigcap_j M_j$. As $M \subseteq M_j$, $M^{\perp\perp} \subseteq M_j^{\perp\perp} = M_j$. Thus

$$M^{\perp\perp} \subseteq \bigcap_j M_j = M.$$

This proves that $M$ is a $\langle\,.\,,\,.\,\rangle$-closed linear manifold.

**Corollary 7.36.** *If $M \subseteq V$, $M^-$ is the smallest $\langle\,.\,,\,.\,\rangle$-closed linear manifold containing $M$. In particular, if $M \subseteq N$, then $M^- \subseteq N^-$.*

**Proof.** $M^-$ is $\langle\,.\,,\,.\,\rangle$-closed by (103). It is therefore enough to prove that if $N$ is a $\langle\,.\,,\,.\,\rangle$-closed linear manifold and $M \subseteq N$, then $M^- \subseteq N$. But $M^- = M^{\perp\perp} \subseteq N^{\perp\perp} = N$. Finally if $M \subseteq N$, $M \subseteq N^-$, and as $N^-$ is $\langle\,.\,,\,.\,\rangle$-closed, $M^- \subseteq N^-$.

**Lemma 7.37.** *If $M$ is a finite dimensional subspace of $V$, then $M$ is $\langle\,.\,,\,.\,\rangle$-closed.*

**Proof.** It is enough to prove that $M^{\perp\perp} \subseteq M$. Let $x \in M^{\perp\perp}$. Let $N$ be the subspace spanned by $M$ and $x$. $N \subseteq M^{\perp\perp}$. Since $\langle\,.\,,\,.\,\rangle$- is definite, its restriction to $N \times N$ is definite and hence nonsingular. But $N$ is finite dimensional and hence it follows from (15) of Chapter IV and the definiteness of $\langle\,.\,,\,.\,\rangle$ that $N$ is the direct sum of $M$ and $(M^\perp \cap N)$. Therefore, $x = x' + x''$ where $x' \in M$ and $x'' \in M^\perp \cap N$. Since $N \subseteq M^{\perp\perp}$, $x'' \in M^{\perp\perp} \cap M^\perp$ and hence $x'' = 0$. Thus $x \in M$.

**Lemma 7.38.** *If $\{M_j\}$ is a family of linear manifolds of $V$, and if $\sum_j M_j$ denotes the (algebraic) linear span of the $M_j$,*

$$(104) \qquad \left(\sum_j M_j\right)^- = \left(\bigcap_j M_j^\perp\right)^\perp.$$

**Proof.** Let $M = \sum_j M_j$. Since $M_j \subseteq M$, $M^\perp \subseteq M_j^\perp$ so that $M^\perp \subseteq \bigcap_j M_j^\perp$. This shows that $M^- = M^{\perp\perp} \supseteq (\bigcap_j M_j^\perp)^\perp = N$, say. On the other hand, as $\bigcap_j M_j^\perp \subseteq M_j^\perp$, $M_j \subseteq M_j^- \subseteq N$ for all $j$ so that $M \subseteq N$. Since $N$ is $\langle\,.\,,\,.\,\rangle$-closed, it follows from corollary 7.36 that $M^- \subseteq N$. Therefore $N = M^-$.

**Lemma 7.39.** *If $(V, \langle\,.\,,\,.\,\rangle)$ is Hilbertian and $M_1, M_2, \cdots, M_s$ is a finite set of mutually orthogonal $\langle\,.\,,\,.\,\rangle$-closed linear manifolds, then $\sum_{j=1}^s M_j$ is also a $\langle\,.\,,\,.\,\rangle$-closed linear manifold.*

**Proof.** It is enough to consider the case $s=2$ since the general case follows at once by induction. We want to prove that

$$(M_1 + M_2)^- = M_1 + M_2.$$

Write $M = M_1 + M_2$. Let $x \in V$. Since $(V, \langle\,.\,,\,.\,\rangle)$ is Hilbertian, we have the unique decompositions

$$x = x_1 + y \qquad (x_1 \in M_1, y \in M_1^\perp),$$
$$y = x_2 + z \qquad (x_2 \in M_2, z \in M_2^\perp).$$

Now, as $M_2 \subseteq M_1^\perp$, $x_2 \in M_1^\perp$ so that $z \in M_1^\perp$ also. Therefore,

$$z \in M_1^\perp \cap M_2^\perp,$$

and we have:

$$x = x_1 + x_2 + z \qquad (x_1 \in M_1, x_2 \in M_2, z \in M_1^\perp \cap M_2^\perp).$$

Suppose now that $x \in (M_1 + M_2)^-$. Then the above equation shows that $z \in (M_1 + M_2)^- \cap M_1^\perp \cap M_2^\perp$, which implies that $z=0$ on using (104). Therefore $(M_1 + M_2)^- = M_1 + M_2$.

**Theorem 7.40.** *Let $\mathbf{D}$ be a division ring, $\mathbf{V}$ a vector space over $\mathbf{D}$ with $4 \le \dim V < \infty$, $\theta$ an involutive anti-automorphism of $\mathbf{D}$, and $\langle\,.\,,\,.\,\rangle$ a definite, symmetric, $\theta$-bilinear form on $V \times V$. Let $\mathscr{L}(V, \langle\,.\,,\,.\,\rangle)$ be the set of $\langle\,.\,,\,.\,\rangle$-closed linear manifolds of $V$, partially ordered under inclusion. If $(V, \langle\,.\,,\,.\,\rangle)$ is Hilbertian, then $\mathscr{L}(V, \langle\,.\,,\,.\,\rangle)$ is a complete projective logic, and for any collection $\{M_j\}$ of $\langle\,.\,,\,.\,\rangle$-closed linear manifolds of $V$, the lattice operations in $\mathscr{L}(V, \langle\,.\,,\,.\,\rangle)$ are given by*

(105)
$$\bigvee_j M_j = \left(\sum_j M_j\right)^-,$$
$$\bigwedge_j M_j = \bigcap_j M_j.$$

*Conversely, let $\mathscr{L}$ be any complete projective logic. Then there exists a division ring $\mathbf{D}$, an involutive anti-automorphism $\theta$ of $\mathbf{D}$, a vector space $V$ over $\mathbf{D}$, and a definite symmetric $\theta$-bilinear form $\langle\,.\,,\,.\,\rangle$ on $V \times V$ such that $(V, \langle\,.\,,\,.\,\rangle)$ is Hilbertian and $\mathscr{L}$ is isomorphic to $\mathscr{L}(V, \langle\,.\,,\,.\,\rangle)$.*

**Proof.** Let $\mathbf{D}$, $\theta$, $V$, $\langle\,.\,,\,.\,\rangle$ be as given in the first half of the theorem. Let $\mathscr{L} = \mathscr{L}(V, \langle\,.\,,\,.\,\rangle)$ be the partially ordered set of $\langle\,.\,,\,.\,\rangle$-closed linear manifolds of $V$. Assume that $(V, \langle\,.\,,\,.\,\rangle)$ is Hilbertian. For any linear manifold $M$, $M^-$ is the smallest element of $\mathscr{L}$ containing it. It is clear from lemmas 7.35 through 7.38 that $\mathscr{L}$ is a complete lattice with the lattice operations given by (105). Next we observe that if we define, for any $M \in \mathscr{L}$, $M^\perp$ by (97), then $\mathscr{L}$ becomes a logic. To check this, the only thing not immediately obvious is the weak modularity (2) (ii) of Chapter VI. Suppose then $M_1, M_2 \in \mathscr{L}$ and $M_1 \subseteq M_2$. Let $N = M_1{}^\perp \cap M_2$. By lemma 7.35, $N$ is a $\langle .\,,.\rangle$-closed linear manifold so that $N \in \mathscr{L}$. Clearly $N \subseteq M_2$, $N \perp M_1$. Since $(V, \langle .\,,.\rangle)$ is Hilbertian, $V = M_1 + M_1{}^\perp$ and for any $x \in V$ we have the decomposition $x = x_1 + x_2$, where $x_1 \in M_1$, $x_2 \in M_1{}^\perp$. If now $x \in M_2$, then $x_1$ and $x_2 \in M_2$ also, so that $x_2 \in N$. Therefore $M_2 = M_1 + N$ and *a fortiori* $M_2 = M_1 \vee N$. $\mathscr{L}$ is thus a complete logic. We claim that it is projective. By lemma 7.37, $\mathscr{L}$ contains all finite dimensional subspaces. As dim $V \geq 4$, (i), (ii), and (iv) of (96) follow at once from this fact; (iii) follows from the *algebraic* decomposition $V = M + M^\perp$ for any $M \in \mathscr{L}$. $\mathscr{L}$ is thus a complete projective logic.

We now come to the converse. Let $\mathscr{L}$ be a complete projective logic. Let us now define $\mathscr{L}'$ by

$$(106) \qquad \mathscr{L}' = \{a : a \in \mathscr{L}, \ a \text{ finite}\}.$$

By (ii) of (96), $a \in \mathscr{L}'$ if and only if the underlying lattice of $\mathscr{L}[0,a]$ is a geometry. Under the induced partial ordering, $\mathscr{L}'$ is thus a *generalized geometry*. Therefore there exists by theorem 5.26, a division ring $\mathbf{D}$, a vector space $V$ of dimension at least 4 over $\mathbf{D}$, and an isomorphism of $\mathscr{L}'$ onto the generalized geometry of all finite dimensional subspaces of $V$. Let $\gamma$ denote any such isomorphism.

Fix a nonzero vector $v_0 \in V$. Let $W$ be any finite dimensional subspace of $V$ containing $v_0$ and of dimension at least 3. The isomorphism $\gamma$ transfers the orthocomplementation in $\mathscr{L}[0,a]$ into an orthocomplementation on the projective geometry of subspaces of $W$. Hence, by theorem 4.6 there exists an involutive anti-automorphism $\theta_W$ of $\mathbf{D}$ and a symmetric, definite $\theta_W$-bilinear form $\langle .\,,.\rangle_W$ on $W \times W$, inducing the orthocomplementation in question, with $\langle v_0, v_0 \rangle_W = 1$. We now argue as in lemma 7.2 to conclude that $\theta_W = \theta$ is independent of $W$ and that there exists a symmetric, definite $\theta$-bilinear form $\langle .\,,.\rangle$ on $V \times V$ such that (i) $\langle v_0, v_0 \rangle = 1$, and (ii) if $x$ and $y$ are points of $\mathscr{L}$, $x \perp y$ if and only if the rays $\gamma(x)$ and $\gamma(y)$ are orthogonal with respect to $\langle .\,,.\rangle$.

Let $\mathscr{L}^\sim = \mathscr{L}(V, \langle .\,,.\rangle)$ be the lattice of all $\langle .\,,.\rangle$-closed linear manifolds of $V$. We shall now extend $\gamma$ to an isomorphism $\gamma^\sim$ of $\mathscr{L}$ onto $\mathscr{L}^\sim$. For any $a \in \mathscr{L}$, let

$$(107) \quad \gamma^\sim(a) = \{v : v \in V \ \text{ and } \ v \in \gamma(x) \ \text{ for some point } x < a\}.$$

We shall first show that $\gamma^\sim(a)$ is a linear manifold in $V$. This is obvious for $a = 0$ or $a = 1$, as then $\gamma^\sim(0) = 0$ and $\gamma^\sim(1) = V$. Let then $a \neq 0$, $\neq 1$. If $v_1, v_2 \in \gamma^\sim(a)$, there are points $x_1, x_2 < a$ such that $v_j \in \gamma(x_j)$, $j = 1, 2$. Now, as $\gamma$ is an isomorphism of $\mathscr{L}'$ onto the generalized geometry of finite dimensional subspaces of $V$, $\gamma(x_1)$ and $\gamma(x_2)$ are rays in $\gamma(x_1 \vee x_2)$. Thus if $v = c_1 v_1 + c_2 v_2$ where $c_1, c_2 \in \mathbf{D}$, $v$ lies in $\gamma(x_1 \vee x_2)$ and hence $v \in \gamma(x)$ for some point $x < x_1 \vee x_2 < a \cdot \gamma^{\sim}(a)$ is thus a linear manifold. We shall prove next that $\gamma^{\sim}(a)$ is $\langle \ . \ , \ . \rangle$-closed. From lemma 7.34 it follows easily that for a point $x \in \mathscr{L}$, $x < a$ if and only if $x \perp y$ for all $y \in \mathfrak{P}(a^{\perp})$. Therefore,

$$(108) \qquad \gamma^{\sim}(a) = (\gamma^{\sim}(a^{\perp}))^{\perp},$$

which shows that $\gamma^{\sim}(a)$ is $\langle \ . \ , \ . \rangle$-closed. Moreover, as (108) is valid for all $a$ (in particular, for $a^{\perp}$), we have:

$$(109) \qquad \gamma^{\sim}(a^{\perp}) = (\gamma^{\sim}(a))^{\perp}.$$

(109) shows that $\gamma^{\sim}$ preserves orthocomplementation. From (107) we conclude, on using lemma 7.34, that for $a, b \in \mathscr{L}$, $\gamma^{\sim}(a) \subseteq \gamma^{\sim}(b)$ if and only if $a < b$. In particular, $\gamma^{\sim}(a) = \gamma^{\sim}(b)$ if and only if $a = b$. Therefore, in order to prove that $\gamma^{\sim}$ is a lattice isomorphism of $\mathscr{L}$ onto $\mathscr{L}(V, \langle \ . \ , \ . \rangle)$, it remains only to prove that $\gamma^{\sim}$ is surjective. Let $M$ be any $\langle \ . \ , \ . \rangle$-closed linear manifold of $V$ and let the subsets $A$ and $B$ of $\mathscr{L}$ be defined as follows:

$$A = \{x : x \in \mathscr{L}, x \text{ is a point such that } \gamma(x) \subseteq M\},$$
$$B = \{x : x \in \mathscr{L}, x \text{ is a point such that } \gamma(x) \subseteq M^{\perp}\}.$$

Since $M = M^{\perp\perp}$, $x \in A$ if and only if $x \perp B$. Let $a$ and $b$ be the lattice sums of the points of $A$ and $B$, respectively; these exist as $\mathscr{L}$ is complete. It follows from lemma 7.34 rather easily that $a$ and $b$ are orthogonal complements of each other and $A = \mathfrak{P}(a)$, $B = \mathfrak{P}(b)$. The equation $A = \mathfrak{P}(a)$ implies that $\gamma^{\sim}(a) = M$. The proof that $\gamma^{\sim}$ is surjective is complete. $\gamma^{\sim}$ is thus a lattice isomorphism of $\mathscr{L}$ onto $\mathscr{L}(V, \langle \ . \ , \ . \rangle)$.

We observe finally that $(V, \langle \ . \ , \ . \rangle$ is Hilbertian. In fact, let $M$, $\neq 0$, $\neq V$, be any $\langle \ . \ , \ . \rangle$-closed linear manifold, and $v \in V$, $v \neq 0$. Let $a \in \mathscr{L}$ be such that $\gamma^{\sim}(a) = M$. Clearly, $a \neq 0$, $\neq 1$. Then $\gamma^{\sim}(a^{\perp}) = M^{\perp}$. Choose $x \in \mathscr{L}$ such that $v \in \gamma(x)$. By (iii) of (96), there are points $y, z$ of $\mathscr{L}$ such that $y < a$, $z < a^{\perp}$ and $x < y \vee z$. Hence $\gamma(x) < \gamma(y) \vee \gamma(z) = \gamma(y) + \gamma(z)$. This shows that $v \in \gamma(y) + \gamma(z) \subseteq M + M^{\perp}$ and demonstrates the Hilbertian character of $(V, \langle \ . \ , \ . \rangle)$. This completes the proof of the theorem.

The division ring $\mathbf{D}$ which enters the second half of theorem 7.40 is uniquely determined by $\mathscr{L}$ (up to isomorphism of course), as can be easily deduced from theorem 3.1. If $\mathbf{D}$ were one of $\mathbf{R}$, $\mathbf{C}$, or $\mathbf{Q}$, and $\mathscr{L}$ is a complete projective logic, we shall say that $\mathscr{L}$ is *associated with* $\mathbf{D}$ if the involutive anti-automorphism $\theta$, constructed in theorem 7.40, is continuous. This is a restriction only in the complex case. If $\mathscr{L}$ is associated with $\mathbf{D}$, $\theta$ must coincide with the conjugation $*$, which is complex conjugation when $\mathbf{D} = \mathbf{C}$, the identity when $\mathbf{D} = \mathbf{R}$, and the canonical conjugation when $\mathbf{D} = \mathbf{Q}$. In view of theorem 7.40 and these comments we can assert that, given any complete projective logic $\mathscr{L}$ associated with $\mathbf{D}$ which is one of $\mathbf{R}$, $\mathbf{C}$, $\mathbf{Q}$, there exists a pre-Hilbert space $V$, with inner product $\langle\,.\,,.\,\rangle$, such that (i) $(V, \langle\,.\,,.\,\rangle)$ is Hilbertian and (ii) $\mathscr{L}$ is isomorphic to the complete projective logic of all $\langle\,.\,,.\,\rangle$-closed linear manifolds of $V$. It is natural to expect that $V$ is then actually a Hilbert space. This essentially leads to Piron's theorem. We shall obtain it as a consequence of a few lemmas.

It is an interesting problem to examine what natural assumptions on a geometry imply that the associated division ring is isomorphic to one of $\mathbf{R}$, $\mathbf{C}$, $\mathbf{Q}$. This is a classical question and is intimately connected with the topologies on a geometry (cf. Kolmogorov [1], Weiss and Zierler [1]).

**Lemma 7.41.** *Let $V$ be a pre-Hilbert space over $\mathbf{D}$ (one of $\mathbf{R}$, $\mathbf{C}$, or $\mathbf{Q}$) and let $\mathscr{H}$ be its completion. If $x_0$, $x_0' \in \mathscr{H}$ are orthogonal, there exists a pair of sequences $x_n$ and $x_n'$ such that*

$$(110) \qquad \begin{array}{ll} \text{(i)} & x_n \perp x_m' \qquad (n, m = 0, 1, 2, \cdots), \\ \text{(ii)} & x_n, x_m' \in V \quad \text{and} \quad x_n \to x_0, x_m' \to x_0'. \end{array}$$

**Proof.** We shall prove first that if $z \in \mathscr{H}$ is a nonzero vector, then $\{z\}^\perp \cap V$ is dense in $\{z\}^\perp$. In fact, let $y \perp z$, and let $\{y_n\}$, $\{z_n\}$ be sequences of elements of $V$ such that $y_n \to y$, $z_n \to z$. Write

$$(111) \qquad y_n' = y_n - \langle y_n, z \rangle \langle z_n, z \rangle^{-1} z_n.$$

Then $y_n' \in V$ and $\langle y_n', z \rangle = 0$ for all $n$. As $y_n \to y$ and $z_n \to z$,

$$\langle y_n, z \rangle \langle z_n, z \rangle^{-1} z_n \to \langle y, z \rangle \langle z, z \rangle^{-1} z = 0,$$

showing that $y_n' \to y$. This proves our assertion. Suppose next that $y, y_1, \cdots, y_s$ are mutually orthogonal nonzero vectors. Applying repeatedly the result proved just now, we conclude in succession that $\{y_s\}^\perp \cap V$ is dense in $\{y_s\}^\perp$, $\{y_s, y_{s-1}\}^\perp \cap V$ is dense in $\{y_s, y_{s-1}\}^\perp$ and so on. In other words, given any finite dimensional subspace $Y$ of $\mathscr{H}$ and a vector $y \perp Y$, there exists a sequence $\{z_n\}$ in $V$ such that $z_n \perp Y$ for all $n$ and $z_n \to y$.

This said, we come to the proof of the lemma. Let $x_0$, $x_0' \in \mathscr{H}$ be given with $x_0 \perp x_0'$. We shall show by induction that there are sequences $\{x_n\}$ and $\{x_n'\}$ in $V$ such that

$$(112) \qquad \begin{array}{c} \|x_n - x_0\| \le 2^{-n}, \qquad \|x_n' - x_0'\| \le 2^{-n}, \\ x_n \perp x_m' \qquad (n, m = 0, 1, 2, \cdots). \end{array}$$

Suppose $x_1, x_2, \cdots, x_k$ and $x_1', x_2', \cdots, x_k'$ have been constructed so that (112) is satisfied for all $n$, $m = 0, 1, 2, \cdots, k$. By the result proved in the previous paragraph, there is a vector $x_{k+1}' \in V$ such that

$$x_{k+1}' \perp x_n \qquad (n = 0, 1, \cdots, k),$$

$$\|x_{k+1}' - x_0'\| \le 2^{-(k+1)}.$$

Applying the same argument again, we can find $x_{k+1} \in V$ such that

$$x_{k+1} \perp x_n{}' \qquad (n = 0, 1, \cdots, k+1),$$
$$\|x_{k+1} - x_0\| \leq 2^{-(k+1)}.$$

Thus $\{x_n\}_{0 \leq n \leq k+1}$ and $\{x_n{}'\}_{0 \leq n \leq k+1}$ satisfy (112) for $n$ and $m \leq k+1$. This proves by induction the existence of a pair of sequences satisfying (112). This immediately proves lemma 7.41.

**Lemma 7.42.**† *Let $V$ be a pre-Hilbert space over* **D** *such that* $(V, \langle \, . \, , . \rangle)$ *is Hilbertian. Then $V$ is complete.*

**Proof.** Let $\mathscr{H}$ be the completion of $V$ and $x_0$ an arbitrary unit vector of $\mathscr{H}$. We denote, for any subset $L$ of $\mathscr{H}$, its orthogonal complement in $\mathscr{H}$ by $L'$. We must prove that $x_0 \in V$. Since $V$ is dense in $\mathscr{H}$, there is a $y \in V$ such that $\langle y, x_0 \rangle \neq 0$, and by changing $y$ to a suitable multiple of it we may assume that $\langle y, x_0 \rangle = 1$. Let $z_0 = y - x_0$. Then $y = x_0 + z_0$ and $x_0 \perp z_0$. By lemma 7.41 there are sequences $\{x_n\}$ and $\{z_n\}$ in $V$ such that

$$(113) \qquad x_n \to x_0, \quad z_n \to z_0, \quad x_n \perp z_m \qquad (n, m = 0, 1, 2, \cdots).$$

Let $M \subseteq V$ be the lattice sum in $\mathscr{L}(V, \langle \, . \, , . \rangle)$ of the rays $\mathbf{D} \cdot x_n$ $(n = 1, 2, \cdots)$. Then, as $(V, \langle \, . \, , . \rangle)$ is Hilbertian,

$$V = M + M^{\perp}.$$

Now $z_m \perp x_n$ for all $n$ so that $z_m \in M^{\perp}$ for all $m$. Hence $x_0 \in M^{\mathrm{cl}}$ and $z_0 \in (M^{\perp})^{\mathrm{cl}}$ where cl denotes closure in $\mathscr{H}$. Moreover, it is obvious that $(M^{\perp})^{\mathrm{cl}} \subseteq (M^{\mathrm{cl}})'$. Therefore,

$$(114) \qquad y = x_0 + z_0, \quad x_0 \in M^{\mathrm{cl}}, \quad z_0 \in (M^{\mathrm{cl}})'.$$

On the other hand, as $V = M + M^{\perp}$, we can also write

$$(115) \qquad y = x_0{}' + z_0{}', \quad x_0{}' \in M, \quad z_0{}' \in M^{\perp}.$$

As $M^{\perp} \subseteq (M^{\mathrm{cl}})'$, a comparison of (114) and (115) shows that $x_0{}' = x_0$ and $z_0{}' = z_0$. In particular, $x_0 \in V$. This completes the proof of the lemma.

**Lemma 7.43.** *Let $\mathscr{L}$ be a projective logic with the property that any family of mutually orthogonal points of $\mathscr{L}$ is at most denumerable. Then $\mathscr{L}$ is complete.*

**Proof.** It is enough to prove that arbitrary lattice unions exist in $\mathscr{L}$. Let $\{a_j : j \in F\}$ be a family of elements of $\mathscr{L}$. For any countable subset $D \subseteq F$, let

$$c(D) = \bigvee_{j \in D} a_j.$$

---

† Piron's original proof of this lemma in [1] contained a gap. I am indebted to Professor J. M. Jauch who communicated the proof of lemmas 7.41 and 7.42 to me. The proof is due to H. Araki.

Let $B$ be a family of mutually orthogonal points $x$ such that (i) for each $x \in B$ there is a countable set $D \subseteq F$ such that $x < c(D)$, and (ii) $B$ is maximal with respect to (i). By hypothesis, $B$ is at most countable. Let

$$B = \{x_1, x_2, \cdots\},$$

and for each $n$ let $D_n \subseteq F$ be a countable set such that

$$x_n < c(D_n)$$

for all $n$. Write $D = \bigcup_n D_n$. If we define $x$ by

$$x = \bigvee_n x_n,$$

then $x < c(D)$. If $x \neq c(D)$, there will exist, by virtue of (i) of (96), a point $y < c(D)$ such that $y \perp x$. Since $D$ is countable, this contradicts the maximality of $B$. Therefore $x = c(D)$. We claim that $a_j < x$ for all $j \in F$. If $j \in D$, this is trivial. If $j \notin D$ and $a_j \not< x$, $a_j \vee x \neq x$, and hence by (i) of (96) there will exist a point $t$ such that $t \perp x$ and $t < a_j \vee x$. Since $t < c(D \cup \{j\})$ and $t \perp B$, we have a contradiction. Consequently, $a_j$ must be $< x$. This proves that $x = \bigvee_{j \in F} a_j$.

**Theorem 7.44.** (*Piron* [1]). *Let $\mathscr{L}$ be any logic. Then, a necessary and sufficient condition that $\mathscr{L}$ be isomorphic to the logic of all closed linear manifolds of a separable Hilbert space over* **D** (*which is one of* **R**, **C**, *or* **Q**) *is that $\mathscr{L}$ be a projective logic associated with* **D** *and have the property that every family of mutually orthogonal points of $\mathscr{L}$ be at most countable.*

**Proof.** The proof follows at once from theorem 7.40 and lemmas 7.41 through 7.43.

# BIBLIOGRAPHY

BAER, R.
  [1] *Linear Algebra and Projective Geometry*, Academic Press Inc., New York, 1952.
BARGMANN, V.
  [1] *On unitary ray representations of continuous groups*, Annals of Mathematics, **59** (1954), pp. 1–46.
  [2] *Note on Wigner's theorem on symmetry operations*, Journal of Mathematical Physics, **5** (1964), pp. 862–868.
BARGMANN, V., AND WIGNER, E. P.
  [1] *Group theoretical discussion of relativistic wave equations*, Proceedings of the National Academy of Sciences, U.S.A., **34** (1948), pp. 211–223.
BIRKHOFF, G.
  [1] *Lattice Theory*, American Mathematical Society Colloquium Publications, Vol. 25, 1960.
BIRKHOFF, G., AND VON NEUMANN, J.
  [1] *The logic of quantum mechanics*, Annals of Mathematics, **37** (1936), pp. 823–843.
BLACKWELL, D.
  [1] *On a class of probability spaces*, Proceedings of the Third Berkeley Symposium on Mathematical Statistics and Probability, Vol. II (1956), pp. 1–6.
BOCHNER, S., AND CHANDRASEKHARAN, K.
  [1] *Fourier Transforms*, Princeton University Press, Princeton, 1949.
BOURBAKI, N.
  [1] *Eléments de Mathématique, I, Livre II, Algèbre*, Chs. 4 and 5, Hermann, Paris, 1959.
  [2] *Eléments de Mathématique, I, Livre V, Espaces vectoriels topologiques*, Chs. 1 and 2, Hermann, Paris, 1953.
  [3] *Eléments de Mathématique, I, Livre III, Topologie Générale*, Chs. 1 and 2, Hermann, Paris, 1961.
BRAUER, R., AND WEYL, H.
  [1] *Spinors in n dimensions*, American Journal of Mathematics, **57** (1935), pp. 425–449.
CALABI, L.
  [1] *Sur les extensions des groupes topologiques*, Annali de Matematica Pura ed Applicata, **32** (1951), pp. 295–370.
CARTAN, E.
  [1] *Leçons sur la théorie des spineurs*, I, II, Hermann, Paris, 1938.
CHEVALLEY, C.
  [1] *Theory of Lie Groups*, Princeton University Press, Princeton, 1946.
  [2] *Théorie des Groupes de Lie*, Tome II, Hermann, Paris, 1951.
  [3] *Théorie des Groupes de Lie*, Tome III, Hermann, Paris, 1955.
  [4] *The Algebraic Theory of Spinors*, Columbia University Press, New York, 1954.
CHEVALLEY, C., AND EILENBERG, S.
  [1] *Cohomology theory of Lie groups and Lie algebras*, Transactions of the American Mathematical Society, **63** (1948), pp. 85–124.

DIRAC, P. A. M.

[1] *The Principles of Quantum Mechanics*, Oxford University Press, London, 1958.

[2] *The quantum theory of the electron*, Proceedings of the Royal Society (London), **A 117** (1928), pp. 610–624.

DIXMIER, J.

[1] *Les algebres d'opérateurs dans l'espace Hilbertien*, Gauthier-Villars, Paris, 1957.

DUNFORD, N., AND SCHWARTZ, J.

[1] *Linear Operators*, Part 1, Interscience Publishers, Inc., New York, 1958.

[2] *Linear Operators*, Part 2, Interscience Publishers, Inc., New York, 1963.

EILENBERG, S.

[1] *Topological methods in abstract algebra. Cohomology theory of groups*, Bulletin of the American Mathematical Society, **55** (1949), pp. 3–37.

FEDERER H., AND MORSE, A. P.

[1] *Some properties of measurable functions*, Bulletin of the American Mathematical Society, **49** (1943), pp. 270–277.

FEYNMAN, R. P.

[1] *Concept of probability in quantum mechanics*, Proceedings of the Second Berkeley Symposium on Mathematical Statistics and Probability, Berkeley, (1951), pp. 533–541.

[2] *Space-time approach to non-relativistic quantum mechanics*, Reviews of Modern Physics, **20** (1948), pp. 367–387.

FINKELSTEIN, D., JAUCH, J. M., SCHMINOVICH, S., AND SPEISER, D.

[1] *Foundations of quaternion quantum mechanics*, Journal of Mathematical Physics, **3** (1962), pp. 207–220.

GEL'FAND, I. M.

[1] *On one-parametrical groups of operators in a normed space*, Doklady Akademii Nauk, SSSR, **25** (1939), pp. 713–718.

GEL'FAND, I. M., AND NAĬMARK, M. A.

[1] *Unitary representations of the group of linear transformations of the straight line*, Doklady Akademii Nauk, SSSR, **55** (1947), pp. 567–570.

GLEASON, A. M.

[1] *Measures on the closed subspaces of a Hilbert space*, Journal of Mathematics and Mechanics, **6** (1957), pp. 885–894.

GUDDER, S. P.

[1] *Spectral methods for a generalized probability theory*, Transactions of the American Mathematical Society, **119** (1965), pp. 428–442.

HALMOS, P. R.

[1] *Measure Theory*, D. van Nostrand Company, Princeton, 1950.

[2] *Introduction to the Theory of Hilbert Space and Spectral Multiplicity*, Chelsea Publishing Co., New York, 1957.

HEISENBERG, W.

[1] *The Physical Principles of Quantum Theory*, Dover Publications, Inc., New York, 1930.

HELGASON, S.

[1] *Differential Geometry and Symmetric Spaces*, Academic Press Inc., New York, 1962.

HELSON, H.

[1] *Lectures on Invariant Subspaces*, Academic Press Inc., New York, 1964.

HELSON, H., AND LOWDENSLAGER, D.

[1] *Invariant subspaces*, Proceedings of the International Symposium on Linear Spaces, pp. 251–262 (Jerusalem, 1960), Pergamon Press, Inc., Oxford, 1961.

HEYTING, A.
  [1] *Axiomatic Projective Geometry*, Interscience Publishers, Inc., New York; P. Noordhoff N. V., Groningen, North Holland Publishing Company, Amsterdam, 1963.

HOCHSCHILD, G.
  [1] *Group extensions of Lie Groups*, I, Annals of Mathematics, **54** (1951), pp. 96–109.
  [2] *Group extensions of Lie Groups*, II, Annals of Mathematics, **54** (1951), pp. 537–551.

INONU, E., and WIGNER, E. P.
  [1] *Representations of the Galilei group*, Il Nuovo Cimento, **9** (1952), pp. 705–718.
  [2] *On the contraction of groups and their representations*, Proceedings of the National Academy of Sciences, U.S.A., **39** (1953), pp. 510–524.

JACOBSON, N.
  [1] *Lectures in Abstract Algebra*, Vol. II, D. Van Nostrand Company, Inc., Princeton, 1953.
  [2] *Lie Algebras*, Interscience Publishers, Inc., New York, 1962.

JORDAN, P., VON NEUMANN, J., AND WIGNER, E. P.
  [1] *On an algebraic generalization of the quantum mechanical formalism*, Annals of Mathematics, **35** (1934), pp. 29–64.

KAKUTANI, S., AND MACKEY, G. W.
  [1] *Ring and lattice characterizations of complex Hilbert space*, Bulletin of the American Mathematical Society, **52** (1946), pp. 727–733.

KAPLANSKY, I.
  [1] *Any orthocomplemented complete modular lattice is a continuous geometry*, Annals of Mathematics, **61** (1955), pp. 524–541.
  [2] *Infinite Abelian Groups*, University of Michigan Press, Ann Arbor, 1954.

KELLEY, J. L.
  [1] *General Topology*, D. Van Nostrand Company, Princeton, 1955.

KLEPPNER, A.
  [1] *Multipliers on abelian groups*, Mathematische Annalen, **158** (1965), pp. 11–34.

KOLMOGOROV, A. N.
  [1] *Zur Begründung der Projectiven Geometrie*, Annals of Mathematics, **33** (1932), pp. 175–176.

KOOPMAN, B. O.
  [1] *Hamilton systems and transformations in Hilbert space*, Proceedings of the National Academy of Sciences, U.S.A., **17** (1931), pp. 315–318.

KURATOWSKI, C.
  [1] *Topologie*, Vol. I, Warsaw, 1948.
  [2] *Topologie*, Vol. II, Warsaw, 1950.

LANDAU, L. D., AND LIFCHITZ, E. M.
  [1] *Quantum Mechanics, non-relativistic Theory*, Gos. Izd. Phys. Mat. Moscow, 1963.

LOOMIS, L. H.
  [1] *On the representation of σ-complete Boolean algebras*, Bulletin of the American Mathematical Society, **53** (1947), pp. 757–760.
  [2] *An Introduction to Abstract Harmonic Analysis*, D. Van Nostrand Company, Inc., Princeton, 1953.
  [3] *The lattice theoretic background of the dimension theory of operator algebras*, Memoirs of the American Mathematical Society, **18** (1955), pp. 1–36.

MACKEY, G. W.
  [1] *The Mathematical Foundations of Quantum Mechanics*, W. A. Benjamin, Inc., New York, 1963.
  [2] *Imprimitivity for representations of locally compact groups*, Proceedings of the National Academy of Sciences, U.S.A., **35** (1949), pp. 537–545.

[3] *Induced representations of locally compact groups*, I, Annals of Mathematics, **55** (1952), pp. 101–139.

[4] *Induced representations of locally compact groups*, II, Annals of Mathematics, **58** (1953), pp. 193–221.

[5] *Borel structure in groups and their duals*, Transactions of the American Mathematical Society, **85** (1957), pp. 134–165.

[6] *Unitary representations of group extensions*, I, Acta Mathematica, **99** (1958), pp. 265–311.

[7] *Infinite dimensional group representations*, Bulletin of the American Mathematical Society, **69** (1963), pp. 628–686.

[8] *Les ensembles Boreliens et les extensions des groupes*, Journal de Mathématiques Pures et Appliquées, **36** (1957), pp. 171–178.

[9] *A theorem of Stone and von Neumann*, Duke Mathematical Journal, **16** (1949), pp. 313–326.

MALČEV, A.

[1] *On the simple connectedness of invariant subgroups of Lie groups*, Doklady Akademii Nauk, SSSR, **34** (1942), pp. 10–13.

MAUTNER, F. I.

[1] *Unitary representations of locally compact groups*. I, Annals of Mathematics, **51** (1950), pp. 1–25.

[2] *Unitary representations of locally compact groups*. II, Annals of Mathematics, **52** (1950), pp. 528–556.

MONTGOMERY, D., AND ZIPPIN, L.

[1] *Topological transformation groups*, Interscience Publishers, Inc., New York, 1955.

MOORE, C. C.

[1] *Extensions and low dimensional cohomology theory of locally compact groups*, I, Transactions of the American Mathematical Society, **113** (1964), pp. 40–63.

MOYAL, J. E.

[1] *Quantum Mechanics as a statistical theory*, Proceedings of the Cambridge Philosophical Society, **45** (1949), pp. 99–124.

MURRAY, F. J., AND VON NEUMANN, J.

[1] *On rings of operators*, Annals of Mathematics, **37** (1936), pp. 116–229.

[2] *On rings of operators*, II, Transactions of the American Mathematical Society, **41** (1937), pp. 208–248.

[3] *On rings of operators*, IV, Annals of Mathematics, **44** (1943), pp. 716–808.

NAKANO, H.

[1] *Unitärinvariante hypermaximale normale operatoren*, Annals of Mathematics, **42** (1941), pp. 657–664.

NEWTON, T. D., AND WIGNER, E. P.

[1] *Localized states for elementary systems*, Reviews of Modern Physics, **21** (1949), pp. 400–406.

PAULI, W.

[1] *Die allgemeinen Prinzipen der Wellenmechanik*, Handbuch der Physik, 2 Aufl. Band **24**, 1 Teil (Reprint, Edwards Brothers, Inc., Ann Arbor, Michigan), 1950.

PIRON, C.

[1] *Axiomatique Quantique*, Thèse, Université de Lausanne, Faculté des Sciences, Bale, Imprimerie Birkhauser S. A. (1964), pp. 439–468.

PONTRJAGIN, L. S.

[1] *Topological Groups*, Princeton University Press, Princeton, 1939.

RIESZ, F., AND NAGY, B. SZ.

[1] *Leçons d'analyse Fonctionnelle*, Akadémiai Kiadó, Budapest, 1952.

SCHWARTZ, L.

[1] *Théorie des distributions*, Tome I, Hermann, Paris, 1957.

[2] *Théorie des distributions*, Tome II, Hermann, Paris, 1959.

[3] *Application of distributions to the study of elementary particles in relativistic quantum mechanics*, Technical Report No. 7, Department of Mathematics, University of California, Berkeley, 1961, pp. 1–207.

SCHWEBER, S.

[1] *An introduction to relativistic quantum field theory*, Row, Peterson and Company, Evanston and New York, 1961.

SEGAL, I. E.

[1] *Postulates for general Quantum Mechanics*, Annals of Mathematics, **48** (1947), pp. 930–948.

[2] *Quantization of nonlinear systems*, Journal of Mathematical Physics, **1** (1960), pp. 468–488.

[3] *Mathematical problems of relativistic physics*, Lectures in Applied Mathematics, American Mathematical Society, Providence, R.I., 1963.

SEIDENBERG, A.

[1] *Lectures in Projective Geometry*, D. Van Nostrand Company, Inc., Princeton, 1962.

SIKORSKI, R.

[1] *Boolean Algebras*, Springer, Berlin, 1964.

STERNBERG, S.

[1] *Lectures on Differential Geometry*, Prentice-Hall, Inc., Englewood Cliffs, N.J., 1964.

STONE, M. H.

[1] *The theory of representation for Boolean algebras*, Transactions of the American Mathematical Society, **40** (1936), pp. 37–111.

[2] *Linear transformations in Hilbert space and their applications to analysis*, American Mathematical Society Colloquium Publications, Vol. 15, 1951.

[3] *Linear transformations in Hilbert space. III. Operational methods and group theory*, Proceedings of the National Academy of Sciences, U.S.A., **16** (1930) pp. 172–175.

VAN HOVE, L.

[1] *Sur certaines représentations unitaires d'un groupe infini de transformations*, Academie Royale de Belgique Classe des Sciences, Memoires Collection in 8°, **29**, No. 6 (1951), pp. 1–102.

VARADARAJAN, V. S.

[1] *Probability in physics and a theorem on simultaneous observability*, Communications in Pure and Applied Mathematics, **15** (1962), pp. 189–217; correction, *loc. cit.*, **18** (1965).

[2] *Groups of automorphisms of Borel spaces*, Transactions of the American Mathematical Society, **109** (1963), pp. 191–220.

[3] *Measures on topological spaces*, Matematiceskiĭ Sbornik, **55** (97) (1961), pp. 35–100.

[4] *Special topics in probability*, mimeographed notes of lectures delivered at the Courant Institute of Mathematical Sciences, New York University, 1962.

[5] *Global theory of representations of locally compact groups*, (Notes by Alan Solomon)—mimeographed notes of lectures delivered at the Courant Institute of Mathematical Sciences, New York University, 1961–62.

VON NEUMANN, J.

[1] *Mathematical Foundations of Quantum Mechanics*, Princeton University Press, Princeton, 1955 (translated by Robert T. Beyer from Mathematische Grundlagen der Quantenmechanik, Springer, Berlin, 1932).

[2] *On rings of operators. Reduction theory*, Annals of Mathematics, **50** (1949), pp. 401–485.

[3] *Die Eindeutigkeit der Schrödingerschen Operatoren*, Mathematische Annalen, **104** (1931), pp. 570–578.

[4] *On an algebraic generalisation of the quantum mechanical formalism* (part I), Rec. Math. Matematiceskiĭ Sbornik, N.S., **1** (1936), pp. 415–484.

[5] *Thermodynamik quantenmechanischer Gesamtheiten*, Göttinger Nachrichten (1927), pp. 273–291.

[6] *Beweis des Ergodensatzes und des H-Theorems in der neuen Mechanik*, Zeitschrift für Physik, **57** (1929), pp. 30–70.

WEIL, A.

[1] *L'integration dans les groupes topologiques et ses applications*, Hermann, Paris, 1938.

WEISS, E., AND ZIERLER, N.

[1] *Locally compact division rings*, Pacific Journal of Mathematics, **8** (1958), pp. 369–371.

WEYL, H.

[1] *The Theory of Groups and Quantum Mechanics*, Dover Publications, Inc., New York, 1931 (translated by H. P. Robertson from Gruppentheorie und Quantenmechanik).

[2] *The Classical Groups*, Princeton University Press, Princeton, 1946.

[3] *Theorie der Darstellung kontinuierlicher halb-einfacher Gruppen durch lineare Transformationen*, Teil I, Mathematische Zeitschrift, **23** (1925), pp. 271–309.

[4] ——, Teil II, Mathematische Zeitschrift, **24** (1926), pp. 328–376.

[5] ——, Teil III, Mathematische Zeitschrift, **24** (1926), pp. 377–395.

[6] *Space, Time, Matter*, Dover Publications, Inc., 1950 (translated by Henry L. Brose from Raum, Zeit, Materie, 1921).

WICK, G. C., WIGHTMAN, A. S., AND WIGNER, E. P.

[1] *The intrinsic parity of elementary particles*, The Physical Review, **88** (1952), pp. 101–105.

WIGHTMAN, A. S.

[1] *On the localizability of quantum mechanical systems*, Reviews of Modern Physics, **34** (1962), pp. 845–872.

[2] *Relativistic Invariance and Quantum Mechanics*, Supplemento al Vol. XIV, serie X, del Nuovo Cimento (1959), pp. 81–94 (Notes by A. Barut).

WIGNER, E. P.

[1] *Unitary representations of the inhomogeneous Lorentz group*, Annals of Mathematics, **40** (1939), pp. 149–204.

[2] *On the quantum correction for thermodynamic equilibrium*, The Physical Review, **40** (1932), pp. 749–759.

[3] *Group theory and its applications to the quantum mechanics of atomic spectra*, Academic Press Inc., New York, 1959.

[4] *Über die Operation der Zeitumkehr in der Quantenmechanik*, Göttinger Nachrichten Math-Physik Kl (1931), pp. 546–559.

[5] *Relativistische Wellengleichungen*, Zeitschrift für Physik, **124** (1947), pp. 665–684.

[6] *Relativistic invariance and quantum phenomena*, Reviews of Modern Physics, **29** (1957), pp. 255–268.

ZIERLER, N.

[1] *Axioms for non-relativistic quantum mechanics*, Pacific Journal of Mathematics, **11** (1961), pp. 1151–1169.

[2] *On the lattice of closed subspaces of Hilbert space* (forthcoming).

# INDEX